ADVANCES IN
CATALYST DESIGN

UNITED NATIONS INDUSTRIAL DEVELOPMENT ORGANIZATION

INTERNATIONAL CENTRE FOR SCIENCE AND HIGH TECHNOLOGY

Proceedings of the Workshop on Catalyst Design

ADVANCES IN CATALYST DESIGN

Trieste, Italy   **11 – 13 December 1990**

Editors

M Graziani
ICC and University of Trieste

C N R Rao
**Indian Institute of Science
Bangalore, India**

World Scientific
Singapore • New Jersey • London • Hong Kong

Published by

World Scientific Publishing Co. Pte. Ltd.
P O Box 128, Farrer Road, Singapore 9128
USA office: 687 Hartwell Street, Teaneck, NJ 07666
UK office: 73 Lynton Mead, Totteridge, London N20 8DH

ADVANCES IN CATALYST DESIGN

ISBN 981-02-0635-6

Printed in Singapore by JBW Printers & Binders Pte. Ltd.

v

PREFACE

This book contains the lectures delivered at the Workshop on Catalyst Design held in Trieste in December 1990, by the International Centre for Pure and Applied Chemistry (ICC). ICC is the chemistry wing of the International Centre of Science and High Technology (ICS). The establishment of the International Centre of Science and High Technology was the brainchild of Professor Abdus Salam, Scientific Director of the International Centre for Theoretical Physics (ICTP). In 1989, pilot activities of ICS were started, financed through the Italian contribution to UNIDO. The aim of ICS is to transfer science and technology to developing countries in order to enable industries to develop there and to promote self-reliance. In the light of recent political changes, this support of technology transfer and consequent collaboration is being extended by ICS to include East European countries and those bordering on the Mediterranean as well.

The proposed activities for the International Centre for Pure and Applied Chemistry include technologies and research areas of utmost importance to the chemical industry, such as reactivity, synthesis, macromolecules, combustion chemistry, catalysis, and computer chemistry.

Research activities of ICC will be carried out at the "Research Area," a science park just outside the city of Trieste, where several other research institutions are already operating, thus ensuring an effective interdisciplinary approach. Another important activity of ICC is to organize workshops, conferences, and research training programmes, open to scientists from developing countries and East Europe.

It has been proposed that the second Workshop on Catalyst Design be held in Trieste in November 1992.

M. Graziani
C. N. R. Rao
Editors

February 1991

CONTENTS

INVESTIGATIONS OF CATALYSTS BY IN-SITU XRD, EXAFS AND MÖSSBAUER MEASUREMENTS AND OF SIMULATED CATALYST SURFACES PREPARED IN-SITU IN AN ELECTRON SPECTROMETER[+]

C.N.R. RAO[*], G.U. KULKARNI, G. SANKAR, G. RANGA RAO and K.R. KANNAN
Solid State and Structural Chemistry Unit
Indian Institute of Science
Bangalore 560012, India

ABSTRACT

In-situ investigations of catalysts by x-ray diffraction (XRD), extended x-ray absorption fine structure (EXAFS) and Mössbauer measurements help to unravel many fascinating and important features of solid catalysts. Some highlights from the studies carried out in the authors' laboratories will be presented. Some of the systems discussed are Ni/TiO_2, Fe/TiO_2, bimetallic $Ni-Cu/Al_2O_3$, $Co-Mo/Al_2O_3$ (HDS) and ammonia synthesis Fe catalysts. Results of x-ray and UV photoelectron spectroscopic studies of Ni/Al_2O_3 and Ni/TiO_2 catalyst surfaces prepared in the electron spectrometer will be discussed with specific reference to the interaction of CO and N_2 with these surfaces. These studies throw light on the strong-metal-support-interaction (SMSI) in the Ni/TiO_2 system.

Introduction

The advent of modern tools of characterization of solids and surfaces has brought out a major change in our understanding of the structure and reactivity of solid catalysts. Amongst the various techniques, special mention must be made of electron microscopy, x-ray diffraction

---

+Contribution No.732 from the Solid State & Structural Chemistry Unit

*To whom correspondence should be addressed

(XRD), extended x-ray absorption fine strucutre (EXAFS) and the various electron spectroscopies. Vital information on the real structure of catalysts can be obtained only when we study them under reaction conditions. This becomes possible by _in-situ_ studies carried out with the aid of specially designed cells. In this paper, we describe some of the results obtained by _in-situ_ x-ray diffraction, EXAFS and Mössbauer measurements on a few catalyst systems. We will discuss Ni/TiO_2 and related catalysts supposed to show strong metal-support interaction (SMSI), bimetallic Cu-Ni/ Υ-Al_2O_3 catalysts and Co-Mo/Υ-Al_2O_3 and Ni-Mo/Υ-Al_2O_3 hydrodesulphurization catalysts. In addition, we also make some observations on iron catalysts used in ammonia synthesis based on _in-situ_ studies.

Techniques of electron spectroscopy such as ultra-violet photoelectron spectroscopy and x-ray photoelectron spectroscopy are very useful for the characterization of catalyst surfaces. There are, however, certain serious limitations with these techniques because of the unreal conditions such as ultra high vacuum employed in these studies. Such limitations have been overcome by carrying out reactions in specially designed chambers operating at ambient or high pressures. We have employed photoelectron spectroscopic techniques to study simulated catalyst surfaces such as Ni/Al_2O_3, Ni/TiO_2 prepared _in-situ_ in the electron spectrometer. Besides characterising the simulated catalyst surfaces, we have examined the adsorption of N_2 and CO on these surfaces.

Experimental

In order to carry out _in-situ_ studies on catalysts, we have designed and fabricated inexpensive cells for x-ray diffraction, EXAFS and Mössbauer measurements. In Fig. 1 we show the schematic diagram of the _in-situ_ XRD cell fabricated by us. It consists of a quartz reaction chamber with a semicircular mylar window at one end. This enables us to carry out the diffraction studies in the reflection mode compatible with the JEOL JDX8P diffractometer facility. The sample-holder carrying a heating element, a thermocouple and the gas-inlet enters the reaction chamber through the ground joint. The correct positioning of the sample can be achieved by a position adjusting screw made

of teflon. The metal holder fixes the <u>in-situ</u> cell to the
diffractometer assembly. Water was circulated through the
metal holder in order to prevent heat-transmission to the
diffractometer.

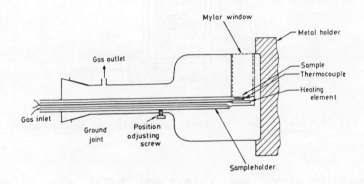

Fig. 1 <u>In-situ</u> x-ray diffraction cell

The <u>in-situ</u> cell for EXAFS and Mössbauer studies
consists of a double-walled quartz tube having a ground
joint at the top and closed at the bottom (Fig. 2). The
sample heating element enclosed in a spiral quartz tube
passes from the sides of the cell along with the gas inlet-
outlet tubes. The sample in the form of a pellet of 20mm
diameter is mounted on a quartz sample holder hanging from
the ground joint at the top. The sample holder contains a
thermocouple just below the sample, to monitor the
temperature accurately. The cell has mylar windows for

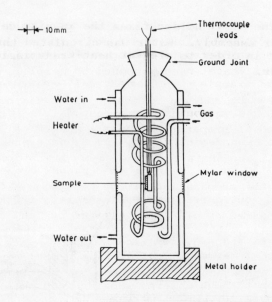

Fig. 2 <u>In-situ</u> cell for EXAFS and Mössbauer measurements

transmission of x- and γ-rays and water was circulated through the double walled cell in order to cool the mylar windows and the surroundings.

We shall not discuss the preparation of the catalysts here, but refer to them while discussing the results.

Results and Discussion

Ni/TiO$_2$ system

An important aspect of heterogeneous catalysis that is yet to be fully understood is the nature of interaction between the oxide support and the dispersed metal.[1] The so-called strong-metal-support-interaction (SMSI) systems show unusual characteristics such as small surface area and suppression of chemisorption of H$_2$ and CO. The most commonly used oxide support in such catalysts is TiO_2. Metal-support interaction manifests itself in Ni/TiO_2 catalysts when subjected to hydrogen reduction above 773K. Several models have been proposed to explain the SMSI effect. For example, there is some evidence for the reduction of TiO_2 and the formation of Ni-Ti bonds.[2] The importance of the various factors responsible for SMSI such as the method of preparation and the polymorphic form of TiO_2 have not been demonstrated. It is noteworthy in this context that[3,4] the anatase form of TiO_2 transforms to the rutile form in a temperature range close to that employed for the preparation of the Ni/TiO_2 catalysts. We have carried out careful investigations of the Ni/TiO_2 catalyst prepared by different methods by employing both in-situ x-ray diffraction (XRD) and extended x-ray absorption fine structure (EXAFS) measurements. The study has revealed that the wet-impregnation method which favours metal-support interaction[5] also promotes the anatase-rutile transformation through a ternary oxide intermediate. This observation is likely to be of significance in heterogeneous catalysis. In addition, we have also examined the Ni/TiO_2 system by a study of the interaction of CO and N_2 with simulated surfaces, prepared in-situ in an electron spectrometer which we shall discuss in a later section.

Ni/TiO_2 catalysts (10 wt% Ni) were prepared by two methods: (i) wet-impregnation method; and (ii) ion-exchange method. This was necessary since there are indications that catalysts prepared by the two methods behave differently.[5] For the support, we used a TiO_2 sample (Degussa) containing 75% anatase and 25% rutile as indicated by x-ray diffraction.[3,4] In the wet-impregnation method, nickel nitrate solution of the appropriate concentration was added to TiO_2 under stirring and the product then dried at 373K before subjecting to calcination and reduction. In the ion-exchange method[5] the nickel nitrate solution was mixed with NH_4OH and then added to TiO_2. In-situ XRD measurements were carried out using a controlled atmosphere[6] cell, the details of which are described elsewhere.[6] In-situ EXAFS measurements were carried out with a specially designed reaction[7] cell fitted to a Rigaku x-ray absorption spectrometer.[7] Besides studying samples calcined in air (for 3 hrs) at different temperatures, we have examined samples after subjecting them to hydrogen reduction at 673K and 773K in the **in-situ** cell. Analysis of the EXAFS data was carried out by the procedure[7] applicable to multiphasic-multicomponent systems.

XRD patterns of the Ni/TiO_2 catalyst prepared by the wet-impregnation procedure and calcined at different temperatures are shown in Fig. 3. We see reflections due to NiO, anatase(A) and rutile(R) in the samples calcined below 773K. Samples calcined above this temperature show

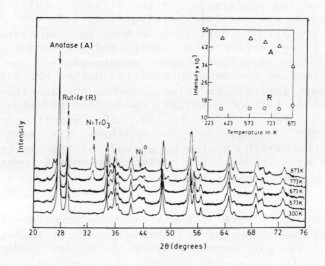

Fig. 3 XRD patterns of Ni/TiO_2 catalyst prepared by wet impregnation, calcined at various temperatures. Inset shows the integrated intensity of the Anatase(100) reflection (triangles) and the intensity of Rutile (110) reflection (circles) plotted as a function of calcination temperature. Notice the decrease in anatase

the emergence of reflections due to $NiTiO_3$ accompanied by a decrease in the intensities of the anatase reflections; intensities of the rutile lines remain essentially invariant. It appears that only the anatase form reacts with NiO clusters to form $NiTiO_3$. We show the variation of the proportion of anatase with the calcination temperature in the inset of Fig. 3. Under these conditions, there is no transformation of anatase to rutile.

The formation of $NiTiO_3$ above 773K in the samples prepared by the wet-impregnation method is supported by EXAFS measurements. We show typical Fourier transforms (FT) of the Ni K-edge EXAFS in Fig. 4. The intensity and the position of the first peak are similar to those of Ni-O

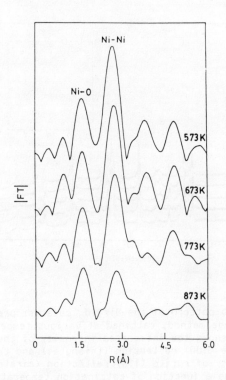

Fig. 4 FT of the catalyst prepared by wet impregnation method, calcined at a. 573K; b. 673K; c. 773K; d. 873K

in NiO, but the intensity of the second peak (due to Ni-Ni) decreases and shifts to higher R values with increase in the calcination temperature. This observation suggests that instead of forming larger clusters of NiO with the increase in calcination temperature, the titanate is formed. The structural parameters obtained from EXAFS studies are shown in Table 1. We see that the coordination numbers decrease with increase in the calcination temperature due to the formation of the titanate; the increase in the distance and the coordination number in the second peak are noteworthy.

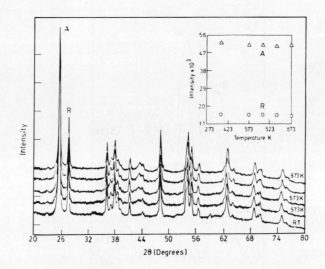

Fig. 5 XRD pattern of the Ni/TiO$_2$ catalyst prepared by ion exchange method, calcined at various temperatures. Inset shows the integrated intensity of the anatase (100) reflection (triangles) and the intensity of rutile (110) reflection (circles) plotted as a function of calcination temperature; we see no change in either

Table 1. Structural parameters of Ni/TiO$_2$ calcined
at various temperatures

Calcination temperature		First shell			Second shell		
Wet impreg-nated	Ion ex-changed	N	R (Å)	$\Delta\sigma^2$	N	R (Å)	$\Delta\sigma^2$
573K		6.3	2.08	0.0006	10.3	2.93	0.0008
673K		6.4	2.08	0.0008	9.4	2.95	0.0006
773K		5.8	2.08	0.0007	7.9	2.94	0.0015
873K		5.6	2.08	0.002	5.2	2.99	0.003
	573K	5.9	2.08	0.0008	5.7	2.93	0.001
	673K	6.0	2.08	0.0004	7.3	2.94	0.0025
	873K	5.8	2.08	0.0018	9.0	2.94	0.0013

XRD patterns of the Ni/TiO$_2$ samples prepared by the ion-exchange method and calcined at different temperatures do not show the formation of NiTiO$_3$ in the 573-873K range, but only show reflections due to NiO and TiO$_2$, the latter maintaining a constant proportion of the anatase and the rutile phases (Fig. 5). The FT's of the Ni K-edge EXAFS show only features due to NiO, the intensity of the second peak increasing with the increase in calcination temperature as expected (Fig. 6). The structural

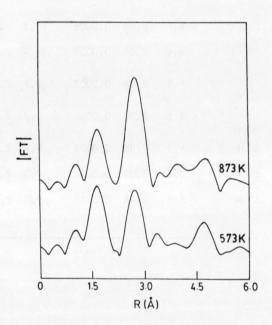

Fig. 6 FT of the Ni K-edge EXAFS of Ni/TiO$_2$
catalyst prepared by ion exchange method, calcined
at a. 573K; b. 373K

parameters (Table 1) also reflect this and show an increase in coordination number of the second shell (due to bulk NiO) with increase in calcination temperature.

We have examined Ni/TiO$_2$ catalysts subjected to H$_2$ reduction subsequent to calcination. XRD patterns of catalysts prepared by the wet-impregnation method and calcined at 773K are shown in Fig. 7. The reduction of

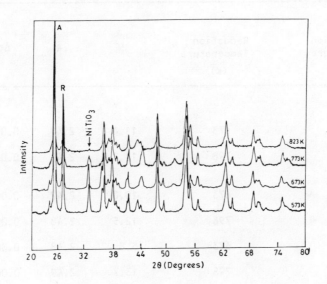

Fig. 7 XRD pattern of Ni/TiO$_2$ catalyst
prepared by wet impregnation method, calcined at 773K
and reduced at various temperatures

NiTiO$_3$, however, occurs only above 773K, giving Ni metal and the rutile form of TiO$_2$. EXAFS data also support the occurrence of partial reduction below 773K and complete reduction above 773K (Figs. 8 and 9). In contrast, the catalyst prepared by the ion-exchange method shows complete reduction to Ni metal below 773K, the TiO$_2$ remaining unaffected. The size of the Ni clusters is generally smaller in catalysts prepared by this method the size increasing with the reduction temperature. EXAFS results fully support these conclusions (Tables 2 and 3). The decrease in the Ni-Ni coordination with calcination temperature in the 673K-reduced samples in Table 2 is due to partial reduction arising from the pressure of the

Table 2.   Structural parameters of Ni/TiO$_2$ catalyst prepared
            by wet impregnation, calcined at various temperatures
            and reduced at 673K and 798K

Calcination Temperature (K)	Reduction Temperature (K)	N	R	$\Delta\sigma^2$
573K	673	11.4	2.48	0.0003
	798	12.2	2.48	0.00078
673K	673	10.0	2.47	0.0008
	798	12.5	2.48	0.0001
773K	673	5.8	2.48	0.0008
	798	13.7	2.49	0.0007

Table 3. Structural parameters of Ni/TiO$_2$ catalyst prepared
by ion exchange method, calcined at various temperatures
and reduced at 673K and 798K.

Calcination Temperature (K)	Reduction Temperature (K)	N	R	$\Delta\sigma^2$
673	673	6.6	2.48	0.00042
	798	8.3	2.49	0.00041
873	673	6.5	2.48	0.00068
	798	8.8	2.48	0.0008

14

titanate phase.   This does not happen   in   the   case   of
samples prepared by ion-exchange.

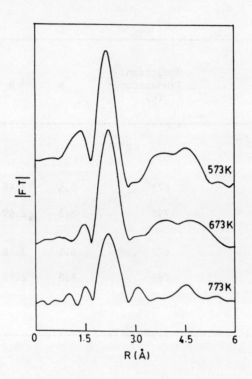

Fig. 8 FT of the Ni K-edge EXAFS of the catalyst
prepared by wet impregnation method, calcined
at a. 573K; b. 673K; c. 773K and reduced at
673K. Notice   the 2.2Å peak (similar to that of Ni metal)
as calcination temperature increases

Reduction   of Ni/TiO_2 above   773K   is   known   to   be
necessary to observe SMSI. This is probably because the
reduction of the $NiTiO_3$ intermediate (occurring above 773K)
is   a   necessary step in imparting this   behaviour   to   the
catalyst. We have further confirmed this conclusion by the
impregnation of freshly prepared pure anatase gel with

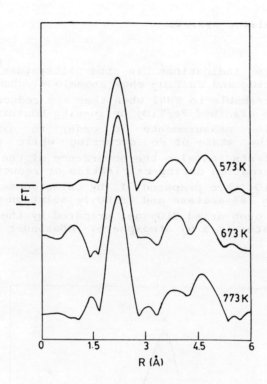

Fig. 9 FT of the Ni K-edge EXAFS of the catalyst
prepared by wet impregnation method,
calcined at a. 573K, b. 673K
and c. 773K and reduced at 793K. The main
feature is similar to that of Ni metal

Ni^{2+}. As expected, there was complete conversion of the
Ni^{2+} to $NiTiO_3$ on calcination above 773K; on reduction
above 773K, $NiTiO_3$ gave metallic Ni and rutile. In Fig. 10
we show the x-ray diffractograms of the calcined sample
(showing $NiTiO_3$ and anatase) and of the reduced sample
showing anatase and rutile.

Fe/TiO_2 and related systems

There are indications in the literature[8-10] that Fe/TiO_2, Rh/TiO_2 and Cu/TiO_2 show anomalous chemisorption behaviour ascribable to SMSI when they are reduced around 770K. We have examined Fe/TiO_2 by <u>in-situ</u> Mössbauer and x-ray diffraction measurements in order to explore the changes in the state of Fe occurring while processing Fe/TiO_2 catalysts and also the occurrence of the anatase-rutile transformation during calcination or reduction. Two types of Fe/TiO_2 were prepared: I, by using commercial TiO_2 (Degussa) with 70% anatase and $Fe(NO_3)_3$ solution and II, by starting with oven-dried TiO_2 gel prepared by the addition of $TiCl_4$ to water in a N_2 atmosphere. Mössbauer spectra of

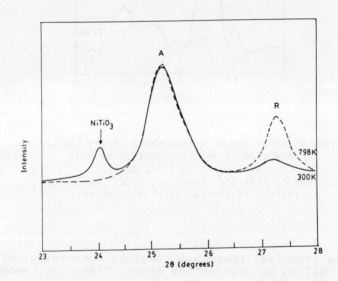

Fig. 10 XRD pattern of calcined Ni/TiO_2 prepared from TiO_2 gel and reduced at 798K

the $Fe/TiO_2(I)$ catalyst subjected to reduction at different temperatures are shown in Fig. 11. We see that the sample as prepared shows a doublet, characteristic of Fe^{3+} as in Fe_2O_3. On reduction at a relatively low temperature (620K), we see evidence for the formation of lower oxides of iron in mixture with metallic iron (Fe^o) and unreduced Fe_2O_3 (Fig. 11b). A sample reduced at 700K shows predominantly Fe^o and only a small amount of unreduced Fe^{2+} (see Fig. 11c). Complete reduction occurs at 770K as can be seen from the characteristic six-finger spectrum in Fig. 11d. XRD patterns of the $Fe/TiO_2(I)$ catalyst reduced at different temperatures showed that the fraction of rutile in the support does not change significantly up to 770K. The anatase-rutile transformation seems to become marked only above 770K. It is noteworthy that the SMSI effect also manifests itself when the reduction is carried out around 770K.

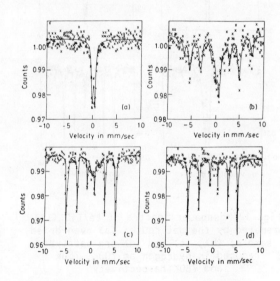

Fig. 11 Mössbauer spectra of $Fe/TiO_2(I)$ prepared from commercial TiO_2: (a) oven-dried sample; (b), (c) and (d) are catalysts reduced in hydrogen at 620K, 700K and 780K respectively

In Fig. 12 we show the Mössbauer spectra of the Fe/TiO$_2$(II) catalyst prepared from the TiO$_2$ gel. This catalyst shows Fe^{3+} in the oven-dried sample similar to Fe/TiO$_2$(I). The TiO$_2$ support is, however, present entirely in the anatase form in this catalyst preparation as can be seen from Fig. 13. On reduction at 620K, a small amount of Fe^{2+} is formed. The formation of Fe^{2+} becomes significant when the catalyst is reduced at 700K, with the proportion of Fe^{2+} and Fe^{3+} becoming equal (see Fig. 12b). The catalyst reduced at 750K shows only features characteristic of Fe^{2+} (Fig. 12c). It is significant that there is no

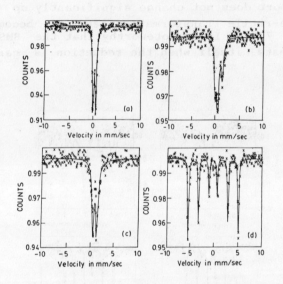

Fig. 12 Mössbauer spectra of Fe/TiO$_2$(II) prepared by the gel route: (a) oven-dried sample; (b), (c) and (d) are catalyst reduced in hydrogen at 700K, 750K and 780K respectively

metallic iron in the Fe/TiO$_2$(II) sample reduced at or below
750K unlike in the case of Fe/TiO$_2$(I). Complete reduction
of Fe/TiO$_2$ (II) to metallic iron occurs when it is reduced
above 770K (see Fig. 12d).

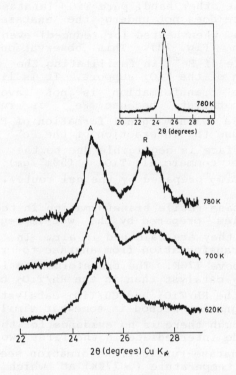

Fig. 13 XRD patterns of Fe/TiO$_2$(II) catalyst reduced
at different temperatures. Notice the
transformation of anatase to rutile occur even
at 750K. Inset shows the XRD pattern of pure
TiO$_2$ gel heated to 780K in hydrogen atmosphere

The XRD patterns of the Fe/TiO_2(II) catalyst reduced at different temperatures (Fig. 13) are revealing. The TiO_2 support, present only in the anatase form to start with, transforms to the rutile form at as low a temperature as 650K.   The transformation becomes marked around 700K and higher. On the other hand, pure TiO_2 (anatase) prepared by the gel route does not undergo the anatase-rutile phase transformation when heated (or reduced) even at 780K (see the inset to Fig. 13). This observation suggests the important role of Fe^{2+} in facilitating the anatase-rutile transformation of the TiO_2 support. It is likely that the anatase-rutile transformation is not favoured in the Fe/TiO_2(I)   catalyst, because Fe^{3+} is reduced almost directly to Fe^O with marginal formation of Fe^{2+} en route and also because the interaction of the Fe^{2+} so formed with the TiO_2 surface is negligible due to the lower surface area   of   the commercial TiO_2 ($50m^2$/gm) (compared to $\sim 800m^2$/g of TiO_2 prepared by the gel route).

The anatase-rutile transformation in the Cu/TiO_2 and Rh/TiO_2 samples prepared by the wet-impregnation method occurs when they are calcined in air. In these systems also, the transformation from anatase to rutile becomes significant above 770K. The transformation is more marked in the Cu/TiO_2 catalyst than in the Rh/TiO_2 catalyst. The behaviour of the Rh/TiO_2 and Cu/TiO_2 catalysts prepared by the wet-impregnation method is somewhat similar to that of Ni/TiO_2, although there is no evidence for the formation of a ternary oxide intermediate in the first two systems.   In general the anatase-rutile transformation seems to occur at or below the temperature ($\sim 770K$) at which strong-metal-support-interaction manifests itself.

Ni-Cu/ γ -Al$_2$O$_3$ bi-metallic catalyst system

The catalytic performance of bimetallic catalysts is known to differ significantly from that of the individual components often showing mutual promotion effects towards reduction.[11-13]   We have carried out a detailed investigation on this aspect on the bimetallic Cu-Ni/ γ -Al$_2$O$_3$ catalyst system prepared by different procedures, by _in-situ_ EXAFS measurements. The study has established that copper promotes the reduction of nickel, whereas copper itself is easily reducible.

In order to understand the interaction of Ni with γ-Al$_2$O$_3$, we initially carried out _in-situ_ EXAFS measurements on Ni/γ-Al$_2$O$_3$ system as a function of the calcination temperature as well as metal loading. The samples were prepared by the wet-impregnation of γ-Al$_2$O$_3$ (200 m^2/g) with aqueous solution of Ni(NO$_3$)$_2$; the metal loading was 5 wt%. The samples were calcined at different temperatures (370, 570, 770 and 970K) for 3 hours and were reduced _in-situ_ at 770K for 3 hours. Multiphasic curve-fitting analysis[7,14] of the inverse Fourier-transformed data was carried out employing phase and amplitude parameters of Ni-O in NiO and Ni-Ni in Ni metal. The sample dried at 370K showed only the NiO-like octahedral environment for Ni. Peaks due to Ni with tetrahedral and the octahedral coordinations of NiAl$_2$O$_4$ develop progressively with the increasing temperature of calcination. Multiphasic analysis of the data of the reduced samples shows that the sample dried at 370K gets completely reduced to Ni, whereas the sample calcined at 970K undergoes little reduction. Employing the additive EXAFS relation,[7,14] we have calculated the compositions of Ni/γ-Al$_2$O$_3$ samples both in the calcined and reduced states. We find that the amount of Ni metal in the reduced sample to be roughly proportional to that of the NiO-like phase in the calcined sample. A similar observation has been made on the Ni/γ-Al$_2$O$_3$ catalyst with different metal loadings (2.5 and 5 wt%, both calcined and reduced at 770K). The sample with higher metal loading shows greater concentration of NiO-like phase and undergoes greater reduction, consistent with the earlier observations.[15-18] It therefore, appears that the reducibility of Ni in the Ni/γ-Al$_2$O$_3$ catalyst depends on the concentration of the NiO-like phase in the calcined sample.

In order to understand the promotion effect of Cu towards the reduction of nickel in the bimetallic catalyst, we have studied co-impregnated Cu-Ni/γ-Al$_2$O$_3$ with a fixed

Ni loading of 2.5 wt% (because the reducibility of nickel varies with its loading), but with varying Cu/Ni ratios (0, 0.33, 1.0 and 3.0; all calcined and reduced at 770K). Multiphasic analysis in this case shows that with increasing Cu loading, the proportion of the NiO-like phase increases accompanied by a decrease in the $NiAl_2O_4$-like phase (see Table 4 and Fig. 14a). The Fourier-transforms of

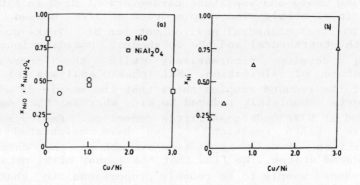

Fig. 14 (a) Variation of the fractions of NiO and
$NiAl_2O_4$ of calcined Cu-Ni/ γ -Al_2O_3 catalysts
with Cu/Ni ratio
(b) Variation of the fraction of metallic Ni
produced on reduction of Cu-Ni/ γ -Al_2O_3,
with Cu/Ni ratio

these catalysts after reduction show that the extent of reduction to metallic Ni increases from ~25% (in the absence of any Cu in Ni/Al_2O_3) to nearly 75% when the Cu/Ni ratio is 3.0 (Fig. 15). In Fig. 14b, we depict the variation of metallic Ni obtained on reduction with Cu/Ni ratio.

TABLE 4: Structural parameters from Ni K-EXAFS of unreduced and reduced Cu-Ni/γ-Al₂O₃ catalysts (with fixed 2.5 wt% Ni loading)

| Cata-lyst with Ni:Cu | Calcined at 770K | | | | | | Reduced at 770K | | | | | |
| | Ni-O tet(NiAl₂O₄) | | Ni-O oct(NiAl₂O₄) | | Ni-O oct(NiO) | | Ni-O tet(NiAl₂O₄) | | Ni-O oct(NiAl₂O₄) | | Ni-Ni (Ni metal) | |
	N	R	N	R	N	R	N	R	N	R	N	R
100:0	1.0	1.84	4.0	1.97	1.0	2.08	1.0	1.84	4.0	1.97	2.7	2.5
75:25	0.8	1.84	3.5	1.98	2.5	2.08	0.8	1.84	3.5	1.98	4.0	2.51
50:50	0.8	1.84	2.5	1.97	3.2	2.08	0.8	1.84	2.5	1.97	7.5	2.54
25:75	0.5	1.83	2.0	1.97	3.5	2.08	0.5	1.83	2.0	1.97	9.0	2.53

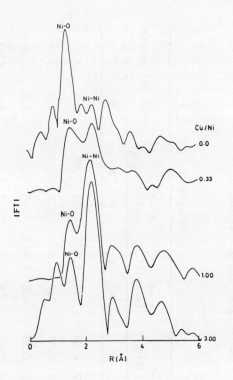

Fig. 15 Fourier-transforms of Ni
K-EXAFS of reduced Cu–Ni/ γ -Al$_2$O$_3$
catalysts with different Cu loadings

Comparing Figs. 14a and 14b, we see that the proportion
of reduced Ni formed is directly proportional to the NiO-
like phase present before reduction. This would imply that
if one can, by some means, prevent the Ni^{2+} ions from
interacting with γ -Al$_2$O$_3$ during calcination, thereby
preferentially promote the formation of the NiO-like phase
(instead of the NiAl$_2$O$_4$-like phase), there would be greater
proportion of metallic Ni on reduction. We have confirmed
this conjecture by two stage impregnations of the
bimetallic catalysts. In this method, the support was
impregnated by one metal after another with an intermediate

calcination at 770K for 3 hours (Cu/Ni = 1.0, each 2.5 wt%). In Fig. 16 we show the Fourier-transforms of Ni K-EXAFS of the two-stage impregnated samples before and after reduction. The concentration of NiO-like phase is low after calcination in the sample where Ni is first impregnated compared to that where Cu was first impregnated. Accordingly, the reduction to metallic Ni is significantly higher in the case where Cu was first

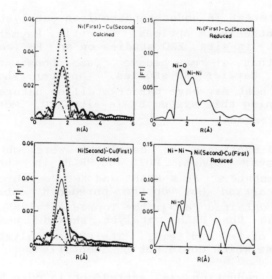

Fig. 16 Fourier-deconvolution of the fitted Ni K-EXAFS
data of two-stage impregnated Cu-Ni/ Υ -Al$_2$O$_3$
(Cu/Ni = 1.0, each 2.5 wt%) employing three Ni-O distances.
Experimental, crosses; NiO-like phase , full line; Ni-O
(tetrahedral) in NiAl$_2$O$_4$, broken line; Ni-O
(octahedral) in NiAl$_2$O$_4$, triangles. Fourier-
transforms of Ni K-EXAFS of these catalysts on
reduction are also shown

impregnated. These observations establish that the promotion effect of Cu on Ni is through enhancing the formation of the NiO-like phase during calcination.

Copper in all copper-containing systems undergoes almost complete reduction. The Cu-Cu distance in the reduced samples does not differ much from the Cu metal bulk; there is about 25% reduction in the Cu-Cu coordination which accounts for the dispersion of metallic Cu on γ-Al$_2$O$_3$.

Ammonia Synthesis Fe Catalyst

The interest in understanding iron catalysts used in ammonia synthesis is obvious. Recently, Rayment et.al.[19] carried out in-situ XRD studies on an Fe catalyst and suggested that it may become amorphous under reaction conditions. Earlier XRD studies,[20] however, show that the catalyst at best may have paracrystalline nature. We have been examining this system by in-situ XRD, Mössbauer and EXAFS measurements.

Ammonia-synthesis Fe catalysts were obtained from three sources: Topsøe, PDIL and RRLH in the unreduced state. Mössbauer, Fe K-EXAFS and XRD measurements were initially carried out on the unreduced catalysts. All catalysts contained Fe$_3$O$_4$; the Topsøe catalyst had little FeO whereas the RRLH catalyst showed nearly equal proportions of FeO and Fe$_3$O$_4$. The PDIL catalyst contained a minor phase which could not be identified.

In-situ reduction was carried out in pure hydrogen at 770, 700 and 625K. Mössbauer spectra showed iron in the reduced catalysts to exist as α-iron. However, the Mössbauer peak-widths were larger compared to bulk α-iron. In general, catalysts reduced at 625K showed largest peak widths whereas those reduced at 770K showed peak widths close to that of the bulk α-iron. At a given temperature of reduction, the RRLH catalyst showed sharpest Mössbauer peaks compared to the other two.

In-situ XRD measurements showed that iron in the reduced catalysts exists as paracrystalline α-iron (BCC). We did not find any features due to amorphous iron. A reduction temperature dependent line-broadening was observed, the behaviour of which was similar to that of the peak-widths in Mössbauer spectra. The iron particles-size was calculated using the Debye-Scherrer formula and the results are tabulated in Table 5.

In-situ Fe-K EXAFS of the reduced catalysts showed features of α-iron. Intensities of the peaks in the Fourier-transform vary significantly with the reduction temperature and are much lower than the values for bulk iron (8 and 6).[21] The effective coordination numbers calculated by curve-fitting analysis are shown in Table 5.

HDS Catalysts

Cobalt or nickel promoted molybdenum catalysts are used extensively for hydrotreating (hydrodesulphurization-HDS, hydrodenitrogenation-HDN etc.) the crude feed stocks in petroleum industry. Under reaction conditions, the catalysts are sulphided and the sulphided surface is responsible for the catalytic activity.[22-24] Previous studies[25,26] have established that Mo in these catalysts is present as small crystallites of MoS_2 (10-20 Å), but the nature of the Co(Ni) species is not entirely understood. Many models have been suggested for the HDS catalysts. These include the pseudo-intercalation model,[27] the contact synergy model[28] and the 'Co(Ni)-Mo-S' model,[29] of which recently the 'Co(Ni)-Mo-S' model has drawn more attention for its merit in explaining the known trends in the hydrodesulphurization activity.[30] According to this model, the promotion of molybdenum-sulphide catalyst is associated with an increase in the electron density on Mo (i.e. formal reduction of Mo) while poisoning is associated with a decrease in the electron density. Of the first row transition metal promotors, Co and Ni serve as promotors by donating electrons to Mo; Cu, on the other hand, serves as a poison, by withdrawing electrons from Mo. This model provided an electronic basis to explain the trends in HDS activity with different promotors. We have investigated this problem by in-situ EXAFS measurements on M-Mo/ Y -Al$_2$O$_3$, M = Fe, Co, Ni and Cu. The association of the M atoms with Mo has been studied using M/ Y -Al$_2$O$_3$ catalysts (without Mo) prepared under the same conditions.

Table 5. Effective Coordination Numbers from Fe K-EXAFS and Particle Size from X-ray line broadening

Reduction Temperature (K)	TOPSØE			PDIL			RRLH		
	EXAFS (coordination No.) I	II	XRD(a) (particle size) Å	EXAFS (coordination No.) I	II	XRD (particle size) Å	EXAFS (coordination No.) I	II	XRD (particle size) Å
770	6	4	250	6	4	280	6	3	3000
700	4	2	250	5	2	180	5	3	430
625	4	2	250	4	1	160	4	2	310

(a) 200 reflection

The catalysts were prepared by two-pore impregnation of γ-Al₂O₃ by the aqueous solutions of the transition metal-salts and ammonium heptamolybdate. The concentration of the transition metal and Mo were 2 and 12 wt% respectively. Monometallic catalysts were prepared with the same loading of the transition metals. The catalysts were calcined at 770K for 3 hours and sulphided _in-situ_ in a stream of H₂S:H₂ (10% H₂S) at 670K for 3 hours.

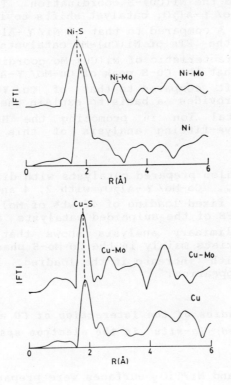

Fig. 17 Fourier-transforms of Ni and Cu K-EXAFS
of sulphided Ni-Mo/γ-Al₂O₃, Ni/γ-Al₂O₃, Cu-Mo/γ-Al₂O₃
and Cu/γ-Al₂O₃. (Ni and Cu loading,
2 wt%; Mo loading, 12 wt%)

Recent EXAFS studies[31,32] on Co(Ni)-Mo catalysts show that the Co(Ni)-S distance (~2.2 Å) is smaller by about 0.2 Å compared to that of the bulk sulphides such as NiS, NiS$_2$ (~2.4 Å). They conclude that the promotor Ni atom is situated in the plane of the Mo atoms with a 5-fold sulphur coordination. In Fig. 17 we show the Fourier-transforms of the Ni and the Cu K-EXAFS of sulphided Ni-Mo/ γ -Al$_2$O$_3$, Ni/ γ -Al$_2$O$_3$, Cu-Mo/ γ -Al$_2$O$_3$ and Cu/ γ -Al$_2$O$_3$ catalysts. The main peak in the FT around 1.8 Å corresponds to the Ni(Cu)-S coordination. This peak, in the FT of Ni-Mo/ γ -Al$_2$O$_3$ catalyst shifts to lower R values by about 0.15 Å compared to that of Ni/ γ -Al$_2$O$_3$ catalyst. Furthermore, the FTs of Ni(Cu)-Mo catalysts show a peak around 3 Å characteristic of Ni(Cu)-Mo coordination. It is interesting that the Cu-S peak of Cu-Mo/ γ -Al$_2$O$_3$ does not show any shift compared to that of Cu/ γ -Al$_2$O$_3$. This observation provides a basis to explain the role of the transition metal ion in promoting the HDS activity. Detailed curve-fitting analysis of this data is in progress.

We have also prepared catalysts with different metal loadings (e.g., Co-Mo/ γ -Al$_2$O$_3$ with 2, 4 and 6 wt% Co-loading, at a fixed loading of 12 wt% of Mo). The FTs of the Co K-EXAFS of the sulphided catalysts are shown in Fig. 18. Preliminary analysis shows that at low Co-loadings, Co exists mainly in the Co-Mo-S phase (short Co-S distance). With increase in the loading, bulk sulphide phases start appearing.

UPS and XPS studies of the interaction of CO and N$_2$ with Ni/TiO$_2$ prepared in-situ in the electron spectrometer

Ni/Al$_2$O$_3$ and Ni/TiO$_2$ surfaces were prepared <u>in-situ</u> in the electron spectrometer as follows. The oxide supports were grown on clean polycrystalline Al and Ti foils by exposing them to oxygen in the preparation chamber. The thickness of the Al$_2$O$_3$ layers was in the range of 8-18 Å and that of the TiO$_2$ was in the range of 30-50 Å. Ni was dispersed on the oxide supports so prepared by evaporating pure Ni metal from a tungsten filament. The concentrations of Ni[33-35] on these supports were estimated to be in the range of (0.1-8)x10^{15} atoms/cm^2.

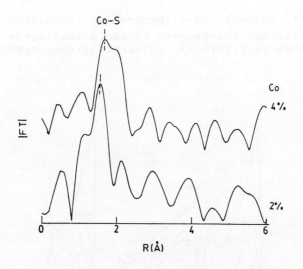

Fig. 18 Fourier-transforms of Co K-EXAFS
of sulphided Co-Mo/γ-Al$_2$O$_3$ with Co loading
of 2 and 4 wt% at a fixed
loading of Mo (12 wt%)

In the case of titania catalysts, different types of Ni/TiO$_2$ surfaces were prepared in order to examine the possible role of electronic and morphological effects associated with the SMSI state. Ni metal was dispersed on prereduced TiO$_2$ under UHV to avoid encapsulation of reduced titanium oxide (referred as TiO$_x$) on Ni. This way, it was possible to study the effect of the reduced TiO$_2$ support on Ni and on the subsequent CO or N$_2$ adsorption. We have simulated the SMSI state of the Ni/TiO$_2$ system by UHV reduction after depositing Ni on TiO$_2$ at 300K. This enabled us to study the morphological effects (migration of TiO$_x$ on Ni) on adsorption. We have also prepared TiO$_2$ (without annealing) as well as TiO$_x$ surfaces and studied N$_2$ adsorption for purpose of comparison. The simulated catalysts were characterized by valence band (He II) and core level (XPS) spectra.

He II valence band spectra of simulated Ni/Al_2O_3 catalysts for two thicknesses of the oxide layers (8 and 18 Å) are shown in Figure 19. Systematic development of the

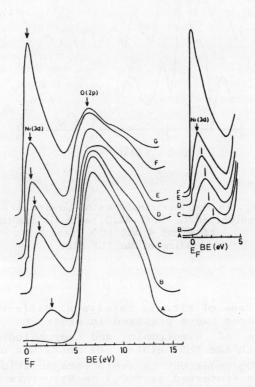

Fig. 19 He II valence band spectra of simulated Ni/Al_2O_3 catalysts: (a) Al_2O_3 layer of thickness 8Å, (B) to (G) are valence bands of Ni deposited on (A) with the following Ni concentration in atoms/cm^2: B, 0.15×10^{15}; C, 0.4×10^{15}; D, 0.55×10^{15}; E, 2.3×10^{15}; F. 4.8×10^{15}; G, $>8 \times 10^{15}$. In the inset, valence bands of Ni/Al_2O_3 with 18Å thick oxide layer are shown; (A) 0.15×10^{15} Ni atoms/cm^2 and (F) $>8 \times 10^{15}$ atoms/cm^2

Ni valence band is clearly seen as the concentration of Ni is increased from 0.1×10^{15} atoms/cm^2 (spectrum B) to 4.8×10^{15} atoms/cm^2 (spectrum F). At low Ni concentration, the valence band does not show the presence of clear Fermi surface (spectra B and C). However, at high concentrations, ($> 8 \times 10^{15}$ Ni atoms/cm^2), a valence band which is comparable to that of metallic Ni is emerged (spectrum G). The thickness of Al$_2$O$_3$ layer does not show any effect on the growth of the valence band (see inset of Figure 19). The Ni(2p) core level spectra show a shift to higher binding energies at low Ni concentrations, similar to that observed in the Ni(3d) valence band due to the decreased screening effect.

In Fig. 20, we show the He II difference spectra and the corresponding C(1s) core level spectra of CO adsorbed on simulated Ni/Al$_2$O$_3$ catalysts described above. At high Ni concentration, the adsorption is molecular just as in the case of metallic Ni even up to 300K (spectrum E). At low Ni concentration, however, the adsorption is molecular at 80K and partly dissociative at 200K; complete dissociation of CO occurs around 300K (spectra A to D). The occurrence of dissociative chemisorption is independent of the thickness of the Al$_2$O$_3$ layer. The separation between the $(1\pi + 5\sigma)$ and the 4σ levels of CO(ad) is large (3.6 eV) at low Ni concentrations compared to 3.1 eV observed on metallic Ni. This shows that the C-O bond is more fissile on simulated Ni/Al$_2$O$_3$ catalysts. The observation of CO dissociation on these catalysts also indicates the structure sensitivity of this phenomenon.

The occurrence of CO dissociation on Ni/Al$_2$O$_3$ surfaces is corroborated by the C(1s) spectra shown in Fig.20b. The C(1s) spectrum shows both molecular and dissociative adsorption of CO at 200K with binding energies of 285.9 and 284.2 eV respectively. At 300K, the spectrum shows only dissociated species.

In Fig.21, we show the Ti(2p) spectra of various titania surfaces prepared in the spectrometer. The Ti(2p) spectrum A of TiO$_2$ is identical with the spectrum D of Ni/TiO$_2$ (non-annealed). The Ti(2p) spectra of TiO$_x$, Ni/TiO$_x$ and Ni/TiO$_2$ (annealed) show the presence of reduced Ti^{3+} species. Figure 22 shows the corresponding He II spectra for the same catalyst surfaces. Spectrum A of the

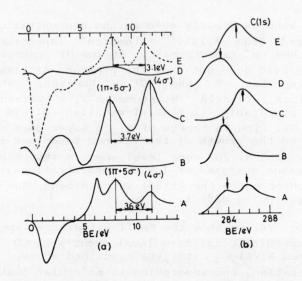

Fig. 20 (a) He II difference spectra of CO
adsorbed on Ni/Al$_2$O$_3$ (A) 20L CO on Ni/Al$_2$O$_3$ at
200K (8Å thick oxide, 1 x 10^{15} Ni atoms/cm^2); (B) after
warming to 300K; (c) 30L CO on Ni/Al$_2$O$_3$ at 80K
(18Å thick oxide, 0.5 x 10^{15} Ni atoms/cm^2); (D) after
warming to 300K; (E) 30L CO on Ni/Al$_2$O$_3$ at 300K (8Å
thick oxide, >8 x 10^{15} Ni atoms/cm^2)

(b) C(1s) region corresponding to conditions
in Fig. 20(a)

TiO$_2$ surface shows only a major feature between 4-10 eV due
to O(2p). After annealing, spectrum B shows Ti(3d) defect
states at 0.8 eV above E$_F$ characteristic of the reduced
TiO$_2$(i.e., TiO$_x$). The spectra (C and D) of Ni/TiO$_x$ and
Ni/TiO$_2$ surfaces exhibit a small Ni d-band near E$_F$. On

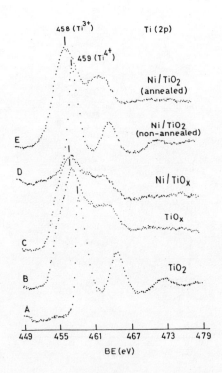

Fig. 21 Ti(2p) core level spectra of (A) TiO_2, (B) TiO_x,
(C) Ni/TiO_x, (D) Ni/TiO_2 (non-annealed) and
(E) Ni/TiO_2 (vacuum-annealed) surfaces

annealing the Ni/TiO_2 surface, however, we notice that the Ni d-band (seen in spectrum D) nearly vanishes accompanied by the appearence of the Ti(3d) states near E_F (spectrum E). This indicates that TiO_x covers the Ni particles when Ni/TiO_2 is annealed at 770K in UHV. Accordingly, the intensity of $Ni(2p_{3/2})$ spectrum of the annealed Ni/TiO_2 is lower than that of the non-annealed Ni/TiO_2 surface (see the inset of Fig. 22). In Fig. 23, the N(1s) core level spectra are displayed for N_2 adsorbed on various simulated

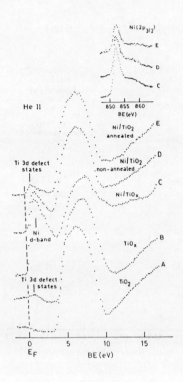

Fig. 22 He II spectra of (A) TiO$_2$, (B) TiO$_x$,
(C) Ni/TiO$_x$, (D) Ni/TiO$_2$ (non-annealed) and
(E) Ni/TiO$_2$ (vacuum-annealed), same as in Fig. 21. Inset
shows the relevant Ni($2p_{3/2}$) spectra

catalyst surfaces described above. The N(1s) spectrum of
N$_2$ on Ni-Ti alloy (prepared by Ni deposition on Ti followed
by annealing at 750K) is also presented. On the Ni/Al$_2$O$_3$
surface, N$_2$ adsorbs molecularly at 80K exhibiting N(1s)
peaks at 401.6 and 406.8 eV due to screened and unscreened
final states (spectrum A). This molecular species is
similar to that found on a polycrystalline Ni surface.[36]
Physisorbed nitrogen with a characteristic N(1s) feature
around 403.5 eV is found on TiO$_2$ and TiO$_x$ surfaces;

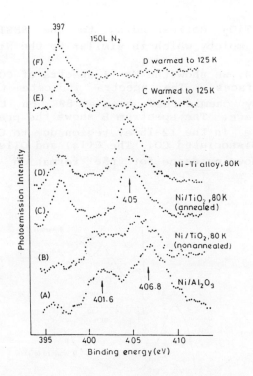

Fig. 23 N(1s) core-level spectra of nitrogen adsorbed
on different simulated catalyst surfaces at 80K

dissociation also takes place on TiO$_x$ surface.[34]

On the non-annealed Ni/TiO$_2$ surface, we observe
molecular chemisorption with N(1s) features at 401 and 405
eV just as on the Ni/Al$_2$O$_3$ surface (spectrum B). On the
annealed Ni/TiO$_2$ surface, however, adsorbed nitrogen gives
two features at 397 and 405 eV, the former due to
dissociated nitrogen and the latter, due to weakly
chemisorbed molecular nitrogen (spectrum C). On warming
the surface, the weakly chemisorbed species desorbs leaving
the dissociative nitrogen at 125K (spectrum E).
Significantly, on the Ni-Ti alloy surface also, we see weak
molecular chemisorption and dissociative adsorption at 80K
(spectrum D), with only the dissociated species remaining
above 125K (spectrum F). These results bring out the
similarity between the surfaces of the annealed Ni/TiO$_2$
catalyst and Ni-Ti alloy. It is rather possible that

annealed Ni/TiO_2 corresponding to the SMSI state may contain Ni-Ti moiety which is similar to the Ni-Ti alloy.

In Fig. 24, we show the He II spectra of CO adsorbed on Ni/TiO_2 surfaces. The spectra indicate that CO is dissociatively chemisorbed even at 80K on the annealed Ni/TiO_2 surface. The spectrum B shows the presence of a broad feature in the 12-15 eV region due to CO_2 or CO_3^{2-} formed from dissociated CO. The C(1s) and O(1s) regions in XPS also show evidence for the formation of CO_2/CO_3^{2-}

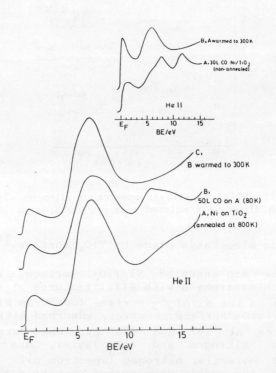

Fig. 24 He II spectra of CO adsorbed on annealed Ni/TiO_2 surface. Inset shows He II spectra of CO adsorbed on non-annealed Ni/TiO_2 surface

species.[37] This is in contrast to the molecular adsorption found on non-annealed Ni/TiO_2 surface at 80K (see inset). These results again suggest the formation of Ni-Ti bonds upon annealing the Ni/TiO_2.[2]

In conclusion, both N_2 and CO chemisorb molecularly on a non-annealed Ni/TiO_2 surface. On an annealed Ni/TiO_2 surface, N_2 adsorbs molecularly as well as dissociatively at 80K, whereas CO adsorbs only dissociatively. On an Ni/Al_2O_3 surface, however, both CO and N_2 adsorb molecularly at 80K and the former dissociates at 300K.

Acknowledgement: The authors thank the Department of Science and Technology and the University Grants Commission for support of this research.

REFERENCES

1. S.J. Tauster, S.C. Fung, R.T.K. Baker and J.A. Horsley, *Science*, 211(1981) 1121.

2 G. Sankar, S. Vasudevan and C.N.R. Rao, *J. Phys. Chem.*, 92(1988) 1879.

3. C.N.R. Rao, *Canad. J. Chem.* 39(1961) 498.

4. S.R. Yoganarasimhan and C.N.R. Rao, *Trans. Farad. Soc.*, 58(1962) 1579.

5. H.C. Zurloye, J.A. Faltens and A.M. Stacy, *J. Am. Chem. Soc.*, 108(1986) 8104..

6. A.P. Walker, T. Rayment and R.M. Lambert, *J. Catal.*, 117(1989) 102.

7. G. Sankar, G.U. Kulkarni and C.N.R. Rao, *Progr. Cryst. Growth and Charact.*, 18(1989) 67.

8. G.L. Haller and D.E. Reasco, *Adv. Catal.* 36(1989) 173.

9. L.M. Tau and C.O. Bennett, *J. Catal.*, 89(1984) 285.

10. F.S. Delk and A. Vavere, *J. Catal.*, 85(1984) 380.

11. H, Charcosset, R. Frety, A. Soldat and Y. Trambouze, *J. Catal.*, 22(1971) 204.

12. A. Roman and D. Delmon, *J. Catal.*, 30(1973) 333.

13. S.J. Gentry, N.W. Hurst and A. Jones, *J. Chem. Soc.*, *Faraday Trans.-1*, 77(1981) 603.

14. G.U. Kulkarni, G. Sankar and C.N.R. Rao, *Z. Phys.*, B73(1989) 529.

15. M. Lo Jacono, M. Schiavello and A. Cimino, *J. Phys. Chem.*, 75(1971) 1044.

16. R.B. Greegor, F.W. Lytle, R.G. Chin and D.M. Hercules, *J. Phys. Chem.*, 85(1981) 1232.

17. G. Ertl, R. Hierl, H. Knozinger, N. Thiel and H.P. Urbach, *Appl. Surf. Sci.*, 5(1980) 49..

18. P.K. Bokx, W.B.A. Wassenberg and J.N. Geus, *J. Catal.*, 104(1987) 86.

19. T. Rayment, R. Schlogl and J.M. Thomas and G. Ertl, *Nature.*, 315(1985) 311.

20. H. Ludwiczek, A. Preisinger, A. Fischer, R. Hosemann, A. Schonfeld and W. Vogel, *J. Catal.*, 51(1978) 326.

21. W. Niemann, B.S. Clausen and H. Topsøe, Int. Symp. on Physics and Chemistry of small clusters, Virginia, 1986.

22. P. Ratnaswamy and S. Sivasankar, *Catal. Rev. Sci. Eng.*, 22(1981) 401.

23. R.R. Chianelli, *Catal. Rev. Sci. Engg.*, 26(1984) 361.

24. H. Topsøe and B.S. Clausen, *Catal. Rev. Sci. Engg.*, 26(1984) 395.

25. B.S. Clausen, H. Topsoe, R. Canadia, J. Villadsen and B.J. Lengellar, *J. Phys. Chem.*, 85(1981) 3868.

26.   T.G. Parham and R.P. Merill, *J. Catal.*, 85(1984) 295.

27.   A.L. Farragher and P. Cossee in Proc. 5th Int. Congress Catalysis, ed. J.W. Hightower (North-Holland, Amsterdam, 1973), P.1301.

28.   D. Pirotte, J.M. Zaballa, P. Grange and B. Delmon, *Bull. Soc. Chim. Belg.*, 90(1981) 1239.

29.   H. Topsøe, B.S. Clausen, R. Candia, C. Wivel and S. Morup, *J. Catal.*, 68(1981) 433, 453.

30.   S. Harris and R.R. Chianelli, *J. Catal.*, 98(1986) 17.

31.   S.M.A.M. Bouwens, D.C. Koningsberger, V.H.J. deBeer, S.P.A. Louwers and R. Prins, *Catal. Lett.*, 5(1990) 273.

32.   W. Niemann, B.S. Clausen and H. Topsøe, *Catal. Lett.*, 4(1990) 355.

33.   M.S. Hegde, M.K. Rajumon and C.N.R. Rao, *J. Chem. Soc., Chem. Commun.*, (1986) 323.

34.   G. Ranga Rao and C.N.R. Rao, *J. Phys. Chem.*, 94(1990) 7986.

35.   G. Ranga Rao and C.N.R. Rao, *J. Chem. Soc., Chem. Commun.*, (1990) 357.

36.   G. Ranga Rao, K. Prabhakaran and C.N.R. Rao, *Surface Sci.*, 176(1986) L835.

37.   M.K. Rajumon, M.S. Hegde and C.N.R. Rao, *Catal. Lett.*, 1(1988) 351.

ON THE STRUCTURE AND ROLE OF PROMOTERS AND MODIFIERS IN HYDROTREATING CATALYSTS

R. Prins

Technisch-Chemisches Laboratorium, ETH Zürich, 8092 Zürich, Switzerland

ABSTRACT

The structures and roles of the Ni promoter and P modifier in sulphided Ni-Mo-P/Al$_2$O$_3$ hydrotreating catalysts are discussed. EXAFS investigations have proved that the Ni promoter atoms are located at the edges of the MoS$_2$ crystallites, as originally proposed by Topsøe. At the high Ni loading of commercial catalysts the Ni atoms fully cover the Mo atoms at the MoS$_2$ edges and the hydrogenation activity is solely coming from the Ni atoms. In addition to increasing the solubility of molybdate during impregnation and improving the mechanical and thermal stability of the Al$_2$O$_3$ support, phosphate also modifies the catalytic properties of the Ni-Mo/Al$_2$O$_3$ catalyst. It has almost no influence on the HDS of thiophene, but doubles the HDN conversion of quinoline. The effect of phosphate is due to a combination of structural and catalytical factors. Phosphate improves the activity by inducing the formation of the type II Ni-Mo-S structure, but also, especially at high Ni loading, lowers the activity by inducing a decrease in the Ni-Mo-S dispersion and a segregation of Ni$_3$S$_2$. Phosphate promotes the S- and N-elimination reactions, but this only influences the overall catalyst activity if the preceding hydrogenation reactions are not rate determining.

INTRODUCTION

The removal of sulphur, nitrogen, oxygen, and metals from oil by reductive treatments in so-called hydrotreating processes has been of paramount importance ever since oil began to be used as an energy source. Oil and oil products must be purified to diminish air-polluting emissions of sulphur and nitrogen oxides which contribute to acid rain. Furthermore, most catalysts which are used for the processing of oil products cannot tolerate sulphur and metals. Hydrotreating catalysts contain molybdenum as catalyst and cobalt or nickel as promoters, supported on γ-Al$_2$O$_3$ (1, 2). Cobalt is mainly used as a promoter for sulphided Mo/Al$_2$O$_3$ in hydrodesulphurization (HDS), while nickel is favoured in hydrodenitrogenation (HDN). Often hydrotreating catalysts also contain so-called modifier elements, such as P, B, F or Cl (3), which may influence the catalytic as well as the mechanical properties of the catalyst.

Although the origin of hydrotreating catalysts goes back to the 1920s when German researchers developed catalysts to liquefy coal, it was not before the '70s that a fair understanding of the structure of these catalysts and of the mechanism of their catalytic action was developed. Thus, in the '70s it was established that under actual catalytic conditions the majority of the molybdenum in industrial hydrotreating catalysts is present in the form of small MoS_2 particles in the pores of the γ-Al_2O_3 support. Although there was already much discussion on the role and structure of the cobalt and the nickel promoters, it was only in the '80s that a full understanding of the location of the promoter ions in the hydrotreating catalysts was developed.

In this review we will discuss the properties of Al_2O_3-supported Mo and Ni-Mo, modified with phosphorus, but because of the similarity in chemical properties, most of the information on Ni also applies for Co. First we will discuss the structures of Ni and P in such catalysts and especially recent Extended X-ray Absorption Fine Structure (EXAFS) investigations of the local Ni structure will be reviewed. Secondly we will discuss the roles of the Ni promoter and P modifier in the HDS of thiophene and the HDN of quinoline in relation to the mechanisms of the HDS and HDN reactions (4).

CATALYST STRUCTURE
MoS_2/Al_2O_3

Hydrotreating catalysts are normally made by pore volume impregnation of γ-Al_2O_3 with an aqueous solution of $(NH_4)_6Mo_7O_{24}$, H_3PO_4, and $Co(NO_3)_2$ or $Ni(NO_3)_2$, followed by drying and calcination (2). The resulting oxidic catalyst precursor is transformed into the actual HDS catalyst by a sulphiding procedure which may consist of treating in a mixture of H_2S and H_2 or thiophene and H_2, or in a liquid feed of sulphur-containing molecules and H_2. The resulting catalyst is almost completely sulphided. That is, the MoO_3 is transformed into MoS_2 and the cobalt or nickel ions have passed from an oxidic into a sulphidic environment. During sulphiding, as well as during actual HDS and HDN, the conditions are highly reducing with H_2S always present, and thermodynamics predict that molybdenum should be in the MoS_2 form. Indeed, Extended X-ray Absorption Fine Structure (EXAFS) studies of Mo K-edge absorption spectra demonstrated that in sulphided Mo/Al_2O_3 catalysts the average Mo ion has the same environment as a Mo ion in MoS_2 (5). The only difference is that in the catalyst the number of molybdenum neighbours surrounding each Mo ion is less than 6, the value in pure MoS_2. This indicates either that the MoS_2 particles on the Al_2O_3 surface are small, or that the long-range order in these particles is not perfect. Also, temperature-programmed sulphidation studies have shown that the kinetics of sulphidation are fast enough to transform the majority of Mo and Co into the sulphidic form (6).

MoS_2 has a layer lattice and the sulphur-sulphur interaction between sandwich domains of MoS_2 layers is weak. Crystals grow in the form of platelets, with relatively large dimensions parallel to the basal sulphur planes and a small dimension perpendicular to the basal plane. Topsøe and Clausen claim that MoS_2 on industrial supports is present as very large patches of a wrinkled, one-slab-thick MoS_2 layer (7). In other studies three-dimensional-like structures were described. In a recent high resolution transmission electron microscopy model study of HDS catalysts, MoS_2 crystallites were created on planar Al_2O_3 (9). On this support the MoS_2 crystallites occurred in the form of platelets with a height-to-width ratio between 0.4 and 0.7. Some of these platelets were oriented with their basal plane parallel to the Al_2O_3 surface and some were oriented at a nonzero angle to the surface, suggesting that the MoS_2 platelets are bonded to the Al_2O_3 surface by Mo-O-Al bonds (Fig. 1).

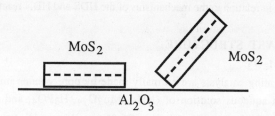

Fig. 1   Schematic view of the orientation of MoS_2 crystallites on the Al_2O_3 support surface.

Models of the active sites in $MoS_2/\gamma\text{-}Al_2O_3$ catalysts are based on the morphology of bulk MoS_2. On the basis of bond energy considerations, Voorhoeve already assumed in 1971 that the sulphur anions in the basal planes of MoS_2 are more strongly bonded to the Mo cations than the anions at edges or corners. Since the removal of sulphur is supposed to start with the adsorption of a sulphur-containing molecule with its sulphur atom in a vacancy around a Mo atom, catalysis most likely occurs at edges and corners, and not at basal planes (9). A surface science study indeed showed that a MoS_2 single crystal, with a large ratio of basal plane over edge surface area, had a negligible activity for the HDS of thiophene, while sputtering of the basal plane and exposure of Mo ions increased the activity (10).

Ni-MoS$_2$/Al$_2$O$_3$

Many spectroscopic techniques are capable of detecting cobalt or nickel in one structure or another, but until the application of Mössbauer spectroscopy no technique could quantitatively determine the simultaneous presence of different cobalt structures. Primarily due to the inverse Mössbauer studies by the Topsøe group, a quantitative picture has emerged in recent years about the structure of cobalt in HDS catalysts (7). Cobalt can exist in several forms in a promoted Mo/Al$_2$O$_3$ catalyst. In the oxidic precursor form, cobalt ions interact strongly with the spinel type γ-Al$_2$O$_3$ lattice and occupy octahedral sites just below the Al$_2$O$_3$ surface or tetrahedral sites in the Al$_2$O$_3$ bulk. At higher loadings cobalt can also form Co$_3$O$_4$ crystallites on the surface of the support. In the sulphidic form, cobalt may be present in three forms, as Co$_9$S$_8$ crystallites on the support, as cobalt ions adsorbed onto the surface of MoS$_2$ crystallites (the so-called Co-Mo-S phase, vide infra), and in tetrahedral sites in the γ-Al$_2$O$_3$ lattice. Depending on the relative concentrations of cobalt and molybdenum and on the pretreatment, a sulphided catalyst contains either a relatively large amount of Co$_9$S$_8$ or of the Co-Mo-S phase (7, 11). The structure of the catalyst in the sulphided state is predetermined by the structure of the oxidic precursor: Co$_3$O$_4$ was found to transform into Co$_9$S$_8$, cobalt ions in octahedral support sites transformed into the Co-Mo-S phase, and cobalt ions in tetrahedral support sites remained in their positions.

By combining the Mössbauer studies with catalytic activity studies, Topsøe et al. established that the promoter effect of cobalt is related to the cobalt ions in the Co-Mo-S phase (7, 11). They have therefore confirmed suggestions made by Voorhoeve and Stuiver (9) and by Farragher and Cossee (12) that the promoter effect is not due to separate Co$_9$S$_8$ crystallites but to cobalt ions in contact with MoS$_2$. Originally the occurrence of this Co on MoS$_2$ adsorption state was somewhat confusing, since thermodynamically the most stable phase of cobalt under sulphidic conditions is Co$_9$S$_8$. Furthermore, solid-state chemistry studies had shown that CoMo$_2$S$_4$ is catalytically inactive and that cobalt and nickel do not form ternary compounds with MoS$_2$, as they do with NbS$_2$ and TaS$_2$ (13). Nevertheless they can adsorb on the surface of MoS$_2$ crystallites. Farragher and Cossee were the first to suggest that the cobalt or nickel is located at the edges of the MoS$_2$ platelets (12). Proof for this suggestion was obtained by Chianelli et al. in scanning Auger studies of cobalt-promoted single crystals of MoS$_2$ (14). Farragher and Cossee suggested that the cobalt ions at the MoS$_2$ edges are located between subsequent MoS$_2$ layers and they therefore called this a pseudointercalation structure, to differentiate it from real intercalation in which the cobalt ions would be randomly distributed between alternate MoS_2 layers. Previously, intercalation proper had been suggested by Voorhoeve to be the structure of the cobalt (9). On the other hand, Topsøe and Topsøe claimed that the cobalt ions were located at the edges of the MoS_2 layers in the molybdenum plane. Evidence for this model came from an infrared study of the adsorption of NO molecules on a series of sulphided Co-Mo/Al_2O_3 catalysts (15). The IR spectrum of NO molecules adsorbed on cobalt ions can be distinguished from that of NO molecules on molybdenum ions. By increasing the cobalt loading at fixed molybdenum loading it was demonstrated that the spectrum of NO adsorbed on Co sites increased in intensity, while that of NO adsorbed on Mo sites decreased in intensity. If the cobalt ions had been in the location proposed by Farragher, the intensity of the NO on Co spectrum should have increased, but the intensity of the NO on Mo spectrum should have stayed constant. Cobalt ions in the locations proposed by Topsøe and Topsøe, however, cover molybdenum ions and block adsorption of NO on these Mo ions. Therefore the observed behaviour is in accordance with the Co location proposed by Topsøe and Topsøe (15). Kasztelan et al. have quantitatively considered the solid-state structure of MoS_2 and the edge location of the promoter by calculating the number of edge and corner Mo and promoter sites as a function of MoS_2 particle size (16). Several geometries for a single MoS_2 slab were taken into consideration. The reasonable fit between predictions and experimental results indicates that the assumptions underlying the model are realistic.

Although less detailed structural information is available for Ni-MoS_2 catalysts as for Co-MoS_2 catalysts, all available information points to a similar structure for both promoter atoms. Thus in a Ni-MoS_2 catalyst the main catalytically active phase is supposed to be a Ni-Mo-S phase in which Ni atoms decorate the edges of MoS_2 crystallites, while also separate Ni_3S_2 and Ni ions in octahedral sites in the Al_2O_3 support may be present.

Ni-MoS_2-P/Al_2O_3

Commercial hydrotreating catalysts for the treatment of heavy feedstocks usually contain P in addition to Ni and Mo. Phosphorus is added during preparation in the form of phosphoric acid or ammonium phosphate since it enhances the solubility of molybdate by the formation of phosphomolybdate complexes like $P_2Mo_5O_{23}^{6-}$, $PMo_{12}O_{40}^{3-}$ and $P_2Mo_{18}O_{62}^{6-}$ (17, 18). During calcination these complexes decompose into molybdate and phosphate which interacts strongly with the Al_2O_3 under the formation of $AlPO_4$. As a consequence the support texture is altered, micropores are closed, the surface area and pore volume decrease and the mechanical and thermal stability of the support increase. Sulphidation does not influence this $AlPO_4$ structure and therefore the support of a sulphided $Ni-MoS_2-P/Al_2O_3$ catalysts consists of $\gamma-Al_2O_3$ with patches of $AlPO_4$ at its surface. The catalyst contains small MoS_2 crystallites which either lie with their basal planes parallel to the support surface or are edge-bonded to the support surface (cf. Fig. 1). The majority of the nickel is present as nickel ions adsorbed on the edges of the MoS_2 crystallites and as Ni_3S_2 crystallites on the support surface. A high Ni/Mo ratio and a high sulphidation temperature of the oxidic precursor favour Ni_3S_2 formation; however, some nickel is always present in the Al_2O_3 lattice. A schematic picture of the resulting structure is presented in Fig. 2.

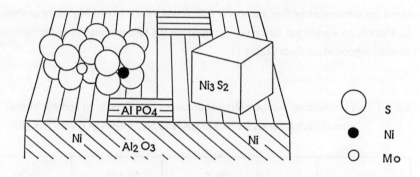

Fig. 2   Structures of the three forms in which Ni can be present in a sulphided $Ni-Mo-P/Al_2O_3$ catalyst: as the active sites at the MoS_2 edges, as segregated Ni_3S_2 and as Ni^{2+} ions in the support lattice.

Local Ni Structure

    Although the Mössbauer (7) and IR studies (15) indicated that the promoter atoms are located at the edges of the MoS_2 crystallites, many edge positions are possible and Mössbauer Emission Spectroscopy could not give an answer as to where exactly the cobalt atoms were located. Also X-ray diffraction or electron diffraction can not answer this question because of a lack of long range order in small MoS_2 crystallites. Since in Extended X-ray Absorption Fine Structure (EXAFS) spectroscopy only short range order is required, this technique is suited for solving the local structure of the promoter atom. In order to do this, however, the problem of the three forms in which the promoter atom can occur had to be solved. EXAFS is a bulk technique and when all three forms of nickel would be present in a sulphided Ni-Mo/Al$_2$O$_3$ catalyst (Ni-Mo-S, Ni$_3$S$_2$ and Ni in Al$_2$O$_3$) a summation of three spectra would be observed, from which it would be extremely difficult to extract the information on the local Ni structure in the Ni-Mo-S phase. Recent work in our group has shown how to overcome these problems (19, 20). Firstly, carbon instead of Al$_2$O$_3$ was used as a support to avoid the dissolution of promoter atoms into the support and secondly a recipe for catalyst preparation was used which exclusively leads to the Ni-Mo-S phase. In this recipe the complexing agent nitrilotriacetic acid (NTA) is added to the impregnation solution and the resulting Ni-Mo-NTA complexes are carefully sulphided to the Ni-Mo-S phase (21).

The EXAFS investigations (19, 20) showed that in all Ni-Mo catalysts the Ni atoms are surrounded by five S atoms at 2.22 Å and by one to two Mo atoms at about 2.8 Å. There is no significant difference between the EXAFS parameters of the carbon and alumina supported catalysts (Table 1).

Table 1   Coordination numbers (N) and distances (R) of the S, Ni and Mo atoms around each Ni atom for Ni-MoS$_2$/C and Ni-MoS$_2$/Al$_2$O$_3$ catalysts (20).

Catalyst	Ni/Mo	Ni-S		Ni-Mo		Ni-Ni	
		N	R Å	N	R Å	N	R Å
Ni-MoS$_2$/C	0.10	5.3	2.22	1.5	2.86	1.1	3.2
Ni-MoS$_2$/C	0.30	5.3	2.21	1.3	2.86	0.6	3.2
Ni-MoS$_2$/C	0.48	5.4	2.22	0.8	2.84	-	-
Ni-MoS$_2$/C	0.77	4.9	2.23	1.0	2.79	0.4	2.58
Ni-MoS$_2$/C	1.25	4.9	2.23	0.5	2.77	0.8	2.56
Ni-MoS$_2$/Al$_2$O$_3$	0.29	5.6	2.22	0.8	2.85	1.0	3.2
Ni-MoS$_2$/Al$_2$O$_3$	0.56	5.2	2.24	1.0	2.82	-	-

At low Ni/Mo ratios the Ni atoms have Ni neighbours at 3.2 Å. Ni neighbours are also present at high Ni/Mo ratios, but the Ni-Ni distance in this case is 2.58 Å (Table 1). This distance of 2.58 Å is due to Ni_3S_2 and is caused by the fact that at high Ni/Mo ratios not enough MoS_2 edge area is available for all Ni to form Ni-Mo-S. The surplus Ni will form Ni_3S_2. The fact that no Ni_3S_2 is observed for Ni/Mo < 0.5 confirms that in the NTA-prepared catalysts with Ni/Mo < 0.5 only the Ni-Mo-S phase is present.

The observed distances and coordination numbers for the local structure around the Ni promoter atoms (Table 1) rule out the pseudo-intercalation model proposed by Farragher and Cossee (12), the octahedral model of Harris and Chianelli (22) and the tetrahedral site model of Ledoux (23). A model that is fully consistent with the EXAFS data is presented in Fig. 3. In this model the Ni atoms are located at the MoS_2 edges in the Mo plane in a square pyramidal coordination. They are connected to the MoS_2 by four sulphur atoms and an additional fifth sulphur atom is attached in front of the Ni atoms. The Ni-Ni distance of 3.2 Å corresponds to neighbouring Ni atoms (cf. Fig. 3).

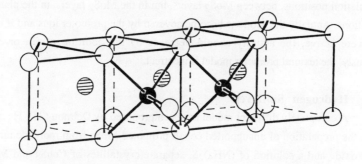

Fig. 3.   Model of the structure of the Ni atoms at the MoS_2 edge, based on EXAFS investigations (19, 20).

The EXAFS results (20) thus clearly prove that the promoter atoms are linked to the MoS_2 edges, as predicted in the Topsøe model (7). EXAFS measurements at the Mo K edge of sulphided Ni-Mo catalysts demonstrated that in the promoted catalysts all Mo atoms are fully surrounded by six sulphur atoms, while in unpromoted supported MoS_2 the Mo atoms have a somewhat lower coordination number (19). This shows that the Ni atoms and the sulphur atoms, which because of stoichiometry come together with the Ni atoms, cover the Mo atoms fully.

ROLE OF THE PROMOTER

Textural Promoter

The strong increase in the catalytic activity of a MoS_2/Al_2O_3 catalyst by addition of Co or Ni has been attributed to an increase in the number of Mo sites at the catalyst surface. By altering the texture of the catalyst surface, the promoter creates more active sites, without itself being involved in the catalysis. Thus, Voorhoeve proposed that the role of Ni in the hydrogenation of cyclohexene and benzene over $Ni-WS_2/Al_2O_3$ is to create more W^{3+} sites (9), which he assumed to be the catalytically active sites. Farragher and Cossee assumed that the promoter atoms induced a surface reconstruction of the edges of the MoS_2 layers, leading to more exposed Mo cations and thus to an enhanced activity (12). Assuming that the normal MoS_2 surface is relaxed (24), so that most Mo cations are covered by sulphur ions, promoter ions in pseudointercalation positions may reconstruct the MoS_2 edge surface, uncover the Mo ions and thus lead to a substantial enhancement in activity. The EXAFS investigations described in the foregoing (19, 20) have, however, clearly demonstrated that the promoter atoms are not present in pseudo intercalation positions, between MoS_2 layers, but in the MoS_2 layers, in the plane of the Mo cations. Actually the Mo ions become covered by the promoter ions and if only Mo ions were active, the activity should decrease by the addition of Co or Ni ions. Obviously, the textural promoter model is incorrect.

Hydrogen Spillover

A completely different model has been proposed by Delmon (25). He observed that in the preparation of unsupported cobalt-promoted MoS_2 from molybdenum oxide, cobalt oxide and a solution of $(NH_4)_2S$, separate crystallites of Co_9S_8 and MoS_2 are formed, and that such a mixture shows a promotion effect. As explanation he proposed that the role of the cobalt sulphide promoter is to provide hydrogen atoms to MoS_2. These spilled-over H atoms would create reduced centers on the MoS_2 surface, which would be the catalytically active sites. The Co_9S_8 then has a "remote control" over the MoS_2 surface. Combined Mössbauer and activity studies demonstrated, however, that even when the presence of minor amounts of Co_9S_8 could be excluded (at Co/Mo < 0.4), the catalytic activity was still increased by a factor of 30 by the addition of cobalt (7). Furthermore, when at high cobalt loading Co_9S_8 became the dominant cobalt phase, the catalytic activity actually decreased. Therefore the promotion effect was attributed to cobalt present in the Co-Mo-S phase, with cobalt ions located at the MoS_2 surface, and a significant contribution of separate Co_9S_8 was excluded (7, 11).

Modified Mo Site

The idea that the promoter ion influences a neighbouring Mo site and in fact creates a much more active site has amongst others been proposed by Chianelli et al. (26). Originally they proposed that a mixed Co-Mo site with a shared sulphur vacancy was responsible for the improved catalytic activity and they argued that the average heat of formation of MoS_2 and Co_9S_8 would be perfect for an optimum reaction rate. The average heat of formation would be intermediate between a too strong and a too weak heat of formation and as a result the mixed Co-Mo site would have an activity near the maximum of the Balandin volcano curve. In their theoretical calculations on the promoter effect, however, Harris and Chianelli rejected this mixed site model, because they calculated that the M-S bond strength did not change significantly upon introduction of a promoter ion (22). Instead, they proposed that the electron density at the Mo sites is increased by Co and Ni promoter ions, and that the modified, reduced Mo sites have a higher activity. Their conclusions are based on SCF-Xα scattered wave calculations of $(MS_6)^{n-}$ and $(S_3MS_3MoS_3)^{m-}$ complexes (22, 27). They assumed that such complexes are representative of the environment of the metal cations at the catalyst surface. In their calculations they took all cations to be octahedrally surrounded by sulphur anions and gave the cations the same oxidation state as they have in the bulk of the most stable metal sulphides. For instance, the Mo cations were taken to be Mo^{4+} ions, and the Co and Ni cations to be M^{2+} ions. Furthermore it was assumed that the catalytic activity is proportional to the product of the M-S bond strength and the number of electrons in the highest occupied molecular orbital (HOMO).

From their calculations on $(MS_6)^{n-}$ complexes, Harris and Chianelli concluded that differences in catalytic activities between different transition metal sulphides are due to electronic factors, such as electron occupancy of the HOMO and covalency of the d-orbitals (27). The calculations on $(S_3MS_3MoS_3)^{m-}$ complexes, in which M was varied from V to Zn, indicated that the promotion effect is related to the donation of electrons from promoter ion to Mo^{4+}. The energy levels of the e_g HOMOs of the Co and Ni complexes are especially well suited for electron donation to the t_{2g} HOMO of Mo^{4+} (22). This electron-donation model of Harris and Chianelli is very similar to the qualitative models proposed earlier by Voorhoeve (9), de Beer and Schuit (28), and Gates et al. (29). Electron donation leads to weakening of the Mo-S bond in all these models.

A way to determine if the promoter ion just creates more sulphur vacancies (textural promoter), or if it changes the nature of the active site (modifier of Mo), would be to determine the number of active sites. Tauster et al. reported that the O_2 uptake of unsupported MoS_2 samples, measured by pulsed, dynamic O_2 chemisorption, varied linearly with HDS activity (30). On the other hand, Zmierczak et al. concluded that O_2 chemisorption is corrosive and that a stable O_2 adsorption is only obtained at -78 °C (31). At higher temperatures a continued O_2 consumption indicated that slow oxidation of the sulphided Mo and Co-Mo catalysts occurs. TEM studies of Chianelli and Daage support these results. They showed that short exposure of unsupported MoS_2 to oxygen during dynamic O_2 chemisorption resulted in substantial oxidation of the crystals (32). A ring of oxidized material was observed around the edges of the crystals. The fact that this oxidation was topotactic explains why a linear relationship is observed between O_2 chemisorption and HDS activity for a certain class of catalysts (e.g., MoS_2), but another relationship for another class of catalysts such as promoted MoS_2. Both O_2 chemisorption and HDS activity are linearly dependent on the crystal edge surface area and therefore there is also a linear relationship between chemisorption and activity. However, this relationship will depend on factors such as O_2 pressure, temperature and exposure time during chemisorption and on the type of crystal surface (e.g., promoted or unpromoted). Since O_2 chemisorption reflects the general state of dispersion of the (un)promoted catalyst rather than the specific sites, at present O_2 chemisorption cannot be used for the quantitative determination of active sites (31).

The use of the less aggressive CO as an adsorbent for the determination of the active surface area of a sulphide catalyst has been investigated by Bachelier et al. (33). They observed that CO binds somewhat stronger to MoS_2 than to Al_2O_3 and proposed the use of CO adsorption at 0 °C as a measure for the sulphide surface area. Also, NO has been tried as a selective adsorbent on the active surface of metal sulphides (15, 34, 35). The infrared and adsorption results of Topsøe and Topsøe (15) demonstrated that there is a good correlation between NO chemisorption and HDS activity of MoS_2/Al_2O_3 catalysts, but not for promoted catalysts. On the other hand, Shuxian et al. concluded from XPS studies of the adsorption of O_2 and NO on polycrystalline MoS_2, that NO adsorbs dissociatively above 130 K and that the resulting oxygen atoms lead to surface oxidation above 200 K. They therefore suggested that one should be careful in interpreting IR spectra of adsorbed NO (34). Further work on chemisorption on the active surface area of an HDS catalyst therefore seems appropriate. A method to measure the active catalytic surface area would not only be of importance as a standard test, but also for calculating turnover frequencies and comparing intrinsic activities of catalysts. It would also shed light on the function of the HDS promoter.

New Catalytic Site

A completely different model was based on the observation that the thiophene HDS activities of cobalt and nickel sulphide supported on carbon were higher than that of MoS$_2$/C, which suggested that cobalt and nickel sulphide might act as the catalyst instead of the promoter (36). Sulphided cobalt or nickel on Al$_2$O$_3$ catalysts have a low HDS activity and therefore Co and Ni have never been considered to be able to act as catalysts in sulphided Co-Mo and Ni-Mo systems. But today it is known that during the usual catalyst preparation of sulphided Co/Al$_2$O$_3$ or Ni/Al$_2$O$_3$ catalysts, cobalt and nickel ions interact strongly with Al$_2$O$_3$ and that either the metal ions are not sulphided at all and do not contribute to HDS activity, or that the application of severe sulphidation conditions lowers their dispersion and activity. Consequently, a higher activity for a Co-Mo or Ni-Mo catalyst is obtained when in the preparation procedure the Mo impregnation is applied before the Co impregnation, preventing the strong interaction between cobalt and nickel ions and Al$_2$O$_3$. The carbon-supported cobalt and nickel sulphide catalysts demonstrate that when these catalysts are prepared with a high dispersion, they indeed have a high activity.

That cobalt and nickel sulphide are at least as active, or may be more active than MoS$_2$ is not an isolated case. Pecoraro and Chianelli (37), Vissers et al. (38), and Ledoux et al. (39) have demonstrated that many transition metal sulphides have a higher HDS activity than MoS$_2$ or WS$_2$. Apparently a high HDS activity is not inherent to layer-lattice metal sulphides such as MoS$_2$ and WS$_2$, because most transition metal sulphides have a different crystal structure. For the 4d and 5d metal sulphides, a Balandin volcano-type activity behaviour was observed, with maxima in the HDS of dibenzothiophene for unsupported RuS$_2$ and OsS$_2$ (37) and maxima in the HDS of thiophene for rhodium and iridium sulphide supported on carbon (38, 39).

Recently Vissers et al. made an attempt to solve the problem of the metal sulphide dispersion by measuring the thiophene HDS activities of series of sulphided Mo/C and Co/C catalysts with varying metal loading. They noted that at equal atomic loading the Co catalysts were about two to three times more active than the Mo catalysts (40). XPS intensity measurements indicated, however, that Co was much less well dispersed than Mo. The activity per mole of metal present of both metal sulphides increased with decreasing metal loading, but much more strongly for cobalt sulphide. By extrapolating the activities to zero metal loading, Vissers et al. obtained a sevenfold higher activity for cobalt sulphide than for MoS$_2$. Since the very best dispersion is expected at very low loading, the ratio of 7 for the relative activity of Co to Mo seems the best value to use whenever all or most of the cobalt is exposed. Vissers et al. explained the activity of a sulphided Co-Mo/C catalyst completely by the very high activity of the cobalt sites. Also, the observed ratio of the rates of hydrogenation and HDS for the Co-Mo/C catalyst was close to that of sulphided Co/C, and substantially different from that of MoS_2/C. Accordingly, MoS_2 was regarded as a support for the cobalt sulphide phase, enabling the cobalt sulphide to be optimally dispersed and preventing its disappearance into the Al_2O_3 carrier. The EXAFS results of the Mo and Ni-Mo catalysts, which indicated that the Ni and S atoms cover the Mo atoms in the Ni-Mo catalysts fully (cf. Local Ni Structure), are in agreement with this conclusion.

ROLE OF THE P MODIFIER
Dispersion Improver

The role of phosphorus in hydrotreating catalysts has long been seen as to be restricted to the enhancement of the solubility of molybdate in the impregnation solution (41) and to the improvement of the mechanical and thermal stability of the support by $AlPO_4$ formation (42). As to its direct role in HDS and HDN catalysis, positive effects on HDS (41, 43-45) and HDN (3, 43, 44) have been reported. There have been some attempts to explain these positive effects by changes in active phase dispersion (3, 41, 45), since it is well known that phosphate has a strong interaction with the Al_2O_3 support and forms $AlPO_4$ (3, 46) which decreases the adsorption of molybdate (46) and weakens the interaction between molybdenum and nickel oxide and the support (3, 46, 47). Consequently, the dispersion of the active phase may change. But not only the dispersion, but also the surface structure and crystal morphology of the catalyst may change. Thus metal sulphide catalysts have a higher intrinsic activity on less polar supports like carbon (48) and a high resolution transmission electron microscopy study showed that nickel and phosphate contribute to stacking of the MoS_2 slabs in sulphided Ni-Mo-P/Al_2O_3 catalysts (49). It is not clear if this stacking is related to the structure transformation of Co-Mo/Al_2O_3 catalysts described by Candia et al. (50). By comparing activity data with [57]Co Mössbauer emission data they observed that Co-Mo/Al_2O_3 catalysts sulphided at high temperature were intrinsically more active per Co atom in the Co-Mo-S phase than those sulphided at normal temperatures (400-500 °C). They introduced the notation of type I Co-Mo-S for the Co-Mo-S structure which was formed after low temperature sulphidation and type II for the Co-Mo-S structure formed after high temperature sulphidation. In addition to changing the dispersion and morphology of the active Ni-Mo-S phase, phosphate may also be more directly involved in the HDS or HDN catalysis, for instance in the acid catalyzed N-removal elimination reaction. In relation to this, it has been observed that phosphate changes the acidity of the alumina support (3) and affects the cracking and isomerisation activity of the catalyst (46).

Support And Catalyst Modifier

Recently we studied the effect of phosphate on the activity and selectivity of sulphided Al_2O_3-supported Ni, Mo, Ni-Mo and Rh catalysts in the HDN of quinoline (cf. Fig. 4) and the HDS of thiophene (cf. Fig. 5) (51). Two series of Ni-Mo catalysts were employed, both with a Mo loading slightly less than the adsorption capacity of the Al_2O_3 used, but one with a Ni/Mo atomic ratio low enough (0.24) for all Ni to be incorporated in the Ni-Mo-S phase, and the other, with the high ratio of 0.72, as in commercial catalysts. In addition two Ni-Mo/Al_2O_3 catalysts, with and without P, prepared by coimpregnation in the presence of the complexing agent nitrilotriacetic acid (NTA), were studied. NTA prepared Co-Mo and Ni-Mo catalysts contain Co or Ni almost exclusively in the Co-Mo-S or Ni-Mo-S type II structure (21) and such catalysts thus may allow us to find out if phosphate induces type I to type II structure transformations.

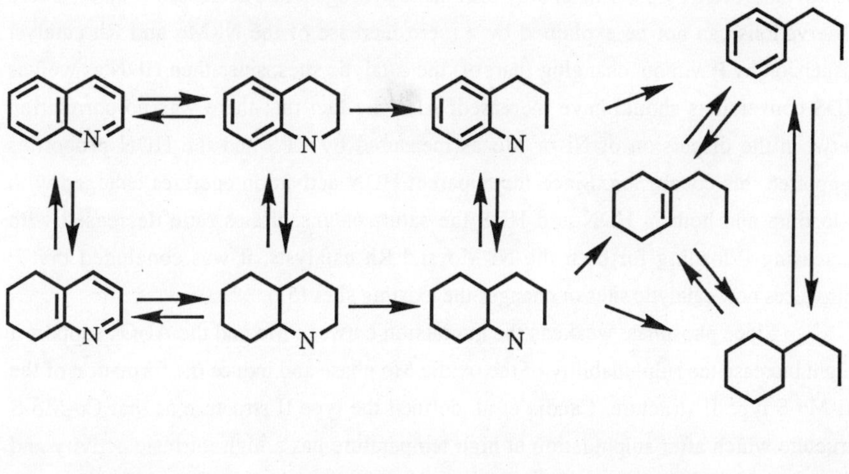

Fig. 4   Reaction network of the hydrodenitrogenation of quinoline to C_9 hydrocarbons and NH_3.

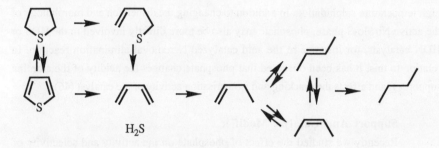

Fig. 5   Reaction network of the hydrodesulphurization of thiophene to C$_4$ hydrocarbons and H$_2$S.

The HDN experiments demonstrated that the addition of Ni to Mo/Al$_2$O$_3$ and the addition of phosphate to Ni-Mo/Al$_2$O$_3$, Ni-Mo(NTA)/Al$_2$O$_3$ and Rh/Al$_2$O$_3$ catalysts significantly increased the conversion of quinoline to hydrocarbons (Fig. 6). Simultaneously the selectivity for propylbenzene increased and that for propylcyclohexane decreased, and the apparent activation energy increased. On the other hand, although the thiophene conversion of Mo/Al$_2$O$_3$ was increased by Ni, the thiophene conversion of Ni-Mo/Al$_2$O$_3$, Ni-Mo(NTA)/Al$_2$O$_3$ and Rh/Al$_2$O$_3$ catalysts was almost unaffected by phosphate, only the butene hydrogenation decreased (Fig. 7). These observations can not be explained by a mere increase of the Ni-Mo and Rh catalyst dispersion by P without changing (part of) the catalytic sites, since then HDN as well as HDS conversions should have increased. Also the fact that there was no correlation between the dispersion of Ni or Mo as measured by XPS and the HDN properties supported this conclusion. Since the apparent HDN activation energies changed with P-loading and both in HDN and HDS the saturates/unsaturates ratio decreased with increasing P-loading for both the Ni-Mo and Rh catalysts, it was concluded that P introduces new catalytic sites or changes the existing sites (51).

        Since phosphate weakens the interaction between Mo and the Al$_2$O$_3$ support it might increase the sulphidability of the oxidic Mo phase and induce the formation of the Ni-Mo-S type II structure. Candia et al. defined the type II structure as that Co-Mo-S structure which after sulphidation at high temperature has a high intrinsic activity and suggested that while the type I structure is characterized by interactions between the Co-Mo-S phase and the support via Mo-O-Al linkages, type II might have few if any

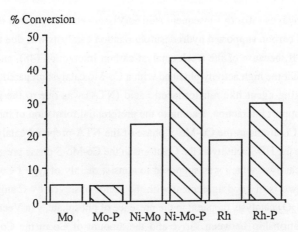

Fig.6   Conversion of Al_2O_3 supported Mo, Ni-Mo and Rh catalysts, with
and without phosphate, in the HDN of quinoline at 30 atm, 370 °C,
0.26 g Q·(g cat.)$^{-1}$ h^{-1} and 2.5×10^3 mol H$_2$·(mol Q)$^{-1}$

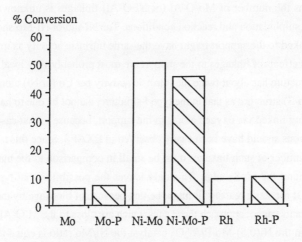

Fig.7   Conversions of Al_2O_3 supported Mo, Ni-Mo and Rh catalysts, with
and without phosphate, in the HDS of thiophene at 1 atm, 400 °C,
0.93 l thiophene.(g cat)$^{-1}$·h^{-1} and 15 mol H$_2$·(mol T)$^{-1}$.

of such linkages (50). In subsequent studies Vissers et al. suggested that the high HDS activity of carbon supported hydrodesulphurization catalysts was due to the presence of Co-Mo-S II, because of the weak catalyst-carbon interaction (48), and van Veen et al. assumed that the high activity obtained with a Co-Mo catalyst prepared in the presence of a complexing agent like nitrilotriacetic acid (NTA) was due to the prevention of the catalyst-support interaction, leading to the preferential formation of the type II structure (21). The Co atoms in the Co-Mo-S phase of the NTA-prepared catalyst were found to have twice the HDS activity as the Co atoms in the Co-Mo-S phase present in a classically prepared catalyst, which was supposed to consist mainly of type I Co-Mo-S (52). This factor of two is in good agreement with the factor observed by Candia et al. (50). For Co-Mo/Al$_2$O$_3$ catalysts prepared in the presence of phosphate, van Veen et al. observed a linear relationship between k$_{HDS}$ and the amount of Co in the Co-Mo-S phase (as determined by Mössbauer spectroscopy) with a slope intermediate between those of the NTA-prepared and classic Co-Mo catalysts, indicating that phosphate-containing Co-Mo/Al$_2$O$_3$ catalysts contain a mixture of the Co-Mo-S types I and II structures (52).

Whether in all cases it is possible to subdivide the M-Mo-S phase into two types is, of course, an open question. Type II, the fully sulphided form with no interactions with the support, appears to be relatively well defined, but type I is certainly less well defined, as the number of Mo-O-Al (or Ni-O-Al) linkages is unknown and is likely to vary with sulphidation and reaction conditions. The Ni and/or Ni-Mo sites in type I which are not linked to the support might have the same intrinsic activity as in type II, since the electronic effects of linkages to the support are most probably very local. The fact that the type II structure has about twice the intrinsic activity per Co (or Ni) atom in the Co-Mo-S (or Ni-Mo-S) structure as that in the type I structure, cannot be due to half of the Co or Ni atoms being linked via oxygen atoms to the support, because in that case Co-O and Ni-O coordinations should have been easily observed in EXAFS. Since this is not the case (19, 20), the number of such linkages must be small in comparison to the number of Co or Ni atoms around the MoS$_2$ edge. This only leaves the possibility that type I is less active than type II for steric reasons. It might be that because of blockage by the support, in type I the reactants cannot approach those sites which are close to the M-O-Al linkages.

In the Ni(0.5)-Mo-P/Al$_2$O$_3$ catalyst the Ni/Mo ratio is equal to 0.24 and this is low enough for all Ni to end up in the Ni-Mo-S phase. The first order specific rate constants for the HDS of thiophene and the zero-order specific rate constants for the HDN of quinoline per atom of Ni per nm^2 of support area, of the Ni(0.5)-Mo-P(0 and 2), Ni(1.5)-Mo-P(0 and 2) and of the Ni(0.6)-Mo (+NTA)-P(0 and 2) catalysts are presented in Table 2. Comparison of the Ni(0.5)-Mo and Ni(0.5)-Mo + NTA results shows that the presence of NTA during catalyst preparation enhances the HDS and HDN activities appreciably. If it is assumed that the NTA based Ni(0.5)-Mo catalyst consist of type II Ni-Mo-S and the conventionally prepared Ni(0.5)-Mo catalyst of type I, this indicates that type II is 2.9 times more active in HDS and 2.3 more active in HDN than type I.

Table 2   First-order thiophene-HDS and zero-order quinoline-HDN specific rate constants per at Ni per nm^2 support surface area (51). The metal loading in at/nm^2 is given in parentheses, the Mo loading was always 2.1 at/nm^2.

	k_{HDS}	k_{HDN}
Ni(0.5)Mo	5.2	0.25
Ni(0.5)Mo P(2)	7.2	0.48
Ni(1.5)Mo	4.4	0.16
Ni(1.5)Mo P(2)	4.0	0.30
Ni(0.6)Mo + NTA	15	0.56
[Ni(0.6)Mo + NTA] P(2)	16	1.15
Rh(0.5)	1.8	0.36
Rh(0.5) P(1)	2.0	0.58

Bifunctionality

If the only effect of phosphate in the Ni-Mo catalysts was to influence the proportion of type I and type II, then the activity of the Ni(0.5)-Mo catalyst should increase upon phosphate addition, since the strong phosphate - alumina interaction can only decrease the molybdate - alumina interaction and thus, after sulphidation, increase the proportion of the type II structure. Even if there would be a simultaneous increase in the MoS_2 crystallite size of the Ni-Mo-S phase(s), this will not lead to Ni_3S_2 segregation and to a decrease of specific activity, because of the low Ni/Mo = 0.24 ratio. Also, phosphate should have no influence on the NTA prepared catalyst, since in that catalyst all Ni is already in the most active Ni-Mo-S II form. Although k_{HDS} and k_{HDN} for the

Ni(0.5)-Mo catalyst indeed increased upon phosphate addition and k_{HDS} for the Ni(0.6)-Mo + NTA catalyst stayed more or less constant, k_{HDN} of the NTA catalyst was doubled by the phosphate addition (Table 2). Thus, although the type I to II structure transformation explains part of the results, it can not explain all, especially not the HDN results. This special position of the HDN results was also evident in the other catalysts. Phosphate influenced the performance of the Rh catalyst in a similar way as that of the Ni-Mo + NTA, or indeed all Ni-Mo, catalysts. The HDN activity improved considerably, while the HDS activity was not much influenced. Apparently the increase in HDN conversion upon phosphate addition is inherent to the mechanism of the HDN of quinoline (Q).

The HDN and HDS reaction networks are complex reaction networks. In the Q-HDN network hydrogenation as well as N-removal (elimination and/or hydrogenolysis) reactions are present (Fig. 4). These reactions occur on different sites, as demonstrated by the fact that addition of H_2S during HDN decreases ring hydrogenation activity and increases aliphatic C-N bond breaking (53). The former reactions take place on Ni, Ni-Mo-S or Mo sites with a sulphur vacancy, while the latter reactions take place on Brønsted acid sites, originating from H_2S adsorption on the metal sulphide (54), the support or from the phosphate promoter. A HDN catalyst is thus a bifunctional catalyst. In the HDN of quinoline, both the N-removal from decahydroquinoline and the preceding hydrogenations are slow, thus precluding a rate-determining-step treatment. The thiophene HDS reaction network is still under debate. At high pressure the mechanism is similar to that of HDN (4), hydrogenation followed by S-removal (Fig. 5). The reaction at 1 atm may, however, take place via the direct hydrogenolysis of thiophene to butadiene, followed by hydrogenation to butene and butane, or via the high pressure mechanism (55). There is general agreement, however, that the first step - be it the hydrogenation or the hydrogenolysis of thiophene - is rate determining. This first step is assumed to take place on a Mo, Ni or Ni-Mo-S site, which has a sulphur vacancy.

The special effect of phosphate on the HDN of quinoline can be explained if it is assumed that in the Q-HDN dual site mechanism phosphate provides (extra) N-removal (elimination and or hydrogenolysis) sites. After all, pure Al_2O_3 is already a good catalyst for the denitrogenation of piperidine and other cyclic amines (56). The bifunctionality was proved in separate experiments with dual catalyst beds containing Ni-Mo/Al_2O_3 in one bed and P/Al_2O_3 in the other (51). Studies by Diez et al. confirmed the bifunctional model. They observed that the rate constants for hydrogenation and N-removal in the HDN of quinoline over Ni-Mo-P/Al_2O_3 catalysts both decreased upon coking, but that the rate constant for N-removal decreased more strongly (57). This confirms that the N-removal reaction takes place, at least partly, at other sites than the hydrogenation sites and that the Ni-Mo-P/Al$_2$O$_3$ HDN catalyst is bifunctional.

In the Ni(1.5)-Mo catalysts the Ni/Mo atomic ratio is quite high (0.72), so that more Ni is present than can be accommodated in the Ni-Mo-S phase. Thus the sulphided catalysts will contain nickel sulphide in addition to the Ni-Mo-S phase. This nickel sulphide phase probably has a low dispersion and may be assumed to have a negligible activity relative to the Ni-Mo-S phase(s). This directly explains why the Ni(1.5)-Mo catalysts have lower specific rate constants than the Ni(0.5)-Mo catalysts (Table 2). Another point is that the type II MoS$_2$ crystallites are larger than the type I crystallites (52), since the former type is generated from molybdenum oxide in weak interaction with the support. As a consequence, the more type II is present, the more Ni will be forced to segregate as nickel sulphide. In the P-containing catalysts not only the interaction between molybdate and support will be weaker, but also, because phosphate decreases the support surface area, a greater extent of formation of bulk MoO$_3$ and polymeric molybdenum oxide will occur, which after sulphiding leads to larger MoS$_2$ crystallites with less interaction with the support (58).

The Ni(1.5)-Mo/Al$_2$O$_3$ catalyst appeared to be about twice as active in the HDS of thiophene and HDN of quinoline as its Ni(0.5)-Mo/Al$_2$O$_3$ counterpart (51), which suggests that about two thirds of the Ni in the Ni(1.5)Mo catalyst is present as Ni-Mo-S I after sulphidation. This estimate would limit the Ni/Mo ratio in the Ni-Mo-S phase to $1/2.1 = 0.5$ and would be in agreement with our EXAFS investigation on Ni-Mo/Al$_2$O$_3$ and Ni-Mo/C catalysts, in which segregated Ni$_3$S$_2$ was only observed for Ni/Mo > 0.5 (20). The presence of phosphate in the Ni(1.5)-Mo/Al$_2$O$_3$ catalyst decreases the specific HDS rate constant slightly, but doubles the specific HDN rate constant (Table 2). The decrease in HDS activity can only be explained by a loss of the Ni dispersion, and thus by a decrease in the Ni-Mo-S edge area and an increase in the amount of Ni$_3$S$_2$. When, as to be expected, the phosphate induces, partly, the formation of Ni-Mo-S II, then the loss of Ni dispersion should even be greater, to compensate for the larger activity of Ni sites in the Ni-Mo-S II phase. The data of Table 2 can semiquantitatively be explained if it is assumed that in the Ni-Mo/Al$_2$O$_3$ catalysts no Ni-Mo-S II is present, that the Ni(1.5)-Mo catalyst contains one third of the Ni in the form of inactive Ni$_3$S$_2$ and that the NTA-based Ni(0.6)-Mo catalysts contain exclusively Ni-Mo-S II. These assumptions seem reasonable, since the high calcination temperature will lead to a high proportion of Ni-Mo-S I and, as discussed before, only the Ni(1.5)-Mo catalyst should contain Ni$_3$S$_2$.

With these assumptions it is calculated that addition of phosphate to be Ni(0.5)-Mo catalyst leads to a change from 100 % Ni-Mo-S I to 80 % Ni-Mo-S I and 20 % Ni-Mo-S II, while the presence of phosphate in the Ni(1.5)-Mo catalyst leads to a change from 67 % Ni-Mo-S I and 33 % Ni_3S_2 to 20 % Ni-Mo-S I, 20 % Ni-Mo-S II and 60 % Ni_3S_2. Thus, for the Ni(0.5)-Mo-P catalyst the specific HDS rate constant is calculated to be 0.8 x 5.2 + 0.2 x 16 = 7.4, compared to 7.2 (Table 2), while the specific HDN rate constant is calculated as 0.43, to be compared with 0.48 (Table 2). For the Ni(1.5)-Mo-P catalyst one predicts 0.2 x 5.2 + 0.2 x 16 = 4.2 for k_{HDS} and 0.28 for k_{HDN} to be compared with 4.0 and 0.30, respectively. Taking into account that the sulphidation procedure was slightly different in the HDS and HDN cases and that the uncertainty in the measurement of the conversion can easily amount to one or two percent, the agreement is reasonable.

CONCLUSIONS

It can be concluded that phosphate is an efficient HDN promoter in the nitrogen removal from quinoline over Ni-Mo/Al$_2$O$_3$ and Rh/Al$_2$O$_3$ catalysts, but that it does not significantly influence the sulphur removal from thiophene. The effect of phosphate is due to a combination of several factors. On the one hand it improves the catalytic properties, both for HDN and HDS, by promoting the formation of the type II Ni-Mo-S phase. On the other hand, it leads to growth of the Ni-Mo-S crystallites, which, especially at high Ni loading, leads to the segregation of Ni_3S_2 and loss of activity. In addition to these structural effects, phosphate also plays a direct role in the HDN reaction, since the removal of nitrogen from cyclic amines is promoted by phosphate and the N-removal in the reaction network of the HDN of quinoline is a slow step.

As a general rule for both HDN and HDS it can be concluded that the effect of phosphate depends on the fact if the C-N or C-S bond breaking steps are slower or faster than the hydrogenation steps. Thus, in the HDN of quinoline (with its slow N-removal from decahydroquinoline) phosphate has a beneficial effect, in the HDS of thiophene it has no effect and in the HDN of pyrrole, in which the first hydrogenation step is rate determining (4), it is predicted to have no effect. Phosphate therefore has a similar effect as H$_2$S, which accelerates C-N bond breaking and slows down hydrogenation (53, 59) and thus accelerates the HDN of quinoline (53) and decelerates the HDN of pyrrole (60) and the HDS of thiophene. Because of its positive effect on the HDN of pyridine-type molecules, but negative effect on that of pyrrole-type molecules, the effect of phosphate on real oil feeds is hard to predict. It may depend on the type of oil.

The nickel and cobalt atoms function in our view as catalysts and not as promoters. They need the MoS_2 as a support in order that the right kind of square pyramidal sites are available. Their main function is to improve the catalyst activity for the hydrogenation of the heteroaromatics, the activity of MoS_2 being low. In addition, the surface of the metal sulphides furnishes sites for the elimination of NH_3 and H_2S from alicyclic amines (like decahydroquinoline) and sulphides (like tetrahydrothiophene), respectively (61).

REFERENCES

1. Prins, R., de Beer, V.H.J. and Somorjai, G.A., Catal. Rev. Sci. Eng. 31, 1 (1989).

2. Knözinger, H., "Proc. 9th Int. Congress Catal." (M.J. Phillips and M. Ternan, Eds.), The Chemical Institute of Canada, Ottawa, 5, 20 (1988).

3. Ramirez de Agudelo, M.M. and Morales, A., "Proc. 9th Int. Congress Catal." (M.J. Phillips and M. Ternan, Eds.), The Chemical Institute of Canada, Ottawa, 1, 42 (1988).

4. Schulz, H., Schon, M. and Rahman, N.M., Stud. Surf. Sci. Catal. 27, 201 (1986).

5. Bouwens, S.M.A.M., Prins, R., de Beer, V.H.J. and Koningsberger, D.C., J. Phys. Chem. 94, 3711 (1990).

6. Arnoldy, P., van den Heijkant, J.A.M., de Bok, G.D. and Moulijn, J.A., J. Catal. 92, 35 (1985).

7. Topsøe, H. and Clausen, B.S., Catal. Rev. Sci. Eng. 26, 395 (1984).

8. Hayden, T.F. and Dumesic, J.A., J. Catal. 103, 366 (1987).

9. Voorhoeve, R.J.H. and Stuiver, J.C.M., J. Catal. 23, 228, 243 (1971).

10. Farias, M.H., Gellman, A.J., Somorjai, G.A., Chianelli, R.R. and Liang, K.S., Surf. Sci. 140, 181 (1984).

11. Topsøe, H. and Clausen, B.S., Appl. Catal. 25, 273 (1986).

12. Farragher, A.L. and Cossee, P., "Proc. 5th Int. Congress Catalysis", North-Holland, Amsterdam, 1301 (1973).

13. Anzenhofer, K., van den Berg, J.M., Cossee, P. and Helle, J.N., J. Phys. Chem. Solids 31, 1057 (1970).

64

14. Chianelli, R.R., Ruppert, A.F., Behal, S.K., Kear, B.H., Wold, A. and Kershaw, R., J. Catal. 92, 56 (1985).

15. Topsøe, N.Y. and Topsøe, H., J. Catal. 84, 386 (1983).

16. Kasztelan, S., Toulhoat, H., Grimblot, H. and Bonnelle, J.P., Appl. Catal. 13, 127 (1984).

17. van Veen, J.A.R., Sudmeijer, O., Emeis, C.A. and de Wit, H., J. Chem. Soc. Dalton Trans. 1825 (1986).

18. Cheng, W.C. and Luthra, N.P., J. Catal. 109, 163 (1988).

19. Bouwens, S.M.A.M., Koningsberger, D.C., de Beer, V.H.J., Louwers, S.P.A. and Prins, R., Catal. Letters 5, 273 (1990).

20. Louwers, S.P.A. and Prins, R., J. Catal. to be published.

21. van Veen, J.A.R., Gerkema, E., van der Kraan, A.M. and Knoester, A., J. Chem. Soc. Chem. Commun. 1684 (1987).

22. Harris, S. and Chianelli, R.R., J. Catal. 98, 17 (1986).

23. Ledoux, M.J., Michaux, O., Agostini, G. and Panissod, P., J. Catal. 96, 189 (1985).

24. Farragher, A.L., Adv. Colloid Interface Sci. 11, 3 (1979).

25. Delmon, B., Bull. Soc. Chim. Belg. 88, 979 (1979).

26. Chianelli, R.R., Pecoraro, T.A., Halbert, T.R., Pan, W.H. and Stiefel, E.I., J. Catal. 86, 226 (1984).

27. Harris, S. and Chianelli, R.R., J. Catal. 86, 400 (1984).

28. de Beer, V.H.J. and Schuit, G.C.A., "Preparation of Catalysts" (B. Delmon, P.A. Jacobs and G. Poncelet, Eds.), Elsevier, Amsterdam, 343 (1976).

29. Gates, B.C., Katzer, J.R. and Schuit, G.C.A., "Chemistry of Catalytic Processes", Mc Graw-Hill, New York, 423 (1979).

30. Tauster, S.J., Pecoraro, T.A. and Chianelli, R.R., J. Catal. 63, 515 (1980).

31. Zmierczak, W., MuraliDhar, G. and Massoth, F.E., J. Catal. 77, 432 (1982).

32. Chianelli, R.R. and Daage, M., private communication.

33. Bachelier, J., Tilliette, M.J., Cornac, M., Duchet, J.C., Lavalley, J.C. and Cornet, D., Bull. Soc. Chim. Belg. 93, 743 (1984).

34. Shuxian, Z., Hall, W.K., Ertl. G. and Knözinger, H., J. Catal. 100, 167 (1986).

35. Miciukiewicz, J., Zmierczak, W. and Massoth, F.E., Bull. Soc. Chim. Belg. 96, 915 (1987).

36. Duchet, J.C., van Oers, E.M., de Beer, V.H.J. and Prins, R., J. Catal. 80, 386 (1983).

37. Pecoraro, T.A. and Chianelli, R.R., J. Catal. 67, 430 (1981).

38. Vissers, J.P.R., Groot, C.K., van Oers, E.M., de Beer, V.H.J. and Prins, R., Bull. Soc. Chim. Belg. 93, 813 (1984).

39. Ledoux, M.J., Michaux, O., Agostini, G. and Panissod, P., J. Catal. 102, 275 (1986).

40. Vissers, J.P.R., de Beer, V.H.J. and Prins, R., J. Chem. Soc. Faraday Trans. I 83, 2145 (1987).

41. Chadwick, D., Aitchison, D.W., Badilla-Ohlbaum, R. and Josefsson, L., Stud. Surf. Sci. Catal. 16, 323 (1982).

42. Hopkins, P.D. and Meyers, B.L., Ind. Eng. Chem. Prod. Res. Dev. 22, 421 (1983).

43. Fitz, C.W. and Rase, H.F., Ind. Eng. Chem. Prod. Res. Dev. 22, 40 (1983).

44. Tischer, R.E., Narain, N.K., Stiegel, G.J. and Cillo, D.L., Ind. Eng. Chem. Res. 26, 422 (1987).

45. Atanasova, P., Halachev, T., Uchytil, J. and Kraus, M., Appl. Catal. 38, 235 (1988).

46. Gishti, K., Iannibello, A., Marengo, S., Morelli, G. and Titarelli, P., Appl. Catal. 12, 381 (1984).

47. van Veen, J.A.R., Hendriks, P.A.J.M., Andrea, R.R., Romers, E.J.G.M. and Wilson, A.E., J. Phys. Chem. 94, 5275, 5282 (1990).

48. Vissers, J.P.R., Scheffer, B., de Beer, V.H.J., Moulijn, J.A. and Prins, R., J. Catal. 105, 277 (1987).

49. Kemp, R.A., Ryan, R.C. and Smegal, J.A., "Proc. 9th Int. Congress Catal." (M.J. Phillips and M. Ternan, Eds.), The Chemical Institute of Canada, Ottawa, 1, 128 (1988).

50. Candia, R., Sørensen, O., Villadsen, J., Topsøe, N.Y., Clausen, B.S. and Topsøe, H., Bull. Soc. Chim. Belg. 93, 763 (1984).

51. Eijsbouts, S., van Gestel, J., van Veen, J.A.R., de Beer, V.H.J. and Prins, R., to be published.

52. van Veen, J.A.R., Gerkema, E., van der Kraan, A.M., Hendriks, P.A.J.M. and Beens, H., J. Catal. to be published.

53. Yang, S.H. and Satterfield, C.N., Ind. Eng. Chem. Proc. Des. Dev. 23, 20 (1984).

66

54. Topsøe, N.Y., Topsøe, H. and Massoth, F.E., J. Catal. 119, 252 (1989).

55. Zdrazil, M., Appl. Catal. 4, 107 (1982).

56. Ledoux, M.J. and Sedrati, M., J. Catal. 83, 229 (1983).

57. Diez, F., Gates, B.C., Miller, J.T., Sajkowski, D.J. and Kukes, S.G., Ind. Eng. Chem. Res. 29, 1999 (1990).

58. Lopez Cordero, R., Esquivel, N., Lazaro, J., Fierro, J.L.G. and Lopez Agudo, A., Appl. Catal. 48, 341 (1989).

59. Fierro, J.L.G., Lopez Agudo, A., Esquivel, N. and Lopez Cordero, R., Appl. Catal. 48, 353 (1989).

60. Perot, G., Brunet, S. and Hamze, N., "Proc. 9th Int. Congress Catal." (M.J. Phillips and M. Ternan, Eds.), The Chemical Institue of Canada, Ottawa, 1, 19 (1988).

61. Eijsbouts, S., de Beer, V.H.J. and Prins, R., J. Catal. 127, 000 (1991).

DESIGN OF ZEOLITE CATALYSTS FOR SOME PETROCHEMICAL APPLICATIONS

P. RATNASAMY
NATIONAL CHEMICAL LABORATORY
PUNE 411 008 - INDIA

CONTENTS

I. INTRODUCTION

Zeolites are crystalline aluminosilicates with a rigid three dimensional network of SiO_4 and AlO_4 tetrahedra wherein cavities and channels of different shapes and sizes are present depending on the structure of a particular zeolite. Zeolites are usually classified on the basis of the diameter of the channels present therein as small, medium or large pore zeolites. These have diameters of 4.1, 5.6 and 7.4 A, respectively. The channels in these zeolites are made up of $Si(Al)O_4$ tetrahedra forming 8, 10 and 12 membered rings, respectively. The catalytic activity of zeolites is associated with the presence of acidic protons in the intracrystalline surface. The concentration and acid strength of these protons are controlled by the number and location of aluminium atoms in the zeolite framework. In addition to acidity, the second most distinguishing characteristic of zeolites is their shape selectivity in catalytic reactions. Only those molecules which are smaller than the zeolite pore diameter can be converted or exit as products from the interior volume of the zeolite catalysts. Figure 1 illustrates the structures of some commercially important zeolites, erionite (small pore), ZSM-5 (medium pore) and Y (large pore) zeolites.

69

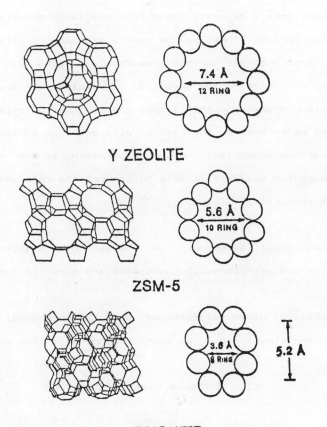

Y ZEOLITE

ZSM-5

ERIONITE

FIG. 1.   EXAMPLES OF STRUCTURES OF LARGE, MEDIUM AND
         SMALL PORE ZEOLITES.

The catalysts used in the various industries can be classified into two broad categories : Heterogeneous and homogeneous. Heterogeneous catalysts, in contrast to homogeneous catalysts, form a separate phase from reactants and products and are often solids. These solids have a microporous structure and a very large internal surface area that may reach 1000 m^2/g. Two features characterise the potential of catalysts in any chemical conversion process. The first one is the activity of the catalyst which defines the rate of disappearance of the reactant into various products. The second parameter is the selectivity with which the catalyst is able to convert the reactant into any desired product(s).

Some major milestones in the use of catalysts in the petroleum and petrochemical industries are given in Table 1.

Table 2 gives examples of some petrochemical processes wherein zeolites are used as major components of the catalysts.

II.   DESIGN OF ZEOLITE CATALYSTS

In the design of zeolite catalysts for any particular petrochemical application the following physicochemical features are particularly controlled and optimised.

1.   Chemical composition — especially Si/Al ratio and Na content.
2.   Crystallinity — minimum of 95 %.

TABLE 1. MILESTONES IN THE USE OF CATALYSTS IN THE PETROCHEMICAL INDUSTRY

DECADE	PROCESS	CATALYST
1900s	BUTTER SUBSTITUTES IN FAT HYDROGENATION	Ni
	METHANE FROM SYNGAS	Ni
1910s	COAL HYDROGENATION TO LIQUID HYDROCARBONS	Fe
	AMMONIA SYNTHESIS - HABER PROCESS	Fe
1920s	METHANOL FROM SYNGAS - BASF HIGH P_R	Zn, Cr OXIDES
	HYDROCARBONS FROM SYNGAS - FISCHER-TROPSCH	PROMOTED Fe, Co
1930s	FIXED BED CAT CRACKING - HOUDRY	Si, Al OXIDES
	ETHYLENE OXIDE	Ag
	PVC	PEROXIDES
	POLYETHYLENE (LD) - ICI HIGH P_R	PEROXIDES
1940s	HYDROFORMYLATION OF OLEFINS TO ALDEHYDES AND ALCOHOLS	Co HOMOGENEOUS
	PLATFORMING OF NAPHTHA TO GASOLINE AND AROMATICS	Pt

DECADE	PROCESS	CATALYST
	CYCLOHEXANONE/CYCLOHEXANOL VIA CYCLOHEXANE OXIDATION (FOR NYLON - 6,6)	CO HOMOGENEOUS
	CYCLOHEXANE VIA BENZENE	NI
	SBR, NBR, BUTYL RUBBER	PEROXIDES, AL
1950s	POLYETHYLENE (HD) - ZIEGLER NATTA AND PHILIPS CATALYSTS	TI OR CR
	POLYPROPYLENE - ZIEGLER NATTA	TI
	POLYBUTADIENE ELASTOMER - ZIEGLER NATTA	TI, CO OR NI
	HDS	CO, MO SULPH.
	ACETALDEHYDE VIA ETHYLENE OXIDATION HOECHST WACKER PROCESS	PD, CU HOMO.
	TEREPTHALIC ACID BY P-XYLENE OXIDATION	CU/MN HOMO
	-OLEFINS VIA ETHYLENE OLIGOMERISATION	AL ET$_3$ HOMO.
	HYDROCRACKING	PT
1960s	MALEIC ANHYDRIDE VIA BUTENE OXIDATION	V, P OXIDES
	ACRYLONITRILE VIA PROPYLENE AMMOXIDATION SOHIO PROCESS	BI, MO OXIDES

DECADE	PROCESS	CATALYST
	HYDROISOMERISATION OF XYLENES	Pt/Al$_2$O$_3$
	ETHYLENE AND 2-BUTENE VIA PROPYLENE METATHESIS	W OXIDES
	ADIPONITRILE VIA HYDROCYANATION OF BUTADIENE	Ni HOMO.
	BIMETALLIC REFORMING CATALYSTS	Pt, Re
	ZEOLITE CRACKING CATALYSTS	ZEOLITE, X, Y
	ACETIC ACID FROM METHANOL - HIGH Pr	Co HOMO.
	VINYL CHLORIDE VIA OXYCHLORINATION OF ETHYLENE	Cu
	VINYL ACETATE VIA ETHYLENE OXIDATION	Pd/Cu
	MODIFIED HOECHST WACKER PROCESS	
	PHTHALIC ANHYDRIDE VIA o-XYLENE OXDN.	V, Ti OXIDES
	PROPYLENE OXIDE VIA PROPYLENE OXDN.	Mo HOMO.
1970s	METHANOL FROM SYNGAS - ICI LOW Pr PROCESS	Cu, Zn, Al OXIDES
	ACETIC ACID FROM METHANOL - MONSANTO LOW Pr	Rh, HOMO.
	XYLENE ISOMERISATION - MOBILs ZSM-5	ZSM-5 ZEOL.
	POLYETHYLENE (LD) VIA ETHYLENE - OLEFINS	Ti, Cr
	COPOLYMERISATION - UNION CARBIDE UNIPOL	

DECADE	PROCESS	CATALYST
	POLYPROPYLENE - IMPROVED CATALYSTS	T_I
	-OLEFINS VIA SEQUENTIAL ETHYLENE OLIGOMERISATION & MATATHESIS - SHELL HIGHER OLEFINS PROCESS	N_I & Mo-W
	IMPROVED HYDROFORMYLATION CATALYSTS UNION CARBIDE - JOHNSON MATHEY	RH, HOMO.
	CHIRAL AMINO ACIDS VIA HYDROGENATION OF -AMINO ACRYLIC ACIDS	RH, HOMO.
1980s	GASOLINE FROM METHANOL - MOBIL	ZSM-5 ZEOL.
	ACETIC ANHYDRIDE FROM SYNGAS VIA CARBONYLATION OF METHYL ACETATE	RH, HOMO.
	METHYL METHACRYLATE BY τ-BUTANOL OXIDATION	Mo OXIDE
	IMPROVED COAL GASIFICATION PROCESS	ALKALI AND ALKALINE METAL SALTS
	SHAPE SELECTIVE TOLUENE DISPROPORTIONATION	SILATED ZSM-5
	AROMATICS FROM LPG CYCLAR PROCESS	PENTASIL ZEOL.

TABLE 2. PETROCHEMICAL PROCESSES USING ZEOLITE CATALYSTS

ALREADY COMMERCIAL

	PROCESSES	PRODUCTS
1	XYLENE ISOMERISATION	PARA AND ORTHO XYLENES
2	TOLUENE DISPROPORTIONATION	BENZENE AND XYLENES
3	ETHYLBENZENE	ETHYLBENZENE
4	PARAETHYL TOLUENE	PARAETHYL TOLUENE
5	PHENOL OXIDATION	PARA METHYL STYRENE HYDROQUINONE AND CATECHOL
6	METHYLAMINE	DI-AND MONO-METHYLAMINES

LIKELY TO BE COMMERCIALISED IN NEAR FUTURE

7	TOLUENE ALKYLATION WITH METHANOL	PARA AND ORTHO XYLENES
8	METHANOL TO OLEFINS	ETHYLENE, PROPYLENE AND BUTENES
9	PARA ALKYL BENZENES	PARA DIETHYL BENZENE PARA DI-ISOPROPYL BENZENE
10	ISOPROPYL BENZENE	INTERMEDIATE FOR PHENOL
11	1.2.4.5 TETRAMETHYL BENZENE	PLASTICISERS

3. Crystallite size - The catalytic activity and stability increase at small crystal sizes (usually smaller than 0.5 micron).

4. The concentration, strength and location of acid sites are modulated by steaming the zeolite under controlled conditions. This procedure removes the Al atoms from the surface of the zeolite crystals leading to lower coke formation and longer life of the catalyst.

5. The relative concentration of the zeolite in the final catalyst formulation.

6. Choice, concentration and location of additional (usually transition group) metals.

7. Shape selectivity - This can be fine-tuned by post-synthesis procedures like silylation which leads to surface passivation and narrowing of the pore mouth. In such molecularly engineered catalysts, the diffusional characteristics of the zeolite is matched with the catalytic requirements.

8. Isomorphous substitution of Al by B or Fe in the lattice framework can lead to significant changes in the selectivity behaviour of the zeolite catalysts. In the methanol-to-olefins process, for example, such changes can enhance the yield of light olefins at the expense of aromatics.

Acid sites in zeolites

Zeolites are converted into their catalytically active form by introduction of protons. The protonation is carried out after the zeolite crystallisation, usually after exchanging the Na^+ ion by NH_4^+ ion and further calcining the zeolite at 400-500°C. Following removal of the base one frequently observes some loss of zeolite crystallinity. This is especially true for aluminium-rich zeolites like A and X, where conversion of the NH_4^+ form to the H^+ form by thermal treatment results in total loss in crystallinity. The same phenomenon occurs, though in an attenuated form, in the case of other zeolites also. Thus, the interaction or 'attack' of the proton with the zeolite framework oxygen causes substantial changes in the bonds surrounding the newly formed hydroxyl groups. This, of course, should be expected considering the very high electron affinity of the proton (13.5 ev) compared to even the smallest alkali metal cation (Li^+ = 5.3 ev). Thus, we should expect that the formation of the acidic O-H groups will cause substantial changes in adjacent T-O-T bonds in the crystal framework. Do these changes that occur during the introduction of active acidic sites by the 'proton attack' on zeolite oxygens remain a local phenomenon limited to atoms adjacent to the O-H group or whether there is a relaxation of the zeolite lattice by a concerted readjustment in order to minimise the loss of lattice vibrational resonance and crystallinity ? The latter phenomenon is more likely.

The acidity and acid strength distribution in zeolites can be quantitatively determined by a variety of techniques like adsorption of bases, thermometric titration, differential scanning calorimetry (DSC), temperature programmed desorption, IR spectroscopy, MASNMR of Al etc. Among the various methods, the calorimetric methods provide the most quantitative data on the strength of the acid-base interaction. Thermometric titration has the advantage of being essentially isothermal but is subject to channel blockage effects due to strongly absorbed bases. DSC provides data similar to thermometric titration but is subject to additional complexities in the calculation of acid strength distribution. TPD is useful, simple and versatile but is strongly affected by heat and mass transfer as well as by multiple adsorption/desorption phenomena.

In addition to acid sites and consequent catalytic activity, zeolites may also be loaded with other catalytically active components (like transition or noble metals) thereby inducing bi or polyfunctional activity in the zeolites.

The design of zeolite catalysts will be illustrated with two examples : (1) Catalysts for the xylene isomerisation process and (2) catalysts for the production of ethylbenzene. Both these processes use ZSM-5 zeolites. Some commercial applications of ZSM-5 zeolites are summarised in Table 3. Table 4 describes the characteristics of other commercially important zeolites used in catalytic applications.

III. ZEOLITE CATALYSTS FOR XYLENE ISOMERISATION

Para and ortho xylenes are important petrochemical intermediates for the production of dimethyl terepthalate (DMT) and purified terepthalic acid (PTA) used for the manufacture of synthetic fibres and pthalic anhydride. They are produced from reformed naptha obtained as the effluent of naptha reformer. The reformed naptha is first fractionated to separate the C_8 fraction ($130-150^{\circ}C$). This fraction contains mainly ethylbenzene and the three xylene isomers (meta, ortho and para) in equilibrium proportions (50 : 26 : 24 %). Therefore, in order to obtain high yields of para and ortho xylenes, a catalytic vapour phase

TABLE 3. COMMERCIAL APPLICATIONS OF ZSM-5 ZEOLITES

	UNITS OPERATING	APPROXIMATE OPERATING CAPACITY
PETROLEUM REFINING		
DISTILLATE DEWAXING (MDDW)	20	110,000 BPSD
LUBE DEWAXING (MLDW)	9	38,000 BPSD
OLEFINS TO GASOLINE & DISTILLATE (MOGD)	-	COMMERCIAL TEST
ZSM-5 IN FCC	OVER 30	
PETROCHEMICALS		
XYLENES ISOMERISATION	19	6 BILLION LBS. YR
TOLUENE DISPROPORTIONATION	3	7,500 B/D
ETHYLBENZENE (MEB)	25	13 BILLION LBS/YR
PARAETHYLTOLUENE	1	35 MILLION LBS/YR
SYNFUELS		
METHANE TO GASOLINE (MTG)	1	14,500 BPSD GASOLINE
METHANE TO OLEFINS (MTO)		100 BPD PILOT PLANT SCALE UP TEST COMPLETED

TABLE 4. COMMERCIALLY IMPORTANT ZEOLITES USED IN CATALYTIC APPLICATIONS

ZEOLITE	CHANNEL SYSTEM[A]	CAVITY[B]
LARGE PORE		
FAUJASITE	(12) 7.4, 3-DIMENSIONAL	6.6, 11.4
(LINDE TYPE X AND LINDE TYPE Y)		
MORDENITE	(8) 2.9 X 5.7, 1D	INTERCONNECTED CHANNELS
	(12) 6.7 X 7.0, 1D	
L	(12) 7.1, 1D	UNIDIMENSIONAL
MEDIUM PORE		
ZSM-5	(10) 5.4 X 5.6, 1D	INTERCONNECTED CHANNELS
	(10) 5.1 X 5.6, 1D	
SYNTHETIC	(8) 3.4 X 4.8, 1D	INTERCONNECTED CHANNELS
FERRIERITE	(10) 4.3 X 5.5, 1D	
SMALL PORE		
ERIONITE	(8) 3.6 X 5.2, 2D	6.3 X 13

A = NUMBER OF OXYGEN ATOMS CONSTITUTING THE SMALLEST RING DETERMINING PORE SIZE (IN PARENTHESES) PORE DIAMETER(S) IN Å, AND NUMBER OF DIRECTIONS IN WHICH THE CHANNEL RUNS.

B = CAVITY FREE DIMENSION(S) IN Å.

process that transforms meta xylene into the para and ortho isomers as well as converting the ethylbenzene into more volatile products like benzene is practised in the petrochemical industry. The various chemical reactions occuring during the xylene isomerisation process are illustrated in Figures 2-5.

Catalysts for xylene isomerisation are evaluated on the basis of the following criteria.

(1)   Per pass conversion of ethylbenzene.
(2)   Xylene loss.
(3) C_8 aromatics loss.
(4)   Para xylene approach to equilibrium (PATE).
(5)   Ortho xylene approach to equilibrium (OATE).
(6)   Ratio of benzene production to conversion of ethylbenzene ($\Delta B/\Delta EB$).

(7)   Hydrogen consumption.
(8)   Throughput ability.
(9)   Purity of ortho xylene produced and
(10) Cycle length and catalyst life.

Brief description of process using ZSM-5 catalyst

Xylene feed is mixed with hydrogen, preheated in feed/effluent exchangers, heated in a heater to the desired reaction temperature and then fed to the reactor. The products leaving the reactor pass through feed/effluent exchangers, fin fan coolers and water coolers into a separator. The liquid from the separator is sent to a stabiliser tower and the gas is sent to the suction of the compressor which discharges the recycle gas to mix with the xylene feed. Isomerisation process is hydrogen consuming. Hence continuous make up of hydrogen is necessary.

FIGURE 2

Xylene Isomerization/Ethylbenzene Conversion Over a Bifunctional Catalyst

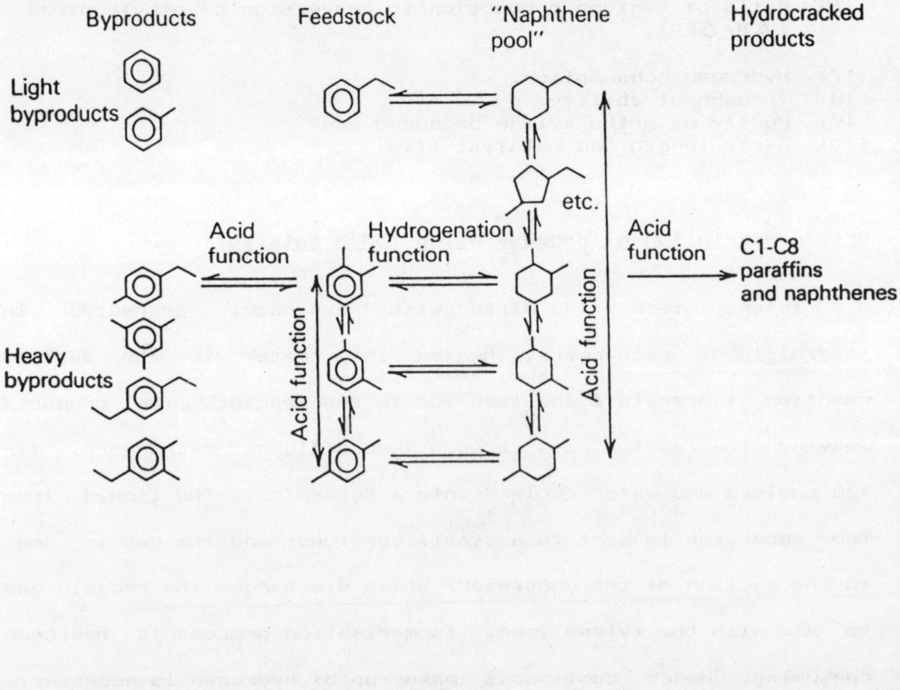

FIGURE 3

Ethylbenzene Conversion Over a Mono-Functional Acid Catalyst
(Formation of Only One Isomer Shown)

Transethylation Reactions

1) Ethylbenzene disproportionation

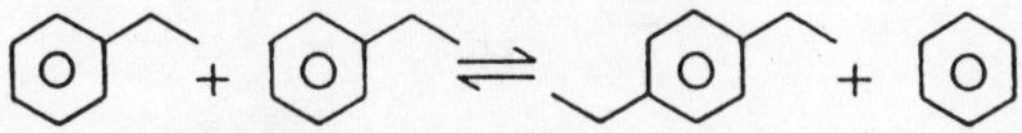

2) Transethylation of xylenes

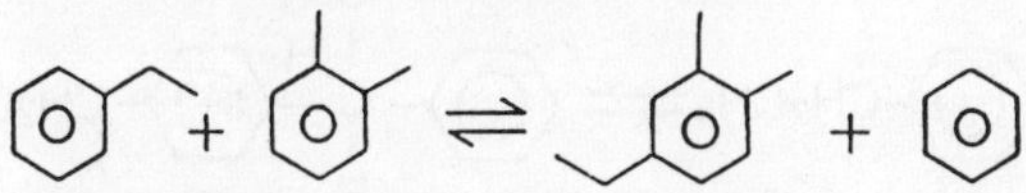

Transmethylation Reactions

3) Xylene disproportionation

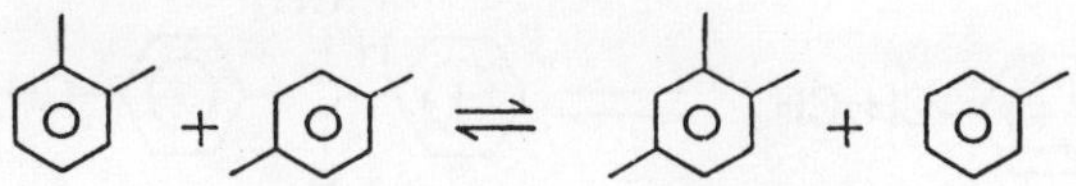

4) Transmethylation of ethylbenzene

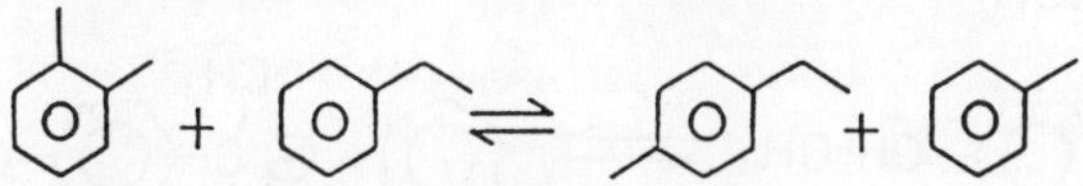

Deethylation Reaction

5) Ethylbenzene Dealkylation

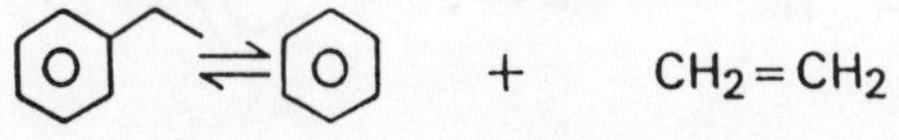

$CH_2 = CH_2$

FIGURE 4

Transethylation Via Biphenyl Ethane

Hydride abstraction

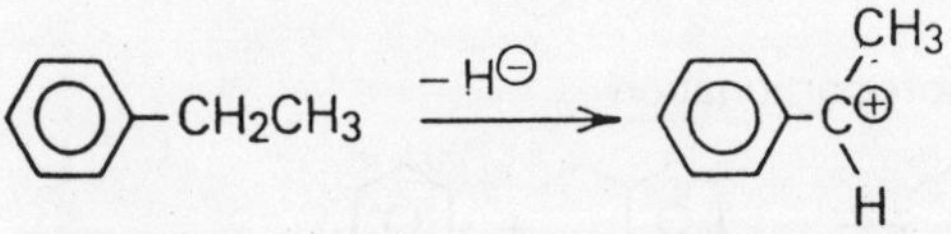

Attack by a second ring

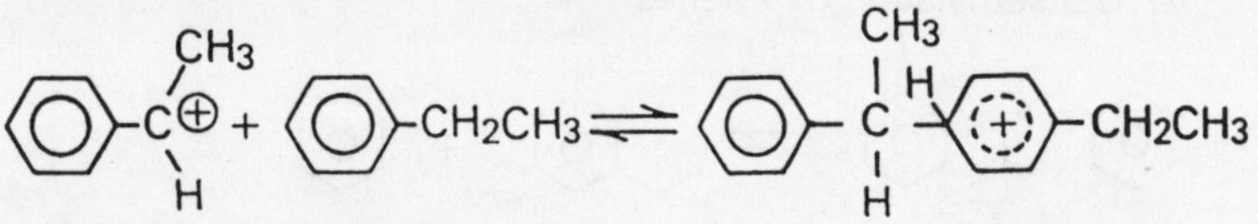

Desorption/adsorption

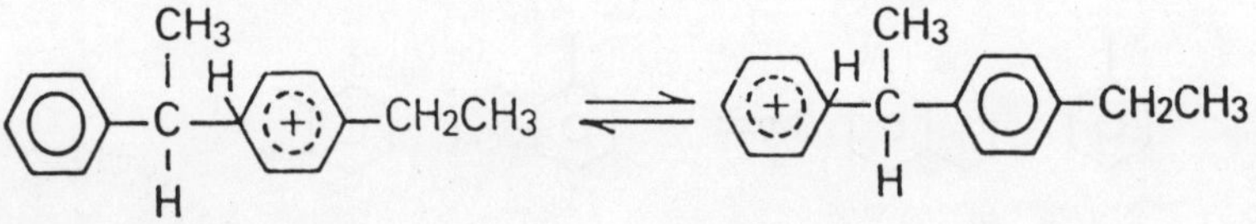

Beta scission

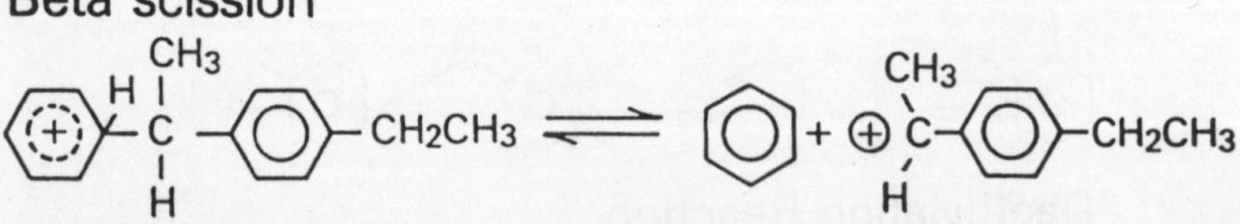

Hydride abstraction

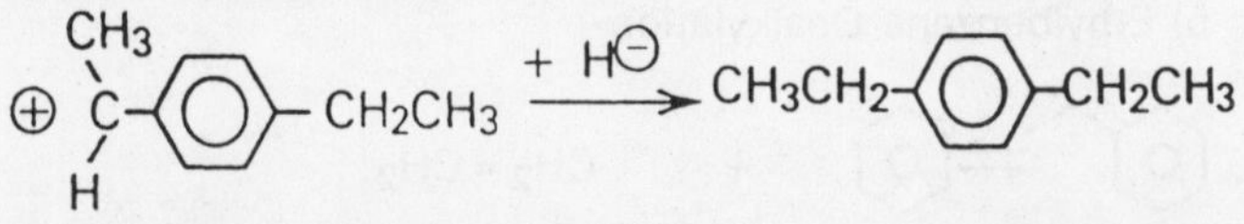

FIGURE 5

Transethylation Via Dealkylation/Realkylation

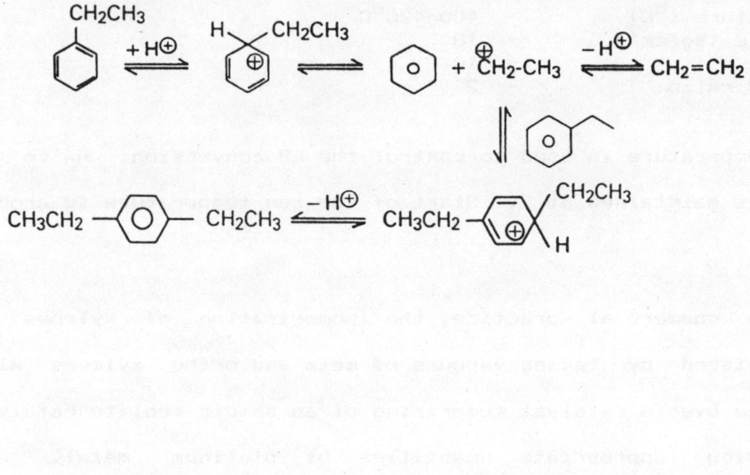

A part of the gas is purged to maintain the purity of the recycle gas. The stabiliser tower removes the light gases as off gas which goes to the fuel gas system. Other light ends are removed as a liquid byproduct from the top. This stream rich in benzene is sent to gasoline blending stock.

The bottom product from the stabiliser tower is sent to distillation unit where xylenes and C_9^+ aromatics are separated.

Operating conditions

The typical operating range for this isomerisation catalyst is :

Temperature (^{O}C)	−	400−420°C
Pressure (kg/cm^2)	−	18
WHSV	−	10
H_2 : HC ratio	−	2

Temperature is used to control the EB conversion. H_2 to HC ratio is maintained at 2. Start of the run temperature is around 400°C.

In commercial practice, the isomerisation of xylenes is accomplished by taking vapours of meta and ortho xylenes with hydrogen over a catalyst comprising of an acidic zeolite catalyst containing appropriate quantities of platinum metal. An important feature of the performance of a good isomerisation catalyst is its capability to handle appreciable amounts (i.e, converting) of ethylbenzene which is present in the feedstock.

Two major xylene isomerisation processes are in world wide practice today. The most widely used one (more than 80 % of plants) is that offered by Mobil Oil Corporation of USA. The octafining process offered by M/s Engelhard and Atlantic Richfield Co. of USA, is the other process. The major advantages of the Mobil process are (1) high throughput of feedstock (WHSV = 10 to 15), (2) high per pass conversion of ethylbenzene to benzene and ethane (upto 60 % ethylbenzene conversion), (3) high production rate of benzene, a valuable by product, (4) high purity of ortho xylene (99 + %) and (5) low consumption of hydrogen (hydrogen/hydrocarbon = 1 to 2). The major significant feature of the octafining process is its ability to hydroisomerise ethylbenzene to xylenes, leading to a net gain of xylenes (2 to 3 %) in the process compared to a loss of 2 to 3 % in the Mobil xylene isomerisation process.

The catalysts are bifunctional in nature containing both acidic and metal functions. The acidic function is necessary to carry out the isomerisation of xylenes by 1.2 alkyl shift and the conversion of ethylbenzene by disproportionation to benzene and diethyl benzene. The metal function removes ethylbenzene by hydrodealkylation to benzene. The hydroisomerisation of ethyl benzene to xylene involves both the acidic and metal functions.

The octafining II catalyst offered by M/s Engelhard, contains about 0.3 % wt. of platinum as the metal function and a blend of mordenite ($SiO_2/Al_2O_3 = 20$) and silica-alumina as the acidic support. The mordenite content is around 20 %. The catalyst offered by Mobil Oil, USA, also contains platinum (but only 0.1 % wt) as the metal function but uses a blend of ZSM-5 zeolite and alumina as the acidic support. A comparison of the performance of the silica-alumina and ZSM-5 based xylene isomerisation catalysts is given in table below :

Table

Comparison of silica-alumina and ZSM-5 based catalysts

	ZSM-5	SiAl
	(Typical values)	
EB conversion, %	Upto 60	30-35
WHSV	10	4
H/HC	1-2	6
PATE, OATE	95-100	95-100
Xyl	-2	+2 to 3
B/ EB	High	Low
Temp. °C	420-450	380-410
PR, ATN	15-20	15-20
H_2 consumption	Low	High
OX purity	High	Lower

In the design of the catalyst for xylene isomerisation, the first decision is the choice of the class of zeolite to be chosen. The table below illustrates the performance of some zeolites in this process. Xylenes disproportionation is not a desirable reaction. The ZSM-5 class of zeolites which gave the lowest disproportionation products was chosen based on the results below :

Table

Selectivity in xylene isomerisation

Zeolite	Si/Al	$\dfrac{k_{Disproportionation}}{k_{Isomerisation}}$
HY	2.5	0.05
Mordenite	7.5	0.014
ZSM-4	3.5	0.01
ZSM-5	35	0.001

Having decided on the ZSM-5 class of zeolites, the influence of some catalyst preparation parameters on activity and selectivity are shown in Figures 6 and 7 and Tables 5 and 6, respectively. The Pt-H-ZSM-5 is seen to be better than the other catalysts tested. Tables 7-12 illustrate the influence of various process parameters including the presence of impurities like S, Cl and NH_3 on the catalyst activity and selectivity. Hence, commercial catalysts for processes using feedstocks containing EB invariably contain platinum or nickel to convert EB into other more easily separable products. When the feedstock does not contain EB, additional metals are not needed and H-ZSM-5 alone may suffice.

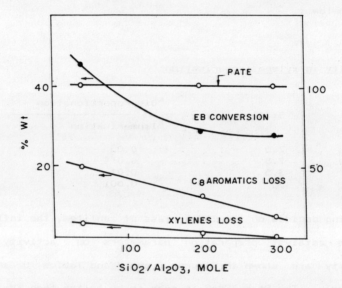

FIG. 6. The influence of the SiO_2/Al_2O_3 ratio in H-ZSM-5 zeolite on catalytic performance. Conditions: Temp. 653 K, pressure 13 bar, molar ratio H_2/oil 8, WHSV 5 h^{-1}.

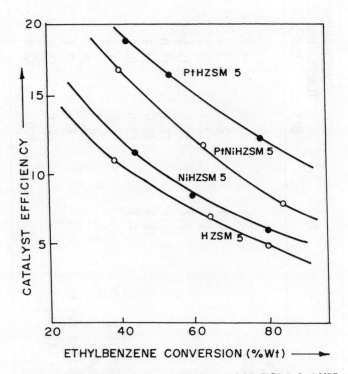

FIG. 7. Comparative evaluation of H-ZSM-5, NiH-ZSM-5, PtH-ZSM-5, and PtNiH-ZSM-5 catalysts at different levels of ethylbenzene conversion.

TABLE 5 . THE INFLUENCE OF THE TEMPERATURE OF CALCINATION OF HZSM-5

COMPOSITION (WT %)	FEED	CALCINATION TEMPERATURE (K)		
		823	933	1123
C_8^- ALIPHATICS	5.6	5.2	4.7	5.0
BENZENE	0.9	2.0	2.2	1.0
TOLUENE	1.5	2.4	2.1	1.1
ETHYLBENZENE	19.2	15.1	15.5	18.5
P-XYLENE	13.5	17.1	17.0	16.0
M-XYLENE	55.0	42.6	44.9	48.7
O-XYLENE	4.3	13.1	10.9	9.0
$C_9 + C_{10}$ AROMATICS	-	1.9	1.6	0.2
Δ XYLENES (WT %)	-	0	0	+0.9
C_8 AROMATICS LOSS (WT %)	-	4.1	3.7	+0.2
EB CONVERSION (%)	-	19.1	15.7	3.5
PATE (%)	-	100	92.8	61.2

NOTE : CATALYST HZSM-5, REACTION TEMPERATURE = 623 K. PRESSURE = 1 BAR, MOLAR RATIO H_2/OIL = 2.3, WHSV = 8 H^{-1}.

TABLE 6. XYLENE ISOMERISATION OVER H-ZSM-5, NiH-ZSM-5, PtH-ZSM-5 AND PtNiH-ZSM-5

	FEED	H-ZSM-5	NiH-ZSM-5	CATALYST PtH-ZSM-5	PtNiH-ZSM-5
COMPOSITION (WT %)					
C_8^- ALIPHATICS	3.5	2.3	2.1	1.5	3.3
BENZENE	1.2	4.3	8.8	10.5	7.8
TOLUENE	3.2	5.0	8.2	3.8	5.1
ETHYLBENZENE	20.8	11.6	6.1	4.4	6.7
P-XYLENE	12.5	16.7	17.2	18.4	18.0
M-XYLENE	54.1	40.2	38.0	44.4	40.4
O-XYLENE	3.8	14.6	17.0	15.8	17.3
$C_9 + C_{10}$ AROMATICS	-	4.6	3.3	1.1	2.2
Δ XYLENES (WT %)	-	+1.0	+1.1	+8.2	+5.0
C_8 AROMATICS LOSS (WT %)	-	8.2	13.0	7.8	9.1
EB CONVERSION (%)	-	38.6	61.1	78.8	64.1
PATE (%)	-	96.3	100	97.2	100

NOTE : TEMP. = 673 K, PRESSURE = 1 BAR, MOLAR RATIO H_2/OIL = 2, WHSV = 5 H^{-1}.

TABLE 7. THE INFLUENCE OF TEMPERATURE

	FEED	REACTION TEMPERATURE (K)		
		623	653	683
COMPOSITION (WT %)				
C_8 ALIPHATICS	4.1	2.2	1.4	1.9
BENZENE	1.9	5.9	9.0	11.0
TOLUENE	2.4	5.1	7.0	9.5
ETHYLBENZENE	27.6	15.9	11.7	8.3
P-XYLENE	9.4	15.0	14.6	14.4
M-XYLENE	48.2	32.0	31.0	30.1
O-XYLENE	6.4	14.4	14.3	14.2
C_9 + C_{10} AROMATICS	-	9.5	10.9	10.5
Δ XYLENES (WT %)	-	-2.6	-4.0	-5.2
C_8 AROMATICS (WT %)	-	14.3	19.9	24.5
EB CONVERSION (%)	-	31.7	45.9	58.8
PATE (%)	-	100	100	100

NOTE : CATALYST HZSM-5, (SiO_2/Al_2O_3 = 36), PRESSURE = 13 BAR, MOLAR RATIO H_2/OIL = 8, WHSV = 5 H^{-1}.

TABLE 8 . THE INFLUENCE OF TOTAL PRESSURE

	FEED	PRESSURE (BAR) 4	10	20	30
COMPOSITION (WT %)					
C_8^- ALIPHATICS	-	-	-	1.2	3.6
BENZENE	2.8	5.8	6.2	7.3	7.8
TOLUENE	2.9	3.9	4.5	5.6	6.6
ETHYLBENZENE	20.0	11.8	11.0	9.8	8.8
P-XYLENE	13.7	18.1	17.7	17.2	17.2
M-XYLENE	55.8	41.4	40.3	37.8	38.0
O-XYLENE	4.7	14.7	15.1	15.4	15.7
$C_9 + C_{10}$ AROMATICS	-	4.2	5.2	5.5	4.5
Δ XYLENES (WT %)	-	-	-1.1	-3.8	-3.3
C_8 AROMATICS LOSS (WT %)	-	8.2	10.2	14.0	14.5
EB CONVERSION (%)	-	41	45	51	56
PATE (%)	-	100	100	100	100

NOTE : CATALYST NiH-ZSM-5, TEMP. = 633 K, MOLAR RATIO H_2/OIL = 8, WHSV = 4 H^{-1}.

TABLE 9 . THE INFLUENCE OF CONTACT TIME

	FEED	CONTACT TIME (S)			
		0.5	1.2	1.8	3.5
COMPOSITION (WT %)					
C_8^- ALIPHATICS	4.4	1.2	1.5	1.3	1.1
BENZENE	1.5	5.7	5.4	6.8	7.3
TOLUENE	3.6	3.6	4.5	6.5	8.3
ETHYLBENZENE	20.0	12.1	7.5	4.2	1.1
P-XYLENE	11.3	18.4	19.3	19.0	19.1
M-XYLENE	55.7	44.1	43.3	41.8	41.9
O-XYLENE	3.5	14.3	16.2	16.9	17.1
$C_9 + C_{10}$ AROMATICS	-	0.4	2.6	3.7	4.1
Δ XYLENES (WT %)	-	+6.3	+8.2	+7.1	+7.7
C_8 AROMATICS LOSS (WT %)	-	1.6	4.2	8.6	11.3
EB CONVERSION (%)	-	38.3	60.6	76.6	93.7
PATE (%)	-	100	100	100	100

NOTE : CATALYST NiH-ZSM-5, TEMP. = 623 K, PRESSURE = 1 BAR,
MOLAR RATIO H_2/OIL = 8.

TABLE 10. THE INFLUENCE OF Cℓ AND S ON XYLENE ISOMERISATION

	FEED	REACTANTS			
		FEED ALONE	FEED + 2 PPM CCl$_4$	FEED + 20 PPM CCl$_4$	FEED + 2 PPM THIOPHENE
COMPOSITION (WT %)					
C$_8^-$ ALIPHATICS	3.4	3.2	3.2	3.4	3.0
BENZENE	1.3	4.9	4.9	5.0	4.3
TOLUENE	3.2	4.1	4.7	4.3	5.0
ETHYLBENZENE	20.1	12.9	12.9	12.8	13.0
P-XYLENE	12.8	17.7	17.7	17.7	17.3
M-XYLENE	54.5	40.3	40.4	39.9	39.9
O-XYLENE	3.8	15.1	15.1	15.1	14.6
C$_9$ + C$_{10}$ AROMATICS	-	1.7	1.7	1.8	3.0
Δ XYLENES (WT %)	-	+2.0	+2.1	+1.6	+0.7
C$_8$ AROMATICS LOSS (WT %)	-	5.2	5.1	5.7	6.4
EB CONVERSION (%)	-	32	32	31.5	30.5
PATE (%)	-	100	100	100	100

NOTE : CATALYST N$_I$H-ZSM-5, TEMP. = 613 K, PRESSURE = 8 BAR,
MOLAR RATIO H$_2$/OIL = 10, WHSV = 3 H^{-1}.

98

TABLE 11. INFLUENCE OF AMMONIA ON SELECTIVITY IN XYLENE ISOMERISATION

	TEMPERATURE, K	633	685		
	PRESSURE, BAR	16	1		
	H$_2$/HC	6	6		
	WHSV	3	3		

PRODUCT COMPOSITION, WT %	FEED	A^A	B^A	A	B
C$_8^-$ ALIPHATICS	6.1	4.1	4.6	3.2	3.5
BENZENE	1.4	5.3	3.9	6.6	5.7
TOLUENE	1.6	4.2	2.8	3.5	2.7
ETHYLBENZENE	19.3	10.4	12.8	5.8	7.5
P-XYLENE	12.9	17.4	17.6	18.7	18.8
M-XYLENE	54.4	38.8	39.5	43.7	43.4
O-XYLENE	4.3	16.5	16.4	17.5	17.5
C$_9$ + C$_{10}$ AROMATICS	-	3.3	2.4	1.0	0.9
C$_8$ AROMATIC LOSS	-	7.8	4.6	5.2	3.7

A A AND B REFER TO THE PRODUCT DISTRIBUTION BEFORE AND AFTER AMMONIA INJECTION, RESPECTIVELY.

TABLE 12. REGENERATION OF ACTIVE SITES AFTER TOTAL POISONING WITH NH_3

COMPOSITION (WT %)	FEED	1	2	3	4	5	6	50
		TIME ON STREAM (AFTER INJECTION OF NH_3) (H)						
C_8^- ALIPHATICS	2.1	2.1	2.2	2.3	2.8	2.8	2.8	2.9
BENZENE	1.4	1.4	1.5	1.4	1.4	2.1	2.3	3.6
TOLUENE	3.3	3.3	3.4	3.4	3.4	3.4	3.4	3.9
ETHYLBENZENE	24.9	24.9	24.9	25.0	23.2	21.6	21.0	18.1
P-XYLENE	7.7	9.4	11.8	13.7	15.2	15.8	15.8	15.8
M-XYLENE	53.9	50.5	46.8	43.4	41.1	39.5	39.4	38.0
O-XYLENE	6.7	8.2	9.4	10.5	12.1	13.1	13.2	13.8
C_9 + C_{10} AROMATICS	-	-	-	0.1	0.1	1.8	1.9	3.9
PX + OX (WT %)	14.4	17.6	21.2	24.3	27.4	28.9	29.0	29.16
Δ XYLENES (WT %)	-	-0.2	-0.3	-0.7	+0.1	+0.1	+0.1	-0.7
C_8 AROMATICS LOSS (WT %)	-	0.2	0.3	0.6	1.6	3.2	3.8	7.5
EB CONVERSION (%)	-	-	-	-	6.8	13.2	15.7	27.3
PATE (%)	-	20.9	50.2	74.3	90.5	97.7	97.7	100

NOTE : CATALYST H-ZSM-5, TEMP. = 633 K, PRESS.= 16 BAR, M.R H_2/OIL = 6, WHSV = 3 H^{-1}.

IV. ZEOLITE CATALYST FOR PRODUCTION OF ETHYLBENZENE

The vapour phase alkylation of benzene with ethylene in the presence of ZSM-5 zeolites is in commercial practice (the Mobil-Badger process) for the manufacture of ethylbenzene. The use of zeolites avoids the environmental and corrosion problems connected with Friedel-Crafts catalysts. The catalyst is regenerated once in every 2-3 weeks. Although, Linde type X and Y zeolites, exchanged with rare earth ions, catalyse the alkylation of benzene with ethanol, the catalyst aging was severe leading to catalyst deactivation in a few hours. Anderson *et al.* have recently investigated the interaction of ethylene/ethanol and deuterobenzene over HZSM-5 zeolite. When ethylene was used as the alkylating agent, the ethylbenzene contained the ethyl group $-CH_2CH_2D$, corresponding to the reaction scheme :

$$
\begin{array}{c}
DO\ Zeol \\
+ \\
C_2H_4
\end{array}
\underset{Slow}{\overset{Slow}{\rightleftarrows}}
DCH_2CH_2^+\ {}^-O\ Zeol
\overset{C_6D_6}{\underset{fast}{\longrightarrow}}
\underset{CH_2CH_2D}{\bigodot}
+\ DO\ Zeol
$$

In the case of ethanol, it was observed that the ethyl group (in ethylbenzene) was undeuterated. Hence, they concluded that the ethyl substituent had not been formed via ethylene. This conclusion, if valid, will have important consequences, especially for catalytic deactivation by carbonaceous deposits since it is known that ethylene (and olefins in general) is a major source of such deposits in alkylation reactions in the vapour phase over solid acid catalysts. In addition to the intrinsic scientific interest, the direct use of ethanol (instead of ethylene) in the manufacture of ethylbenzene is also of economic significance in those countries (like Brazil and India) where biomass-derived alcohol is an additional raw material for the manufacture of chemicals. The manufacture of ethylbenzene by a direct, single stage reaction of benzene and dilute ethanol (the ALBENE process) is in commercial practice in a 15000 tpy plant in India.

The pentasil group of zeolites was chosen since it was known earlier that they have good stability and form less polyalkyl benzenes. In the presence of water strongly acidic aluminosilicate zeolites underwent deactivation due to poisoning by water. Iron analogs, however, retained their activity due to their lower acidic strength. Modification with phosphorous and boron lowered the acid strength even further (Fig. 8). Phosphorous levels were next optimised (Table 13). The level of impurities in the P-containing catalysts was lower, at the same yield of (ethyl + diethyl) benzenes.

Activity and selectivity

Figure 9 illustrates the influence of temperature on the selectivity for various products in the alkylation of benzene with ethanol. The C_9 aromatics consisted mainly of ethyltoluenes. The formation of ethylbenzene passes through a maximum around 675 K. Below this temperature, significant amounts of diethylbenzenes were formed while, above 675 K,

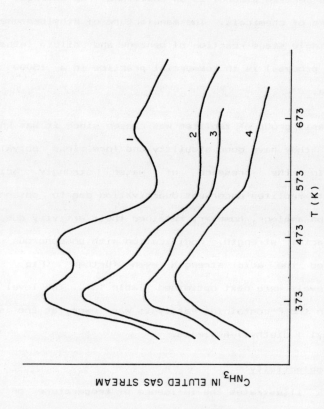

FIGURE 8. The temperature-programmed desorption of NH_3 from HZSM5, p(1%)-HZSM5, P(5%)-HZSM5 and B(3%)-HZSM5 (curves 1-4, respectively).

TABLE 13 . ALKYLATION OF BENZENE WITH ETHANOL OVER MODIFIED ZSM-5 CATALYSTS[A]

PRODUCT DISTRIBUTION WT %	CATALYST			
	HZSM-5	P(1%)-HZSM-5[B]	P(5%)-HZSM-5	B(3%)-HZSM-5
BENZENE	72.1	73.9	90.1	88.1
TOLUENE	1.1	0.12	-	0.08
ETHYLBENZENE	22.3	20.3	8.4	7.9
DIETHYLBENZENES[C]	3.00	4.9	1.5	3.06
XYLENES[D]	0.08	-	-	0.18
ISOPROPYLBENZENE	0.28	0.21	-	0.32
n-PROPYLBENZENE	0.77	0.30	-	0.10
ETHYLTOLUENES	0.08	0.12	-	-
C_{10}^+ AROMATICS	0.24	-	-	-

[A] REACTION TEMP. 623 K; PRESSURE, 1 ATM; BENZENE/ETHANOL MOLE RATIO, 4; WHSV, 5 G/G H.

[B] THE VALUES IN PARENTHESES REFER TO WT % OF THE MATERIAL IN THE CATALYST.

[C] THE DIETHYLBENZENES CONSISTED MAINLY (MORE THAN 90 WT %) OF THE PARA-ISOMER.

[D] THE ORTHO-ISOMER WAS PREDOMINANT AMONG THE XYLENES.

104

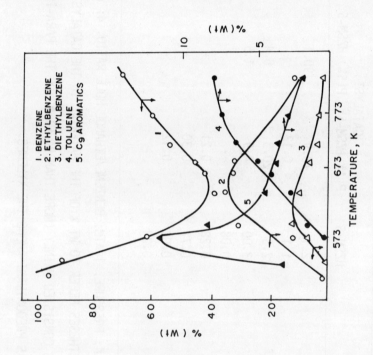

FIGURE 9 The influence of temperature on product distribution in the alkylation of benzene with ethanol. WHSV, 5; pressure, 1 atm.; Benzene/ethanol, 1 mole/mole.

cracking reactions (ethylbenzenes to toluene/benzene) assume importance. Over H-mordenite, the corresponding temperature above which cracking begins to play a role was found to be 623 K. Zeolites of the faujasite family were highly active even at 500-600 K, but underwent fast deactivation. The influence of the mole ratio of benzene to ethanol (in the feedstock) on product selectivity is shown in Figure 10. The selectivity for ethylbenzene increases with increasing benzene content and reaches 100 % at a value of 10:1 (benzene:ethanol). The observed selectivity values are also quite close to those calculated assuming thermodynamic equilibrium. For example, the observed value of 85 % selectivity to ethylbenzene (benzene/alcohol = 5), (Figure 10) compares well with the equilibrium value of 90 %.

Selectivity values (for ethylbenzenes) observed in this study with HZSM-5 zeolite were much higher than those reported over faujasites. Venuto *et al* for the ethylation of benzene with ethanol (477 K, 1 atm, benzene/alcohol = 5) over a rare earth exchanged, Linde X zeolite observed a maximum selectivity of only 74 % for the conversion of alcohol to ethylbenzenes. Over HZSM-5 (Figure 10) at the same value of the benzene/alcohol molar ratio of 5, about 90 % of the alcohol is converted into mono- and diethylbenzenes. Among the ethylbenzenes, the selectivity for the monoalkylate was higher over the HZSM-5 (molar ratio of mono/polyalkylate = 8-10) than the faujasites.

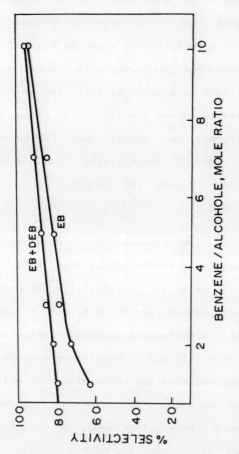

FIGURE 10 The influence of mole ratio of benzene/ethanol on the selectivity of conversion of alcohol to ethybenzene (EB) and ethyl and diethylbenzenes (EB + DEB); Temperature, 673 K; WHSV, 5.

The influence of contact time (defined as the reciprocal of the weight hourly space velocity) on product distribution is shown in Figure 11. The concentration of ethylbenzene passes through a maximum around $W/F = 0.1$ h. The increasing formation of toluene as well as that of benzene at high W/F values is due to further cracking reactions of both ethyl- and diethylbenzenes. Traces of isopropylbenzene and ethyltoluenes were also formed under these conditions.

Stability

One of the distinguishing features observed when ethanol rather than ethylene was used as the alkylating agent was the long stable life of the catalyst. There was no deactivation of the catalyst (in plant operations) even after continuous operation for more than one month (Figure 12). When ethylene was used as the alkylating agent the catalyst was deactivated in about two weeks time in agreement with published results. Since the origin of catalytic deactivation in the ethylation reaction is mainly the formation of 'coke' on the catalyst from olefins like ethylene, this suggest that the ethyl substituent in ethylbenzene is formed from ethanol without the intermediate formation of ethylene. An alternative explanation could be that the presence of water suppresses the reactions of ethylene leading to 'coke'.

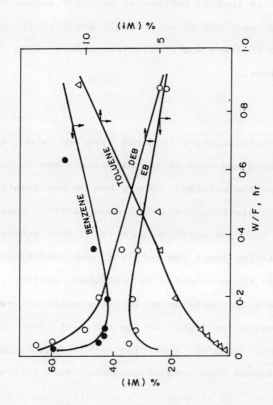

FIGURE 11 The influence of contact time on product distribution. W, weight of catalyst/g; F, the total weight/g of the benzene and ethanol passed per h; temperature, 673 K; benzene/ethanol, 1 mole/mole; pressure, 1 atm.

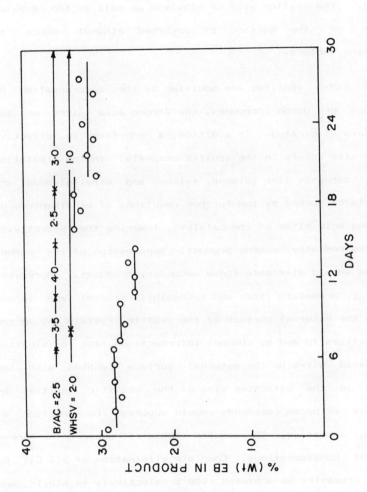

FIGURE 2 Catalytic activity over a prolonged period of time; Temperature, 673 K; benzene/ethanol mole ratio and WHSV values are as indicated in the Figure.

It is probable that free ethylene molecules, if formed from ethanol, diffuse out of the zeolite structure much more readily than ethanol molecules and hence do not contribute to coke formation. The smaller size of ethylene as well as the greater converage of the surface by adsorbed ethanol would be contributing factors.

When ZSM-5 zeolites are modified by the incorporation of phosphorous or boron compounds, the strong acid sites on the surface are eliminated. In addition, a reduction in effective pore size also occurs in the zeolite channels. In the alkylation process, compounds like toluene, xylenes and ethyltoluenes are believed to be formed by the further reactions of ethylbenzene on the strong acid sites of the catalyst, lowering the selectivity for the desired ethylbenzene product. Suppression of the strong acid sites should eliminate these secondary products. Moreover, since C_{10+} aromatics (tri- and tetraethylbenzenes) are formed mainly on the external surface of the zeolite crystals and in the large cavities formed by channel intersections, the elimination of the acid sites on the external surface coupled with the reduction in the effective size of the zeolitic cavities by phosphorous or boron compounds should suppress the formation of these C_{10+} aromatics. The results (Table 13) support the above theoretical considerations. Complete elimination of all C_7, C_9 and C_{10+} aromatics is achieved (100 % selectivity to ethyl- and diethylbenzenes) with the catalyst containing 5 % phosphorous.

V. CONCLUSIONS

Heterogeneous catalysis, has sometimes been called the " last refuge of the alchemist ". Due to advances in our understanding of the structure, especially the surface structure of solid catalysts in the last two decades, the situation has changed dramatically so much so that, today we can design and tailor-make catalysts for specific reactions. This is especially true of zeolite catalysts. Since the three dimensional structure including details of the pore geometry are available from XRD, high resolution electron microscopy, solid state MASNMR, FTIR spectroscopy etc, our understanding of the structure of zeolites, the diffusion of molecules in their internal volume and the interaction effects between the two has advanced to such a level that the design of zeolite catalysts for particular applications can be undertaken with a reasonable level of confidence.

DESIGN AND SYNTHESIS OF NEW PILLARED CATALYSTS FOR HIGHLY SELECTIVE ORGANIC TRANSFORMATIONS

B.M. Choudary, V.L.K. Valli and A. Durga Prasad

Inorganic & Physical Chemistry Division
Indian Institute of Chemical Technology, Hyderabad 500 007, India.

ABSTRACT

The design, synthesis and characterisation of pillared clay catalysts were described. V-PILC1 with small interlayer spacing could induce molecular recognition evident in selective oxidation of para and primary benzyl alcohols distinguishing ortho and secondary ones. On contrast, all the benzyl alcohols described above were readily oxidised with V-PILC2 which has higher interlayer expansion. The same catalyst (V-PILC2) has also been successfully used for the regioselective epoxidation of allylic alcohols. In addition to this, enantioselective epoxidation of primary allylic alcohols is demonstrated using catalytic amounts of Ti-PILC.

1. INTRODUCTION

Smectites have a sandwich structure where negatively charged aluminosilicate layers are separated by positively charged cations. The charge in montmorillonite and fluorhectorite minerals arises from isomorphos substitution mainly in the middle of the clay layers[1]. When large organic and inorganic cations separate the clay sheets, sufficient interlamellar space is created to allow a variety of adsorbed and catalytic uses[2]. Also, clays can be intercalated by covalent bonding to obtain rigid and more expanded interlamellar spacing[3,4]. Control of the free lateral surface and pore size are important factors for reactions such as shape-selective catalysis[5], molecular recognition[3] etc. Keeping these factors in mind, earlier we synthesized covalently bound anchored palladium complexes in the interlamellars of montmorillonite and successfully applied those catalysts to study selective hydrogenation of alkynes[6]. Although these anchored catalysts are very promising, the swellability of montmorillonite interlayers as a factor of solvent polarity made them less important for selective studies. Thus, we proposed to design and synthesize a variety of pillared clay catalysts (PILCS) by crosslinking the interlayers of smectite clays with oxy or hydroxy oligomers of transition metals which governed essentially by charge balance or covalent bonding and hence leads to more stable catalysts[7]. The salient features of the PILCS that make them especially interesting for heterogeneous catalysis are envisaged below :

1. **Large pore openings** ranging from 10-40 Å.
2. High **thermal stabilities** (usually > 600°C).
3. Bascity or acidity can be imparted using suitable basic or acidic clay. Thus, **bi-functionality** can be introduced due to the support as well as the pillaring agent.
4. **Reduction in dimensionality** results high catalytic activity.
5. Exert **shape-selectivity** because of the restricted space availability between the pillars.
6. Can be recycled.
7. Have more approachable metal sites since oligomers constitute the pillars.
8. Migration and agglomeration on to the surface into variety of particles can be minimized.

Although PILCS have been studied extensively in vapour phase, very few liquid phase reactions are known in the literature[8]. Thus, in view of the envisaged advantages combined with the asset of selectivities observed in vapour phase studies[9], it was thought that PILCS would be the ideal choice to carry out some of the selective organic transformations in liquid phase. The present paper describes the design and synthesis of two types of novel vanadium pillared montmorillonite catalysts (V-PILC1 & V-PILC2) with varied physical and chemical properties to study the molecular recognition of substituted benzyl alcohols and regioselective epoxidation of allyl alcohols in liquid phase reactions. In addition to this the utility of the PILCS have been exploited to the asymmetric catalysis for the first time. Thus, the use of Ti-PILC to obtain chiral epoxy alcohols has been demonstrated.

2. EXPERIMENTAL

2.1 Preparation of Pillared Montmorillonites

Natural montmorillonite was used for pillaring. Na^+-montmorillonite and H^+-montmorillonite were prepared by the procedure of Spencer et al.[10]

from natural montmorillonite of general formula $M_x^+[(OH)_4Si_8(Al_{3-x}Mg_x)O_{20}]$. Pillaring agents were NH_4VO_3, $VOCl_3$ and $Ti(OPr^i)_4$.

$$\text{$\not\!\!\!\text{I}$} -Cl + NH_4VO_3 \xrightarrow[\text{reflux}]{\text{Acetone}} V\text{-PILC}1 \quad \ldots \quad \text{(A)}$$

$$\text{$\not\!\!\!\text{I}$} -OH + VOCl_3 \xrightarrow[\text{reflux}]{\text{Benzene}} V\text{-PILC}2 \quad \ldots \quad \text{(B)}$$

$$\text{$\not\!\!\!\text{I}$} -ONa + Ti(OPr^i)_4 \xrightarrow[\text{80°C}]{1N \ HCl} Ti\text{-PILC} \quad \ldots \quad \text{(C)}$$

2.1.A   Preparation of V-PILC1 : A 1wt% suspension of freshly prepared chloromontmorillonite (5g) in dry acetone (100ml) and NH_4VO_3 (0.4g) was refluxed for about 12h.   The V-PILC1 thus obtained was centrifused, and washed thoroughly with de-ionised water.   To remove excess of NH_4VO_3 present, the clay was washed with 2% KOH solution.   The V-PILC1 thus obtained was washed several times with de-ionised water immediately after base washings to remove traces of alkali if present and dried in oven below 70°C overnight.

2.1.B   Preparation of V-PILC2 : V-PILC2 was synthesized by refluxing $VOCl_3$ (0.5 ml) in dry benzene (70 ml) with H^+-montmorillonite (5g) under nitrogen atmosphere until the solid clay suspension turned a deep bottle green colour (within approximately 6h).   The solid was filtered under nitrogen atmosphere, washed repeatedly with dry benzene and moist air was passed over.   It was then dried at 110°C for 6h and analyzed.

2.1.C   Preparation of Ti-PILC : Ti-PILC was synthesized by the procedure reported by Yamanaka et al.[11] $Ti(OPr^i)_4$ was added dropwise to vigorously stirred 1N HCl.   The resulting slurry was stirred for 3h to give a clear titania sol and then mixed with an aqueous suspension of 1wt% Na^+-montmorillonite.   The suspension was then stirred for 3h at 50°C.   The clay was washed with de-ionised water, the mixture centrifused, and the sample dried in air at room temperature.

2.2   Catalyst Characterization

The vanadium and titanium-pillared montmorillonite catalysts were characterized using X-ray powder diffraction (XRD), Plasma analysis for the estimation of metal content, Electron spin resonance spectroscopy (ESR), and Thermogravimetric analysis (TGA).   First, XRD measurements were

carried out as thin films coated on glass plates on a "Siemens D5000 diffractometer" using Ni-filtered, fine focus Cuk_α radiation ($\lambda = 1.54138$). The
amount of metal was estimated on "Inductively coupled plasma emission
spectrophotometer : Lab Tam (Australia)". ESR spectra were recorded
at room temperature on "Brucker ER 200 D-SRC X-band spectrometer"
with 100 kHz modulation using quartz tubes and TGA studies were performed
with a "Dow instruments model 951 thermoanalyzer".

2.2.1 XRD measurements : XRD experiments were conducted to characterize
the length of the pillars as well as the thermal stabilities of the PILCS. The
XRD spectra of V-PILC1, V-PILC2 and Ti-PILC were shown in Fig. 2.1.
It is evident from the Fig. 2.1 that the length of the pillars of V-PILC1,
V-PILC2 and Ti-PILC are 5.8 Å, 13.3 Å and 15 Å respectively. Fig. 2.2
explains the XRD spectra of V-PILC2, heated at different temperature
and it is clear from the Fig. 2.2 that V-PILC2 is thermally stable upto
~ 700°C. A similar experiment conducted on V-PILC1 indicated its thermal
stability as below 500°C.

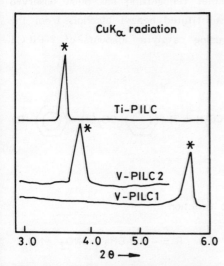

Fig. 2.1 : XRD Patterns of PILCS
recorded at room temperature.

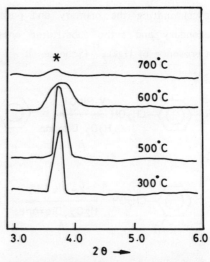

Fig. 2.2 : XRD Patterns of V-PILC 2
calcined at various temperatures.

2.2.2 Plasma analysis : Plasma analysis for metal atom indicated a loading of 0.2, 2.4 and 6 m mol per gram of the clay.

2.2.3 : ESR spectroscopy : ESR spectra were recorded on V-PILC1 and V-PILC2 to find out the local symmetry of vanadium atom present in the pillars. The ESR spectrum of V-PILC1 is a singlet with g_{eff} = 1.97 assigned to the partially reduced V^{4+} species which is resembling that of pure V_2O_5 spectrum[12]. Further, the ESR spectrum of an oriented thin film of V-PILC1 is not affected by the angular invariance in a similar experiment conducted by Kijima et al.[13] In contrast, the ESR spectrum of V-PILC2 is a well-resolved hyperfine spectrum with g_I = 2.040 and g_{II} = 1.970. This indicate that the vanadium atom is present as a dispersed V^{4+} species.

2.2.4 : Thermogravimetric analysis : TGA of V-PILC1 and V-PILC2 indicated their thermal stabilities as 480°C and 668°C respectively.

3. CATALYTIC APPLICATIONS - RESULTS AND DISCUSSION

3.1 Molecular Recognition of Benzyl Alcohols

An unusual phenomenon of molecular recognition has been observed descriminating the primary and para substituted benzyl alcohols from the secondary and ortho substituted ones using catalytic amounts of V-PILC1 in presence of H_2O_2[3] (Scheme 1).

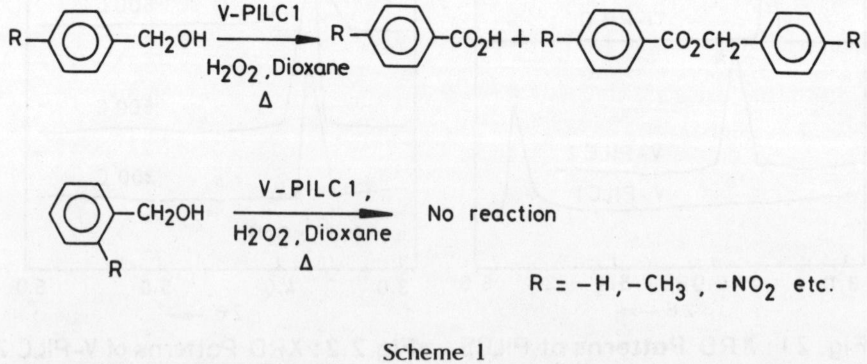

$$R-\langle\bigcirc\rangle-CH_2OH \xrightarrow[\substack{H_2O_2, Dioxane \\ \Delta}]{V-PILC1} R-\langle\bigcirc\rangle-CO_2H + R-\langle\bigcirc\rangle-CO_2CH_2-\langle\bigcirc\rangle-R$$

$$\langle\bigcirc\rangle\substack{-CH_2OH \\ R} \xrightarrow[\substack{H_2O_2, Dioxane \\ \Delta}]{V-PILC1,} \text{No reaction}$$

R = −H, −CH$_3$, −NO$_2$ etc.

Scheme 1

Benzyl alcohols and para substituted benzyl alcohols are readily oxidised by V-PILC1 to afford acids and esters (Table 1).

Table 1 : Shape-selective Oxidation[a] of Benzyl Alcohols $ArCH_2OH$

| Ar | Yield (%)[b] of products using V-PILC1 | | Using V-PILC2 |
	$ArCO_2H$	$ArCO_2CH_2Ar$	$ArCO_2H$
Ph	62	34	96
$p-MeC_6H_4$	86	11	97
$o-MeC_6H_4$	3	–	92
$p-ClC_6H_4$	86	12	91
$o-ClC_6H_4$	29	48	94
$p-O_2NC_6H_4$	82	–	82
$o-O_2NC_6H_4$	–	–	88
$p-MeOC_6H_4$	91	8	99
$o-MeOC_6H_4$	2	–	82
$m-MeOC_6H_4$	5	–	
$o,p-Me_2C_6H_3$	–	–	

[a] All reactions are conducted on 5 m mol substrate, 2.5 ml H_2O_2 and 500/30 mg of V-PILC1/V-PILC2 at reflux temperatures.

[b] Isolated yields (based on consumption of the substrate). Products were characterized by IR, NMR and mass spectrometry.

The significant amount of ester formation is due to the acidic sites of the catalyst. Ortho substituted and secondary alcohols such as 1-phenyl-ethanol are recovered even on prolonged hours.

All the alcohols in Table 1 were oxidised in the presence of V-PILC2 a more expanded pillared catalyst within 4-5 h with no discrimination under the same experimental conditions (Scheme 2).

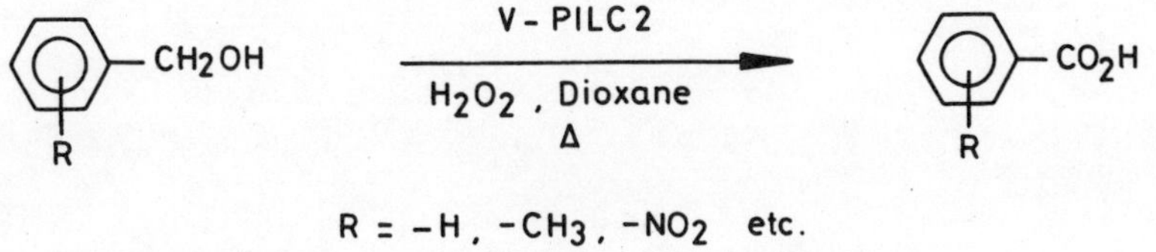

$R = -H, -CH_3, -NO_2$ etc.

Scheme 2

Thus, V-PILC1 with smaller interlayer spacing could induce molecular recognition evident in selective oxidation of para and primary benzyl alcohols distinguishing ortho and secondary ones. On contrast, all the benzyl alcohols described above were readily oxidised with V-PILC2 which has higher inter-layer expansion.

3.2 Regioselective Epoxidation of Allyl Alcohols

Regioselectivity towards internal allylic double bonds in preference to terminal allylic double bonds is displayed using the catalytic amounts of V-PILC2.

Thus, only internal allylic double bonds are reactive towards epoxidation in presence of tert-butylhydroperoxide and terminal ones are found to be totally inert (Scheme 3).

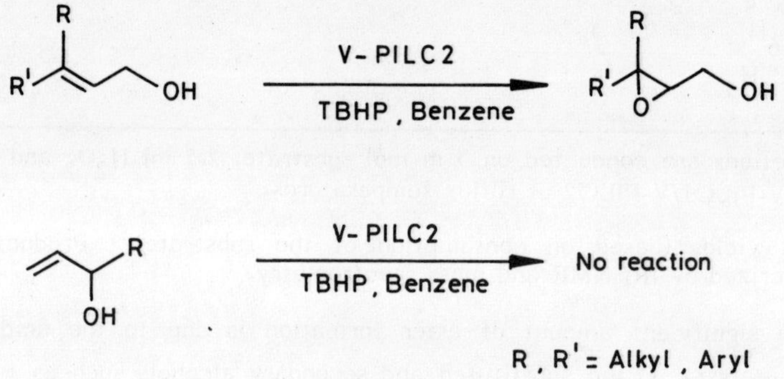

R , R' = Alkyl , Aryl

Scheme 3

The same property of regioselectivity has been observed also in case of homoallylic alcohols. Thus, internal homoallylic double bonds are reactive under the same experimental conditions leaving the terminal ones totally inert[15]

Table 2 : Regioselective epoxidation of allylic alcohols using V-PILC2[a]

Entry	SUBSTRATE	PRODUCT	ISOLATED YIELD	TIME (h)
1			96	5
2			89	5
3	Ph...OH	Ph...OH	92	7
4	OH	OH	94	2.5
5	OH	OH	88	7.5
6	OCH₂Ph OH	NO REACTION	—	15
7	OCH₂Ph OH	NO REACTION	—	15
8		NO REACTION	—	15
9	HO OH	OH	91	7
10	OH	OH	95	7

a All reactions were performed on 7 mmol allylic alcohols in 15 ml dry benzene using 42 mg of V-PILC2 (containing 0.1 mmol of vanadium) and 1.3 ml of azeotropically dried hydroperoxide (ca. 3.1 M in toluene) at room temperature under nitrogen atmosphere.

3.3 Asymmetric Epoxidation of Allyl Alcohols

The work on asymmetric catalysis was initiated using pillared clays as catalysts for the first time by chosing a suitable metal template as pillaring material to perform enantioselective organic reactions with the aid of external chiral auxiliary.

The sharpless reaction has provided a successful general solution to the problem of asymmetric epoxidation. Since asymmetric epoxides are good chiral intermediates in organic synthesis, the validity of the reaction has been tested using the heterogeneous V-PILC2 under straight-forward conditions. However, the use of this catlayst in the asymmetric epoxidation of (E)-hex-2-enol using (+)-diethyl tartrate led to 20% enantiomeric excess (e.e) only and we used Ti-PILC in an attempt to obtain better e.e. The result obtained was highly encouraging with 90% e.e (Scheme 4).

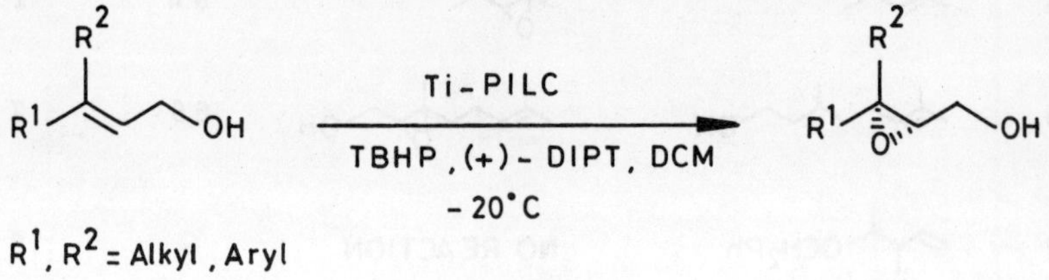

$$R^1, R^2 = Alkyl, Aryl$$

Scheme 4

The epoxidation of allylic alcohols using heterogeneous Ti-PILC catalyst [16] (Table 3) proceed at rates and e.e. comparable with those achieved using homogeneous $Ti(OPr^i)_4$ and molecular sieves[17]. The present system is catalytic without the molecular sieves since the clay itself can act as zeolite. The possible pillaring species of Ti-PILC are long inorganic polymeric oxy-hydroxy cationic species with a large amount of zeolite-like pore space. Thus, during the addition of tartrate, the polymeric oxy or hydroxy titanium species may form a chiral complex which is responsible for the chiral induction. Ti-PILC thus plays a dual role, in replacing both $Ti(OPr^i)_4$ and molecular sieves used in the sharpless reaction[17]. Further, the work up of the reaction is very simple and the solid catalyst can be removed easily by filtration without tedious experimental conditions.

Table 3 : Catalytic asymmetric epoxidation of allylic alcohols using heterogenized Ti-PILC[a]

Substrate	Product	Tartrate	Time / h	Isolated yield %	ee %.
[structure] $\sim\!\!/\!\!\sim$ OH	[epoxide structure] OH	(+) – DIPT	3.5	86	94
[structure] OH	[epoxide structure] OH	(+) – DIPT	9	76	98
[structure] OH	[epoxide structure] OH	(+) – DIPT	7	68	90
Ph [structure] OH	Ph [epoxide structure] OH	(+) – DIPT	4.2	91	95
Ph [structure] OH	Ph [epoxide structure] OH	(+) – DET	3.5	89	98
[structure] OH	[epoxide structure] OH	(+) – DIPT	8	82	$[\alpha]_D^{25} = -17.8$ (C = 1.0, CHCl$_3$)
[structure] OH	[epoxide structure] OAc	(+) – DIPT	9	72	96
[structure] OH	[epoxide structure] OAc	(+) – DET	7.5	79	98

a All reactions were performed on 4 mmol of allylic alcohols in dry CH_2Cl_2 (6 ml) using Ti-PILC (20 mg) containing 0.12 mmol of titanium, (+)-diisopropyl or (+)-diethyl tartrate (0.24 mmol) and azeotropically dried hydroperoxide (1.2 ml, ca. 4 M in toluene) at -15 to -20°C under nitrogen.

With this success of the asymmetric epoxidation reaction using Ti-PILC at mild conditions, the oxidation of prochiral sulfur compounds has been undertaken which is in good progress.

References

1. Grim, R.E., Clay Mineralogy; McGraw-Hill Book Co.: New York, 77 (1968).

2. (a) Pinnavaia, T.J., "Intercalated Clay Catalysts", Science, 220, 365 (1983).

    (b) Barrer, R.M., "Expanded Clay Minerals" : A Major Class of Molecular Sieves", J. Inclusion Phenom., 4, 109 (1986).

3. Choudary, B.M. and Valli, V.L.K., J. Chem. Soc., Chem. Commun., 1115 (1990).

4. Figueras, F., Catal. Rev. Sci. Eng., 30, 457 (1988).

5. Adams, J.M., Martin, K. and McCabe, R.W., "Clays as Selective Catalysts in Organic Synthesis", J. Inclusion Phenom., 5, 663 (1987).

6. Choudary, B.M., Sharma, G.V.M. and Bharati, P., Angew. Chem. Int. Ed. Engl., 28, 465 (1989).

7. Jones, W., Catalysis Today, 2, 357 (1988).

8. Yoneyama, H., Haga, S. and Yamanaka, S., J. Phys. Chem., 93, 4883 (1989).

9. Kikuchi, E. and Matsuda, T., Catalysis Today, 2, 297 (1988).

10. Spencer, W.F. and Gieseking, J.E., J. Phys. Chem., 56, 751 (1952).

11. Yamanaka, S., Nishihara, T. and Hattori, M., Mater. Chem. Phys., 17, 87 (1987).

12. Nag, N.K., Chary, K.V.R., Reddy, B.M., Rao, B.R. and Subrahmanyam, V.S., Appl. Catal., 9, 225 (1984).

13. Kijima, T., Tanaka, J., Goto, M. and Matsui, Y., Nature (London), 310, 45 (1984).

14. Choudary, B.M., Valli, V.L.K. and Durga Prasad, A., J. Chem. Soc., Chem. Commun., 721 (1990).

15. Choudary, B.M. et al., Unpublished results.

16. Choudary, B.M., Valli, V.L.K. and Durga Prasad, A., J. Chem. Soc., Chem. Commun., 1186 (1990).

17. Gao, Y., Hanson, R.M., Klunder, J.M., Ko, S.Y., Masamune, H. and Sharpless, K.B., J. Am. Chem. Soc., 109, 5765 (1987).

ABOUT SOME POSSIBILITIES OF CONTROLLING THE SELECTIVITY OF ZEOLITIC CATALYSTS

P. JIRU, Z. TVARUZKOVA and K. HABERSBERGER
J. Heyrovsky Institute of Physical Chemistry and Electrochemistry,
Dolejskova 3, CS-182 23 Prague, Czechoslovakia

ABSTRACT
   In this paper further possibilities (besides shape selectivity) of controlling the selectivity of catalytic reactions over zeolites are discussed in detail. Special attention is dedicated to the interaction of proton donor sites with the active component, to the effect of the active component and to the way of its introduction into the catalyst (or its surface) and to the influence of the working (reaction) conditions, like total pressure and presence of water vapour. By combining a zeolite with a suitable active component bifunctional catalysts were obtained; over these catalysts methanol is transformed in a one-step process into higher aldehydes.

1. INTRODUCTION

The problem of selectivity control in catalytic reactions is of great current interest. One of the possibilities in this field is offered by the zeolites. Two alternatives of their application are concerned. The first one, considered already as classical, is based on the experimental results obtained by Weiss, Czisery and coworkers in the sixties. These authors characterized and applied three forms of the shape selectivity of zeolites: reactant shape selectivity, product shape selectivity and restricted transition state selectivity. The results of their extensive investigations led to the successful introduction of a number of industrial catalytic processes in the domain of fuel processing (e.g. dewaxing, selectoforming), aromatic processing (e.g. m-p-xylene isomerization, toluene disproportionation) and methanol transformation (MTG, MTO). The second, non-classical alternative (still in the stage of preliminary investigation) is the control of the selectivity by means of other factors (besides the shape selectivity) of the zeolitic catalysts. In our contribution we would like to stress and discuss in more detail some of the possibilities of the zeolitic catalysts in this respect.

2. RESULTS AND DISCUSSION

2.1. The effect of the interaction of proton-donor sites of zeolitic catalysts with supported oxidic redox component

To demonstrate this effect the selective oxidation of butadiene over zeolitic catalysts with a supported P-V-O active component of the types HY-P-O, HZSM5-P-V-O, HZSM11-P-V-O and for comparison also HY-V-O (with comparable amount of V-O), HY-P-O (with comparable amount of P-O) and pure $(VO)_2P_2O_7$, designed P-V-O active component without support, were used. The selective oxidation products were furan and maleic anhydride. A description of the preparation of the catalysts by impregnation together with the characteristic data concerning their crystallinity, OH group concentrations obtained by measurements of their IR spectra and determination of their catalytic activity and selectivity in an integral microreactor are given in refs. 1, 2. All catalysts exhibited good crystallinity also after the impregnation as well as after the catalytic tests; no amorphization was observed.

The experimental data obtained are presented in Table 1. In the catalytic oxidation of butadiene, the type of the zeolitic support affects qualitatively the selectivity, where we may discern two groups A, B (refs. 1, 2). Over catalysts of the group A only furan is formed as a selective oxidation product, whereas over catalysts of the group B (zeolitic support of the type HZSM-11 as well as pure component P-V-O), both furan and maleic anhydride are formed. Pure zeolites are active in the total oxidation to CO and CO_2 only.

The different effect of various types of zeolitic supports on the selectivity of butadiene oxidation over the active component P-V-O may be interpreted by a change in the concentration of OH groups (proton donor centres) in the catalyst after the introduction of the active component in comparison with the concentration of OH groups in the original zeolitic support. From a detailed analysis of the results obtained from measurements of valency vibration absorbances of the proton donor OH groups in the structure (localized in the large cavities of the HY zeolite - Table 1) as well as from measurements of

TABLE 1 - Selectivity of zeolitic catalysts and concentration of their proton-donor centres in butadiene oxidation.

Catalyst	Group	Si/Al	Conc.of V, of PV,% wt	React.temp.for Max selectivity to Furan %	K	Maleic Anh %	K	OH conc* mol.10^3/g
HY	-	2.1	-	-	-	-	-	2.48
HY-PV	A	2.1	5.3	41.5	597	5	-	0.98
HY-V	A	2.1	2.2	35.4	597	5	-	1.52
HY-P	-	2.1	3.0	-	-	-	-	1.87
HZSM5	-	13.6	-	-	-	-	-	1.1
HZSM5-PV	A	13.6	4.2	44.7	651	5	-	0.63
HZSM11	-	49.0	-	-	-	-	-	0.06
HZSM11-PV	B	49.0	4.1	25.0	600	32.3	650	0.06
P-V-O	B	-	-	34.8	683	30.9	706	-

*Calculated from the absorbance at 3640 cm^{-1} with the Y-zeolite and at 3610 cm^{-1} with ZSM

changes in the initial rates of ethylene oligomerization (ref. 1), it was found that the number of these OH groups decreases with catalysts of group A (in contrast to those of group B), this effect being caused by the interaction of the OH groups with the active component P-V-O. This "neutralization effect" affects the bond between phosphorus and vanadium inside the active component by weakening the positive influence of phosphorus on the valency state of vanadium in both of the phases present, i.e. in $VOPO_4$ with vanadium (V) and in the $(VO)_2P_2O_7$, whose existence and role in industrial catalysts has been proved previously. This interaction with vanadium and the weakening of the effect of phosphorus leads to the formation of a specifically-bonded V-O component on the zeolitic support over which butadiene is converted into furan only.

The catalytic behaviour of the catalysts of OH group B is identical with that of the pure active component P-V-O. The main products of the oxidation reaction are here furan and maleic anhydride. In this

Tab.2

AMMOXIDATION OF XYLENES

selectivity ☐ catalyst **A** (impregnated)

▢┈┄ catalyst **B** (synthesized, silical.+ cristob.)

	p - xylene		**m - xylene**	
	p-tolu-nitrile	terephtalo-nitrile CO_2	m-tolu-nitrile	isophtalo-nitrile CO_2
20% conv.	297°C	307°C	334°C	407°C
40% conv.	314°C	437°C	361°C	459°C

case, the concentration of the proton donor OH groups remains unchanged; no interaction of these groups with the active component
P-V-O takes place and the positive effect of phosphorus on vanadium
is preserved.

From these facts it follows that the interaction of proton-donor
centres of the zeolitic carrier with the active redox component may
be used in the control of selectivity of the catalytic oxidation
process.

2.2. The effect of the dispersion of the oxidic redox component on
    the zeolite on its selectivity.

This effect is demonstrated by means of ammoxidation of p-xylene
over zeolitic catalysts with V_2O_5 as a supported active component on
zeolites of the types HZSM5-V-O (Si/Al=13.6, 0.8wt% of V) - type A,
prepared by impregnation, and V-silicalite (Si/Al=558, 0.43 wt% of V)
- type B, prepared by hydrothermal synthesis. Detailed description of
the preparation of the catalysts and characterization of their activity
and selectivity in an integral microreactor are given in ref. 3. The
selective oxidation products were either p-tolunitrile and tere-
phthalonitrile or m-tolunitrile and isophthalonitrile respectively, and
CO_2.

Table 2 presents (as rectangles) the selectivities to the individual
products as well as the reaction temperatures at which 20 or 40% total
conversion of either p- or m- xylene is attained over both types of
zeolitic catalysts. The qualitative difference in their selectivity is
obvious at first sight. Over catalyst A, prepared by the classical
impregnation procedure, both mono- and dinitrile are formed with comparable selectivity, both selectivities being somewhat lower in the
ammoxidation of m-xylene: for a given conversion a higher reaction
temperature is needed)probably thanks to the effect of "shape selectivity". Over catalyst B (V-silicalite), prepared by hydrothermal synthesis, only both types of mono-nitriles are formed. The selectivity
is comparable with the values obtained with the catalyst A. The lower
total activity of catalyst B is indicated by the higher reaction temperatures. In all cases, an increase in the reaction temperature en-

hances, as expected, the deep oxidation to CO_2. The qualitatively
different catalytic behaviour of V-silicalite (B) cannot be interpreted by the effect of "shape selectivity". The selectivity for the
formation of mono-nitrile (i.e. p-tolunitrile or m-tolunitrile) is the
same, although from the analogy with the catalytic xylene isomerization
over ZSM-5 zeolites (where the restricted transition state shape selectivity and product shape selectivity play a dominant role) this selectivity should be lower.

The different catalytic behaviour of V-silicalite (B) may be explained by the way of its preparation. The active V-O component is
finely dispersed and probably partially incorporated in the zeolite
lattice (ref. 3): this interaction causes different catalytic properties giving thus the possibility of influencing the ammoximation
selectivity when compared with the zeolitic catalyst A prepared by the
usual impregnation procedure.

2.3. The effect of position of the cation on the activation of H_2 on
    zeolitic catalysts

The rate of homomolecular exchange (in fact the rate of equilibra-
tion of the non-equilibrium mixture) of H_2+D_2 was selected for the
characterization of the H_2 activation, of the participation of various
types of active centres and of their changes in HY zeolite and four
FeHY zeolites (exchanged with Fe^{3+} to 3, 7, 23 and 63%). The changes of
the homo-exchange rate with temperature pretreatment (18 h in vacuo in
the temperature range of 600-950°C were investigated. Experimental
details and detailed results are given in refs. 4, 5. After the heat
treatment at the chosen temperature the sample of Fe-zeolite was prior
to the homo-exchange·rate measurement always pretreated by a standard
procedure in the atmosphere of dry H_2 (2 kPa) for 6 h at 670 K. In all
cases, the homo-exchange rate was then measured at 670 K and 0.15 kPa
on 0.1 g of Fe-zeolite.

Fig. 1 presents the dependence of the homo-exchange on the heat pretreatment temperature for all five samples (HY and FeHY)- ref. 4.

Up to 800 K the homo-exchange rate is the same with all FeHY
zeolites and is equal to the exchange rate on the original HY (without
Fe). From this fact if follows that in this temperature range the same

active centres take part in the H_2 activation. These are probably the proton-donor centres together with the electron-acceptor centres of the original HY zeolite and the Fe^{n+} cations in accessible cationic sites

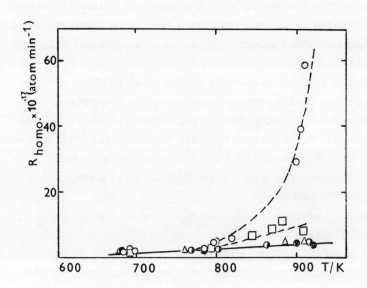

Fig. 1. The dependence of the rate of homoexchange of deuterium on the pretreatment temperature of zeolites ◑ HY, ● FeHY/3, □ FeHY/7, ○ FeHY/23, △ FeHY/63.

which replaced the original OH groups. All three types of active sites may take part in the H_2 activation. A more detailed distinction of their role is impossible because of the very low homo-exchange rate. The same low homo-exchange rate is exhibited by the sample FeHY with the highest content of Fe^{n+}. In this case (heat treatment at 800-950 K) a collapse of the lattice of the zeolite and its amorphization took place (as found by IR spectra registered in the skeletal vibration range). The sample thus behaves in the same way as the original zeolite without Fe in its cationic sites.

The increase in the homo-exchange rate formed with the samples FeHY with 23 or 7% exchanged Fe^{n+} is evidently caused by the formation of new active sites for the H_2 activation. These new sites are not represented by the electron-acceptor centres formed successively with the increasing temperature of the heat pretreatment as the result of the dehydroxylation of the OH groups of the HY zeolite, as it follows from the very slow increase in the homo-exchange rate on the original HY or on FeHY with the lowest content of Fe^{n+}. From the course of the IR spectra (ref. 5) of the adsorbed CO on the samples of FeHY with 7 and 23% of exchanged Fe^{n+} in dependence of the heat pretreatment it follows that the normalized absorbance of the band of adsorbed CO at 2195 cm^{-1} (attributed to the adsorption complex of Fe^{2+} in positions accessible to CO, i.e. in the large cavities of the zeolite) increases. This means that with the increasing temperature of the heat pre-treatment a transfer of Fe^{2+} into accessible zeolite sites takes place, thus causing an increase in the number of active sites of the zeolite for the homo-exchange and in this way also an increase in the homo-exchange value. In the IR spectra of CO adsorbed on FeHY zeolites after heat pretreatment no bands corresponding to Fe^{3+} or to metallic Fe were found. By summarizing these facts we may state that by the thermal treatment of FeHY in vacuo and in the atmosphere of H_2 both the concentration and the valency state of the active Fe sites for H_2 activation may be controled.

2.4 The preparation of bifunctional zeolitic catalysts for the one-step
    oxidation of CH_3OH to higher aldehydes

The aim of this chapter is to show how a selective bifunctional catalyst with both acidobasic and oxidative redox properties for a one-step conversion of CH_3OH to higher aldehydes can be tailor-made. In the preparation of the catalyst the acidobasic properties of the HZSM-5 zeolite (for the conversion of CH_3OH to higher hydrocarbons) and its role as a support for the redox component Bi_2O_3-MoO_3 (for the oxidation of the higher hydrocarbons formed to oxygen compounds) was exploited.

The following types of bifunctional catalysts were prepared: sample A-HZSM-5, containing 3 wt.% of $Bi_2O_3 \cdot 3MoO_3$ prepared by hydrothermal synthesis (with tetrapropylammonium hydroxide as structure directing agent) in the presence of the Bi-Mo-O component in the reaction mixture, sample B- a mechanical mixture of HZSM-5 with 5 wt.% of $Bi_2O_3 \cdot MoO_3$

TABLE 3 - Catalytic oxidation of CH_3OH to higher aldehydes

Cat.	$°C$	WHSV	$\frac{MeOH}{O_2}$	conv. MeOH	CO_2	HCOOH	Fd	ΣC_1^{ox}	Ac	Bz	ΣC_{2+}^{ox}	$S_{C_{2+}}^{ox} = \dfrac{\Sigma C_{2+}^{ox} \cdot 100}{\Sigma C_1^{ox} + C_{2+}^{ox}}$
A	450	1.3	12	99	2.07	0.05	0.17	2.29	0.35	0.4	0.76	24.9
B	450	2	3	70	4.39	0.00	28.13	32.59	1.53	0.21	1.74	5.08
C	450	2	6	82	7.91	0.00	5.16	13.07	2.15	0.20	2.35	15.24

Fd - formaldehyde, Ac - acetaldehyde, Bz - benzaldehyde

(prepared according to ref. 2), sample C - $Bi_2O_3 \cdot MoO_3$ (23 wt.%) supported on HZSM-5, prepared by impregnation. The Si:Al ratio in the HZSM-5 zeolite was 19. Both the activity and the selectivity of the catalysts were investigated in an integral flow microreactor, the products were determined by gas chromatography and (after absorption in water) by polarography. Further experimental details are given in ref. 6.

The reaction conditions and results of the catalytic tests, where the highest value of the criterion $S_{C_{2+}}^{ox}$ were obtained, are presented in Table 3. This criterion is defined as the percentage represented by the sum of the selectivities to acetaldehyde and benzaldehyde in the total sum of the selectivities to the oxygen containing products $C_1^{ox} + C_{2+}^{ox}$. Other methanol transformation products (not given in Table 1) are hydrocarbons. Although C_{2+} oxygen derivatives are formed already over HZSM-5 alone, their yields, mainly those of acetaldehyde and benzaldehyde, are inceased over all catalysts containing also the Bi-Mo-O component. The highest value of the criterion $S_{C_{2+}}^{ox}$ (25 times higher than that obtained over HZSM-5 alone, $S_{C_{2+}}^{ox} = 1\%$) was observed over catalyst A at $450°C$, WHSV = 1.3 h^{-1} and molar ratio $CH_3OH/O_2 = 12$ in the feed. The remaining oxidation products were: carbon monoxide, formic acid and formaldehyde. No acrolein was found in the products. The catalyst A with the highest value of the criterion $S_{C_{2+}}^{ox}$ exhibits in its IR spectrum characteristic bands at 3530 cm^{-1} and at 3610 cm^{-1} in the range of the structural OH groups. These groups are the proton donor centres of the HZSM-5 zeolite which decline of the original band intensities and formation of surface methoxy groups (the latter being indicated by bands at 2985 cm^{-1}, 2950 and 2850 cm^{-1} in the (C-H) vibration range.

Catalyst A represents a typical bifunctional catalyst with two types of active centers, namely: (i) acid-base sites represented by proton proton-donor structural OH groups, (ii) redox sites on the Bi-Mo-O component. At present there is no indication whether this component is only finely dispersed on the HZSM-5 zeolite or at least partially inserted in the zeolite network.

The methoxy groups formed in the interaction of CH_3OH with an OH group seem to act as precursors in the formation of ethylene and higher hydrocarbons according to a mechanism described previously (ref. 7), these products can subsequently interact with the surface oxygen of the Bi-Mo-O redox component of the bifunctional catalyst under formation of the respective aldehydes. The participation of surface oxygen in this process seems to be indicated by the change of the color of the catalyst D after its interaction with CH_3OH in the IR cuvette at higher temperatures from yellow to bluish-green. Such cycle of interactions (alternatively with methanol and with oxygen) may be repeated again.

The priority in the formation of acetaldehyde and benzaldehyde over these catalysts is probably caused (i) by the lower reactivity of these aldehydes in comparison with e.g. acrolein, (ii) by the low reactivity of ethylene and toluene when compared to the olefins C_3-C_4, the latter being more readily oligomerized to surface polyenes than oxidized, so that the possibility of the formation of other aldehydes is reduced.

2.5. The effect of the working conditions of zeolitic catalysts on their selectivity

Fig. 2 illustrates the effect of the total pressure on the selectivity of the conversion of CH_3OH on a classical catalyst (MTG and MTO process) HZSM-5 (Si/Al = 17.5) under the pressures of 2 Pa and 100 Pa. Experimental details are given in ref. 7. When the pressure is reduced 50 times, the product of the catalytic reaction is changed qualitatively. At the total pressure of 100 Pa a composition

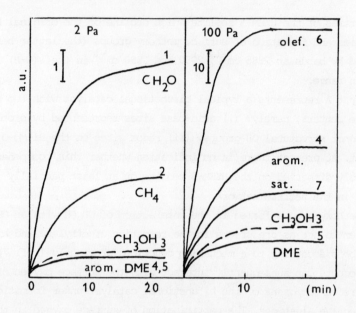

Fig. 2. Composition of the product of catalytic methanol transformation over HZSM-5 as function of time on stream at 670 K.

corresponding to the transformation under atmospheric pressure was attained. At the pressure of 2 Pa formaldehyde and methane were the main products of the transformation. Aromates and dimethyl ether were formed only in low concentrations. Under reduced total pressure a change in the coversion mechanism evidently takes place under the participation of surface methoxy groups in the surface of the HZSM-5 zeolite, identified by means of IR spectra (ref. 7) as the result of the interaction of CH_3OH with proton-donor centres. At a higher pressure their concentration is probably sufficiently high for the formation of dimethyl ether (by mutual interaction of methoxy groups in the surface) as precursor for the formation of ethylene, so that the mechanism of CH_3OH transformation to higher hydrocarbons can be started (ref. 7). At a lower total pressure their surface concentration is so low that practically no mutual surface reaction to dimethyl ether takes place. Under such conditions the methoxy groups in the surface may react only with another molecule of CH_3OH from the gas phase. Such an interaction leads then to the formation of methane and formaldehyde according to the equations 1-3:

$$CH_3OH(g) + Z-OH(s) = Z-OCH_3(s) + H_2O(g) \qquad (1)$$
$$Z-OCH_3(s) + CH_3OH(g) = Z-OH(s) + CH_4(g) + CH_2O(g) \quad (2)$$

over-all reaction: $2CH_3OH = CH_4 + CH_2O + H_2O$ \qquad (3)

where $Z-OH(s)$ is the proton-donor site of the zeolite

and $Z-OCH_3(s)$ is the surface methoxy group

The following example illustrates the effect of the change in the composition of the feed on the selectivity of the catalytic transformation of C_2H_4. In Table 4 are presented the values of the conversion of C_2H_4 to saturated and unsaturated hydrocarbons over a HZSM-5 zeolite, both in presence and in absence of H_2O in the feed, as function of time on stream. Experimental details are given in ref. 9. The aim was to find out in which way the presence of H_2O in the feed may affect the selectivity of CH_3OH transformation to hydrocarbons over HZSM-5 zeolite. In the course of this transformation H_2O as side product

TABLE 4 - Role of $H_2O(g)$ in C_2H_4 conversion (X%) over HZSM-5 at $400^\circ C$ after 50 min. and 100 min.

	X_{sat}/X_{unsat}		X_{sat}		X_{unsat}	
	50min	100min	50min	100min	50min	100min
C_2H_4/HZSM-5	0.4	1.6	2	5	5	5
$C_2H_4 + H_2O$/HZSM-5 ($C_2H_4:H_2O=1:1$)	1.1	1.6	14	32	13	20

(1 mole H_2O formed per 1 mole CH_3OH transformed) is always formed. From the suggested mechanism of CH_3OH transformation to higher hydrocarbons (ref. 7) it follows that ethylene plays an important role as precursor formed from CH_3OH. For this reason, we have investigated its further catalytic transformation to higher saturated and unsaturated hydrocarbons. From the results presented in Table 4 it follows that water vapour in the feed may affect significantly the ratio of the conversion to

saturated and unsaturated hydrocarbons favouring the formation of saturated higher hydrocarbons. In this case, the presence of water vapour in the feed gives rise to new proton-donor centres which enhance the transfer of hydrogen during the formation of higher paraffins, e.g. via the mechanism by Derouane et al. (ref. 7).

3. CONCLUSIONS

The results given above as well as their analysis indicate further general possibilites (besides the "shape selectivity") of controlling the selectivity of catalytic transformations (mainly those of the redox type) over zeolitic catalysts.

4. REFERENCES

1 G. Centi, Z. Tvaruzkova, P. Jiru, F. Trifiro, L. Kubelkova: Appl. Catal. 13, 69 (1984).
2 Z. Tvaruzkova, G. Centi, P. Jiru, F. Trifiro: Appl. Catal. 19, 307 (1985).
3 F. Cavani, F. Trifiro, P. Jiru, K. Habersberger, Z. Tvaruzkova: Zeolites 8, 12 (1988).
4 P. Jiru: Stud. Surf. Science and Catal. 12, 137 (1982).
5 L. Kubelkova, J. Novakova: J. Mol. Catal. 16, 305 (1982).
6 P. Jiru, Z. Tvaruzkova, K. Habersberger: Stud. Surf. Science and Catal. 55, 317 (1990).
7 E.G. Derouane et all: J. Catal. 53, 40 (1978).
8 L. Kubelkova, J. Novakova, P. Jiru: Stud. Surf. Science and Catal. 18, 217 (1984).
9 J. Novakova, L. Kubelkova, Z. Dolejsek, P. Jiru: Coll. Czech. Chem. Commun. 44, 3341 (1979).

ALUMINOPHOSPHATE-BASED MOLECULAR-SHAPE SELECTIVE CATALYSTS FOR METHANOL TO ETHENE CONVERSION

Stanko Hočevar, Jurka Batista

Department of Catalysis and Chemical Reaction Engineering

Boris Kidrič Institute of Chemistry, Hajdrihova 19, P.O.Box 30

61115 Ljubljana, Slovenia (Yugoslavia)

ABSTRACT

A series of aluminophosphate-based catalysts have been synthesized: SAPO-34, MeAPSO-34 (Me = Co, Mn, Cr), SAPO-44, MeAPSO-44 (Me = Co, Mn), $AlPO_4$-5 and $AlPO_4$-14. Acidity was determined by temperature programmed desorption of methanol and catalytic activity and selectivity for ethene production was determined for the methanol dehydration reaction in the gradientless catalytic reactor. It was found that acidity follows the sequence: H-ZSM-5 > MnAPSO > CoAPSO > SAPO >> $AlPO_4$. The catalytic activity of MeAPSO samples does not depend on the structural type of molecular sieve, being it 34 or 44. It slightly depends on the type of isomorphously substituted element, being higher for CoAPSO than for MnAPSO samples. Selectivity strongly depends on both: structural type of molecular sieve and type of isomorphously substituted element. Within series of one structural type the highest selectivity have CoAPSO samples. But SAPO-44 and MeAPSO-44 samples give more than twice higher selectivities than SAPO-34 and MeAPSO-34 samples.

INTRODUCTION

Since the discovery of Wilson et al.[1] that under certain synthesis conditions aluminium phosphate can form open crystalline structures having channels and cavities of molecular dimensions, resembling those in zeolite molecular sieves, the research in many laboratories around the world became oriented to the synthesis and crystallochemistry of these new materials. It was found that, although aluminophosphate molecular sieves are biult from alternating AlO_4 and PO_4 tetrahedra and are therefore forming electroneutral frameworks, they can be modified during the synthesis procedure by isomorphously replacing either aluminum or phosphorus, or, in the case of silicon , both of them, to give negatively charged frameworks, so called SAPO's, MeAPO's, MeAPSO's, ElAPO's [2]. These materials have Bronsted acidities in the range between low- and high-silica zeolites and thus a considerable potential to be used as media for ion exchange and molecular separation as well as for heterogeneous catalysts.

It is usually the case at the beginning of the research of new materials for their possible applications that there are always some controversies between the results obtained by different authors and laboratories. Especially so in using these materials as heterogeneous catalysts [3,4]. The structure of isomorphously substituted aluminophosphate molecular sieves is far more complicated than the structure of zeolites and the functionality of the elements incorporated in the framework of aluminophosphates is, from the standpoint of catalytic action, far from being fully understood [2].

This article represents an attempt to give the possible insight in the mode of catalytic action of a series of SAPO and MeAPSO molecular sieves in the model reaction of methanol dehydration to hydrocarbons. The rationale of this research is following : it is known that molecular-shape selective acid catalyzed synthesis of ethene and propene from methanol proceeds over some types of zeolite molecular sieves in hydrogen forms, having structures with relatively small pores, like erionite, zeolite T, chabazite and ZK-5 [5]. Unfortunately, the coking of these catalysts is very rapid. Since the coking reactions are complex function of the distribution of strength and concentration of Bronsted acid sites in a given topology of molecular sieve, as well as of the topology itself (since it determines the possible forms of molecular-shape selectivity constraints imposed on the reactants, products, transition states and molecular traffic), the right combination of all these factors may leed to the design of active, selective and stable catalyst for the above mentioned reactions. The chabazite-like structures SAPO-34, MeAPSO-34 (Me = Co, Mn, Cr) and SAPO-44, MeAPSO-44 (Me = Co, Mn) have the proper topology for molecular-shape selectivity in methanol dehydration and because of the differences in electronegativities of the elements incorporated in the framework, they broaden the possibilities for the fine tuning of surface acidity to the specific needs of the reaction in question. The scope of our work was therefore to test the acidity, catalytic activity and selectivity of these materials in the reaction of methanol dehydration to olefins.

EXPERIMENTAL

The synthesis procedures and characterization of SAPO-34, MeAPSO-34 (Me = Co, Mn, Cr) and of the reference sample H-ZSM-5 are described elsewhere[6,7]. The SAPO-44 sample was synthesized according to[8], the CoAPSO-44 was synthesized according to[9], MnAPSO-44 was synthesized according to[10] and the $AlPO_4$-5 and $AlPO_4$-14 as reference samples were synthesized according to[1]. All samples were characterized by means of X-ray powder diffraction (XRD)(structural type, degree of crystallinity, phase purity), scanning electron microscopy (SEM)(morphology, particle size, phase purity), thermogravimetry (TG/DTG/DTA)(content of the water and template, thermal stability) and quantitative chemical analysis. The templates were removed from the as-synthesized samples by calcination at 823 K for 4 hours in the flow of dry air. The calcined samples were pressed out in slabs of 30 mm in diameter and 1.5 mm thick at the pressure of 20.3 bar. The slabs were used for catalytic activity measurements and the 0.2 to 0.3 mm fractions of crushed slabs were used for temperature programmed desorption (TPD) measurements as described in detail elsewhere[11,12].

The TPD spectra of methanol adsorbed were scanned under the dynamic vacuum with heating rate of $10°$/min in the temperature interval between 292 K and 673 K. The sample weight changes were monitored in TG/DTG mode by electromagnetic suspension microbalance Sartorius type 4201 and evolved gases were simultaneously analyzed with quadrupole mass spectrometer Leybold MSQ 1002. The catalytic activity of samples in the methanol dehydration was tested in the Caldwell type CST reactor at 623 K, pressure of 0.18 MPa, methanol feed 12.4 mmole/min and reactor impeller rotation of 1500 rpm. At these conditions external and internal resistances were equal for all samples. The reactant and products were analyzed with HP 5890 GC on the stainless steel column filled with PORAPAK T.

RESULTS AND DISCUSSION

Since the results for SAPO-34, MeAPSO-34 (Me = Co, Mn, Cr) and H-ZSM-5 are presented elsewhere[12], we shall present here in detail only the results concerning the SAPO-44, MeAPSO-44 (Me = Co, Mn), $AlPO_4$-5 and $AlPO_4$-14 samples. Some characteristics pertinent to discussion and general conclusions are however gathered for all samples in tables and graphs.

The chemical composition of SAPO-44, MeAPSO-44, $AlPO_4$-5 and $AlPO_4$-14 samples and framework charges, calculated on a TO_2 basis[2] are given in Table 1.

Table 1.

The chemical composition of SAPO-34, MeAPSO-34 (Me = Co, Mn), $AlPO_4$-5 and $AlPO_4$-14 molecular sieves and their framework charge.

Sample	Me	Al	Si	P	Si+P	Framework charge
SAPO-44	–	0.50	0.14	0.36	0.50	-0.14
CoAPSO-44	0.04	0.46	0.11	0.39	0.50	-0.15
MnAPSO-44	0.04	0.44	0.15	0.37	0.52	-0.15
$AlPO_4$-5	–	0.50	–	0.50	–	0.00
$AlPO_4$-14	–	0.50	–	0.50	–	0.00

The quantity of methanol that remains adsorbed after degassing of samples at 292 K in dynamic vacuum of $< 1.33*10^{-3}$ Pa for several hours, until constant weight of samples was reached, was determined gravimetrically. The quantity of species desorbed during TPD was also determined gravimetrically, while the composition of desorbed species was calculated from the integral intensities of desorption peaks for characteristic fragments obtained by QMS in ion-chromatographic mode. These quantities are given in Table 2.

Table 2.

Quantity of methanol that remains adsorbed after degassing of samples at 292 K (TG), quantity (TG) and composition (QMS) of desorbed species during TPD between 292 K and 673 K.

Sample	CH_3OH_{ads} [g/gcat]	Prod.$_{des}$ [g/gcat]	Composition (molar fractions)			
			CH_3OH	H_2O	C_2H_4	$(CH_3)_2O$
SAPO-44	0.023	0.027	0.38	0.55	0.05	0.02
CoAPSO-44	0.049	0.039	0.61	0.25	0.08	0.05
MnAPSO-44	0.038	0.038	0.12	0.65	0.11	0.12
$AlPO_4$-5	0.010	0.011	0.06	0.94	0.00	0.00
$AlPO_4$-14	0.000	0.000	0.00	0.00	0.00	0.00

Table 3 gives a comparison of activity and selectivity data obtained by measurements in the gradientless catalytic reactor and those obtained by TPD measurements of methanol, where the reaction proceeds under nonisothermal static conditions. First column gives the reaction rate, second column gives the weight percents of ethene in hydrocarbon fraction, third column gives the conversion of methanol during TPD, fourth column gives the weight percents of ethene desorbed from converted methanol during TPD.

Figures 1a,b and 2a,b show the TPD spectra of methanol adsorbed on SAPO-34, SAPO-44 and CoAPSO-34, CoAPSO-44 respectively. Closer inspection of these figures reveals the fact that in 44 type structures the dimethylether desorption peaks are narrower than in 34 type structures, although the peak temperatures are about the same. This can be explained in our opinion by the slight differences between the 34 and 44 type structures, although they both belong to the chabazite-like topology. It seems that the 44 type structures are more ordered (less distorted), giving a narrower temperature interval for the intermediates to convert furtheron and/or to desorb.

Table 3.

Catalytic activity and selectivity data for the reaction of methanol dehydration measured in CST catalytic reactor and in TPD experiments under conditions described in text.

Sample	Catalytic reactor		TPD experiment	
	Reac. rate [mole/g.h]	Wt. % of ethene in H.C. frac.	Conv. of CH_3OH	Wt. % of ethene in CH_3OH conv.
SAPO-34	0.192	6.1	0.428	6.4
CoAPSO-34	0.104	12.0	0.374	9.9
MnAPSO-34	0.080	18.6	0.297	5.3
CrAPSO-34	0.105	9.9	0.397	3.1
SAPO-44	0.126	18.6	0.445	14.4
CoAPSO-44	0.102	33.7	0.331	23.2
MnAPSO-44	0.083	19.3	0.848	14.4
$AlPO_4$-5	0.125	0.0	0.0	0.0
$AlPO_4$-14	0.222	0.0	0.0	0.0
H-ZSM-5	0.541	40.8	0.298	9.8

Figure 3 shows the relation between the catalytic activity and selectivity of the SAPO and MeAPSO samples of both 34 and 44 structural types. Figure 3a shows that the equilibrium reaction of methanol dehydration to dimethylether (DME) is fast, but the further dehydration to hydrocarbons (ethene) is slower. As the conversion to hydrocarbons becomes higher, the reaction rate of methanol dehydration decreases. It decreases more with those catalyst samples having lower selectivities for ethene production, i.e. with those catalyst samples favoring oligomerization of ethene to higher hydrocarbons (coke) which can not diffuse out from the chabazite cage through the eight-membered rings (figure 3b, samples MnAPSO-34 and MnAPSO-44). Figures 3c and 3d illustrate the fact that the selectivities for ethene formation obtained by measurements in gradientless catalytic reactor (figure 3c) and by TPD (figure 3d) are qualitatively equal.

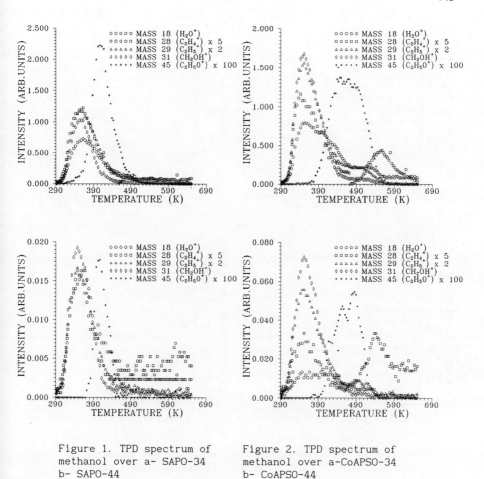

Figure 1. TPD spectrum of methanol over a- SAPO-34 b- SAPO-44

Figure 2. TPD spectrum of methanol over a-CoAPSO-34 b- CoAPSO-44

This is in agreement with Anderson et al.[13], where the authors claim that space velocity does not change oligomerization properties of SAPO-34 sample. From the same figures and Table 3 it is seen that the reaction rate does not depend at all on the structural type of the MeAPSO molecular sieves, being it 34 or 44. But it is affected slightly by the type of transition metal ion incorporated in the MeAPSO systems. On the other hand, selectivity towards ethene formation strongly depends on both structural type of molecular sieve and the type of transition metall ion incorporated in the MeAPSO

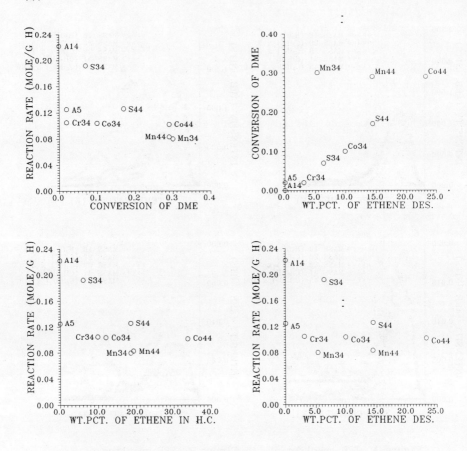

Figure 3. Relationship between activity and selectivity of AlPO$_4$, SAPO and MeAPSO catalysts in methanol dehydration reaction: a- overall reaction rate versus conversion of dimethylether to hydrocarbons (CST catalytic reactor); b- conversion of dimethylether (CST catalytic reactor) versus wt.% of ethene in desorbed products during TPD of methanol; c- overall reaction rate versus wt.% of ethene in hydrocarbon fraction (CST catalytic reactor); d- overall reaction rate (CST catalytic reactor) versus wt.% of ethene in desorbed products during TPD of methanol.

systems. It is clearly seen that the CoAPSO-44 has the highest selectivity to ethene among all aluminophosphate catalysts tested here. This is the evidence that selectivity is a function of both :

molecular-shape selectivity imposed by the structure of molecular sieve and acidity strength determined by the electronegativity of the active center forming element incorporated in the framework of molecular sieve. As the result the 44 type structures are about twice more selective to ethene than the 34 type structures. This is striking difference in molecular-shape selectivity between two "identical" structural types of molecular sieves.

REFERENCES

1. Wilson S.T., Lok B.M.T., Flanigen E.M., EP 0 043 562 (1982)
2. Flanigen E.M., Patton R.L. and Wilson S.T.,
   Stud.Surf.Sci.Catal. 37, 13-27 (1988)
3. Inui T., Matsuda H., Okaniwa H., Miyamoto A., Appl.Catal. 58,
   155-163 (1990)
4. Liang J., Li H., Zhao S., Guo W., Wang R. and Ying M.,
   Appl.Catal. 64, 31-40 (1990)
5. Chang C.D., "Hydrocarbons from Methanol", Chemical Industries
   10, Marcel Dekker, Inc., New York, 1983
6. Rajic N., Kaučič V., Stojakovic D., Zeolites 10, 169-173
   (1990)
7. Rajic N., Žagar T. and Kaučič V., "Studies of MeAPSO olecular
   Sieves (Me = Co^{2+}, Mn^{2+}, Cr^{3+}) with Chabazite Structure",
   Presented at 13th Annual Meeting, British Zeolite Association,
   Chislehurst, July 1990
8. Lok B.M.T., Messina C.A., Patton R.L., Gajek R.T., Cannan
   T.R., Flanigen E.M., U.S. Pat. 4,440,871 (1984)
9. Lok B.M.T., Marcus B.K., Flanigen E.M., EP 0 161 489 (1985)
10. Lok B.M.T., Marcus B.K., Flanigen E.M., EP 0 161 490 (1985)
11. Hočevar S., Rajic N., Žagar T., Levec J. in "Synthesis and
    Properties of New Catalysts: Utilization of Novel Materials
    Components and Synthetic Techniques" (Eds.: E.W.Corcoran, Jr.
    and M.J.Ledoux), Materials Research Society, Pittsburgh, 1990,
    pp.29-32
12. Hočevar S., Levec J., "Acidity and Catalytic Activity of
    MeAPSO-34 (Me = Co, Mn, Cr), SAPO-34 and H-ZSM-5 Molecular

Sieves in Methanol Dehydration reaction",Submitted to J.Catal.

13. Anderson M.W., Sulikowski B., Barrie P.J. and Klinowski J.,
    J.Phys.Chem., <u>94</u>, 2730-2734 (1990)

A TWO-STEP CATALYTIC ROUTE FOR THE PREPARATION OF PYRAZINAMIDE

Lucio Forni

Dipartimento di Chimica Fisica ed Elettrochimica
Universita' di Milano, Via C.Golgi,19 20133 Milano, Italy

INTRODUCTION

2-Amidopyrazine (AP) is one of the five drugs chosen by the World Health Organisation as praesidia against tuberculosis. One of the most important methods for the preparation of AP involves a complex sequence of reactions[1-4] leading to the synthesis of 2,3-diaminopropionic acid hydrochloride, which is further reacted with glyoxal and in presence of air to give 2-pyrazinoic acid. The latter is finally converted into the amide. A very attractive way to simplify the preparation is the insertion of some catalytic reactions[5-8]. From this point of view, the most interesting route is the cyclisation of largely available and cheap reagents, namely ethylene diamine (ED) and propylene glycol (PG) to 2-methyl-pyrazine (MP), followed by ammoxidation with air and ammonia to 2-cyanopyrazine (CP), which is easily hydrolysable to the amide[9].

Of course, the feasibility of this route relies completely on the availability of a sufficiently active and selective catalyst for each one of the two key-steps. The design of such catalysts has been the main goal of an extensive study carried out recently in our laboratory[10-17].

AMMOXIDATION OF MP TO CP

The second step of the process seemed the most difficult in principle. Hence, it was faced first, by starting with an extended exploratory research of a heterogeneous catalyst, including the transition metal oxide mixtures usually employed for ammoxidation of aromatics and heterocycles, such as the oxides of V, Sb, Mo, Sn, Bi, Fe, etc. Owing to their ionic nature, all these oxides are characterised by the ability of rapidly transferring oxygen from the bulk to the surface and from the latter to the adsorbed reacting species, accompanied by a rapid reoxidation by the molecular oxygen coming from the gas phase[18,19].

The performance-comparison runs were carried out under standard conditions by means of a conventional, continuous, fixed-bed microreactor assembly. The screening on over 30 different solid mixtures put soon in evidence the combination of Sb and V oxides, especially when promoted by a small addition of a third component, particularly Mn oxide. Furthermore, it was observed that a large excess of steam in the reacting mixture improves substantially the life of the catalyst. This resulted also easily regenerable by simply burning off the carbonaceous deposits with air under controlled conditions.

The optimal composition of the catalyst and the best reaction conditions were: Sb/V/Mn atomic ratio = 8/2/1; support: α-alumina of less than 1 m^2/g surface area; active oxides loading on the support: 5 to 10 wt%; reaction temperature: 300 to 400 $^\circ$C; total pressure: atmospheric; MP/NH$_3$/H$_2$O/air molar feeding ratio = 1/2.5/13/95. Under these conditions the catalyst showed up to 75% selectivity to CP at 90% conversion of MP, coupled with a good durability.

The present ammoxidation reaction may be described by the formal stoichiometry

$$MP + 3/2\ O_2 + NH_3 \rightarrow CP + 3\ H_2O$$

and it is highly exothermic (ΔH = -120 kcal/mol of reacted MP). As a

Table 1. Effect of particle size in ammoxidation
of MP to CP. Reaction temperature 400°C.

Mesh	C_{MP}(mol%)	S_{CP}(mol%)
10-20	66.6	61.5
20-40	75.9	69.0
40-60	81.8	69.6
60-80	95.2	70.1
80-100	95.9	70.4

consequence, even by employing the smallest catalyst particles, still permitting a reasonable pressure drop (< 10 kPa = 0.1 bar) of the reacting gas through the catalyst bed, some internal diffusion limitation is still present (Table 1). This is confirmed also by the low value (12 kcal/mol) of the apparent activation energy of reaction. Therefore, for a practical application of the process, the catalyst has to be prepared in special form, e.g. by covering the non porous, inert support with a very thin layer of active components. This would shorten considerably the diffusive path of reagents and products within the active phase, with acceptable pressure drop of the gas flowing through the bed of particles. Of course, a careful study on pilot plant scale is needed, to collect the information relative to the behaviour of the catalyst in its final configuration.

CYCLISATION OF ED AND PG TO MP

The formal stoichiometry of the first key-step is:

$$ED + PG \rightarrow MP + 2 H_2O + 3 H_2$$

Hence, a selective catalyst for this reaction should possess at least two functions: dehydration and dehydrogenation. These functions are simultaneously provided by some transition metal oxides, such as ZnO, Fe_2O_3, Cr_2O_3. However, very often mixtures of catalysts typically showing only the dehydration function, such as Al_2O_3 or SiO_2-Al_2O_3, combined with catalysts typically showing only the dehydrogenation function, such as noble metals, were found to exhibit a better performance, with respect to bifunctional single oxides. In the present case, the high thermodynamic stability of the pyrazinic ring may help in favouring the selective formation of such a species, with respect to the competitive formation of unwelcome byproducts.

Our exploratory research[11] was carried out on over 50 different catalysts, ranging from the single-oxide preparations to mixtures of the various transition metals and oxides usually exhibiting the desired functions. The screening put soon in evidence ZnO as an excellent catalyst for our cyclisation. Unfortunately, ZnO is quite unstable under the optimal reaction temperature (ca. 400°C), so at least a textural promoter had to be added, to withstand sintering. Furthermore, the addition of a small amount of Pd enhanced substantially selectivity[11,13,16] by depressing the formation of acetone, the most abundant byproduct (Table 2).

Spinels showed among the best retardants of sintering, particularly Zn-chromite, and a relatively large excess of steam once again proved useful in improving substantially the life of the catalyst. As the previous one for ammoxidation, the present catalyst too was found to be easily regenerable by simple burning off the carbonaceous fouling substance.

Table 2. Selectivity to acetone vs. Pd conc.
Reaction temperature 370°C.

Pd wt %	S_{AC} mol %
0	29.09
0.24	4.77
0.77	4.85
1.00	4.61
1.49	5.58
1.93	4.69
3.15	4.77

The best results (up to 80% selectivity to MP at 100% conversion of the key-reagent ED) were obtained with a $ZnO/ZnCr_2O_4$ mixture of Zn/Cr $\cong$ 3/1 atomic ratio, promoted with ca. 1 wt% Pd, by working at atmospheric pressure and 350 to 430°C and by feeding a 5 to 50 wt% aq. solution of ED+PG with ca. 0.7/1 molar ratio.

CHARACTERISATION AND STRUCTURAL ANALYSIS OF THE CATALYST

The design of a catalyst is usually accomplished essentially on the basis of a continuous feed-back procedure, in which the correlation between physico-chemical properties and catalytic performance plays the most important role. As a result, an invaluable help in improving both conversion and selectivity, together with an increasing understanding of the catalytic process, are simultaneously obtained.

a) Ammoxidation of MP

The characterisation of the Sb-V-Mn-O catalyst has been carried out[14] by analysing the effect of changing the relative ratios of active components, their concentration and the nature of the support on both the physico-chemical properties of the solid and catalytic behaviour. Besides chemical composition, the analysis included the nature and morphology of solid phases, the concentration of active elements at the surface and in the bulk, the surface acidity, the source of the e.s.r. signal generated by the solid, the BET surface area and porosity. The most interesting information so collected can be summarised as follows.

i) The activity of the catalyst is likely connected with the presence of Sb^{4+} species. Only the cervantite-like α-Sb_2O_4 and the $SbVO_4$ crystalline phases were detected by XRD in active catalysts (Fig.1). No other Sb-containing phases, such as Sb_2O_5, Sb_6O_{13}, Sb_2O_3 (either senarmontite- or valentinite-like) and particularly β-Sb_2O_4 were detected in such a way. The Sb^{4+} species is usually cosidered in the literature[20] as a formal oxidation state, determined by the simultaneous presence of Sb^{3+} and Sb^{5+} ions, alternating in the crystal lattice of the oxide. It is thermodynamically unstable, but sufficiently resistant, with respect to reduction to the stable Sb^{3+}, up to 480-530°C, under

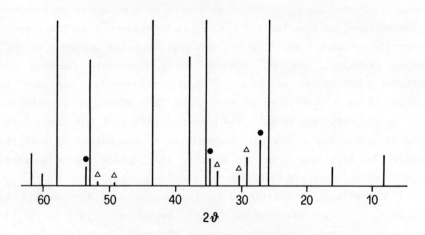

Fig.1 Typical XRD pattern of a supported ammoxid. catalyst.
       ($\triangle$) α-Sb_2O_4, ($\bullet$) $SbVO_4$. Other lines due to support.

at least 0.1 bar (10^4 Pa) oxygen partial pressure. It forms when Sb_2O_5 is heated at ca. $480°C$, through the intermediate Sb_6O_{13}.

ii) The nature of the support affects both surface area and porosity, as expected, leading to a bimodal pore size distribution and the specific yield Y_s, referred to unit surface area of the catalyst, strongly increases with decreasing surface area, i.e. by decreasing the amount of micropore $(10 < R_p(\text{Å}) < 30)$ volume (Table 3).

Table 3. Specific yield Y_s, ref. to unit surface area, vs. S_{BET}.

S_{BET} (m^2/g)	$Y_s \cdot 10^4$ (mol/h x m^2)
0.9	3.4
1.0	3.2
1.4	1.3
4.4	0.3

iii) The e.s.r. signal generated by our catalyst is very weak and is due to the V^{4+} ion (H = 3000 Gauss, g = 1.97). Furthermore, the intensity of the signal in active catalysts is practically independent of temperature, as expected for electrical conductors[14]. In the present system the catalytic activity is connected with the presence of Sb^{4+} species (α-Sb_2O_4), the Sb^{3+} species being completely inactive, as mentioned. The effect of V as a structural promoter may then be interpreted as a stabiliser of the formal Sb^{4+} state, by blocking or delaying its reduction to Sb^{3+}. The promoting effect of V probably takes place by conferring electrical conductivity to the solid, so that the transfer of electrons from the bulk to the surface and *vice versa* becomes easier, strongly favouring the redox mechanism.

iv) The effect of loading of active oxides onto the support is limited to a concentration of ca. 10 wt%. Beyond this limit no further improvement in catalyst performance is observed (Table 4). However, since the higher the loading, the softer is the resulting solid, one may conclude that 10 wt% probably represents the best compromise between good activity and acceptable mechanical strength of the catalyst.

Table 4. Effect of active oxides loading
on support (AMC alumina).
Standard reaction conditions.

Loading (wt %)	C_{ED} (mol %)
2.0	28
5.1	39
9.5	61
11.8	65
22.9	68
100.0	62

v) A similar conclusion can be drawn for the effect of concentration of promoters (Table 5): the higher the amount of promoters, the better the base-component (Sb) is exploited.

Table 5. Specific yield Y_{Sb}, referred to unit mass
Sb, vs. Sb/(V+Mn) atomic ratio.

Sb/(V+Mn)	$10^2 Y_{Sb}$, mol/h x g Sb
0.48	1.14
0.68	0.80
1.04	0.73
1.13	0.76

However, both in the absence and in the presence of a too high amount of promoters, the catalyst life shortens considerably. So the best compromise is attained for Sb/(V+Mn) atomic ratio $\cong$ 1.

b) Cyclisation of ED + PG to MP

The characterisation of the Zn-Cr-O-Pd catalyst for the cyclisation to MP has been carried out essentially by analysing the effect on catalytic behaviour of the method of preparation, of Zn/Cr ratio and of concentration of promoter. The most interesting information may be summarised as follows.

i) Coprecipitation leads to better catalysts, with respect to the wet-mixing technique, due to a different texture of the solid obtained. For instance, surface area is up to five times higher and selectivity usually 10 to 20 % better with coprecipitated catalysts. Furthermore, the ZnO and $ZnCr_2O_4$ phases in coprecipitated catalysts are much less crystalline.

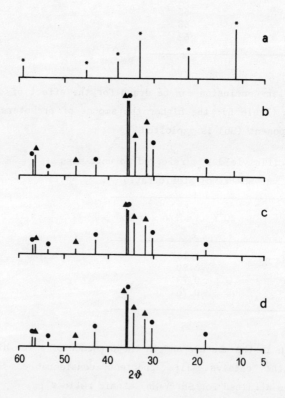

Fig.2　Typical XRD pattern of coprecipitated cyclisation catalyst: a) precursor mix dried at $100°C$, b) calcined at $430°C$ in the absence of Pd, c) reduced at $320°C$ in the absence of Pd, d) calcined and reduced after addition of Pd. (*) hydrotalcite-like phase, (▲) ZnO, zincite, (●) $ZnCr_2O_4$.

ii) In coprecipitated catalysts the crystallinity of the material depends on the Zn/Cr ratio, the less crystalline solid corresponding to Zn/Cr $\cong$ 3. Furthermore, the simple drying of the coprecipitated hydroxycarbonates leads to the formation of a hydrotalcite-like phase, in which no trace of the final structures (ZnO and $ZnCr_2O_4$) are noticed in the XRD pattern (Fig.2). These structures form only after calcining (430°C) in air and the further reduction step, either in the presence or in the absence of the Pd precursor, leads to a considerable decrease of crystallinity.

iii) Another parameter strongly depending on the Zn/Cr ratio is the linewidth of the e.s.r. spectrum, centred at g = 1.98 and connected with the presence of β-Cr^{3+} ions[15]. The linewidth is independent of temperature, as expected for electrical conductors. The change in linewidth is due to two opposite phenomena: spin-exchange coupling and dipolar interaction, leading to line narrowing or broadening, respectively. By magnetic dilution of the sample, the spin-exchange coupling effect weakens more rapidly than dipolar interaction, so that, by increasing the Zn/Cr ratio from 1.8 to 4.4, a change of more that 300% is observed in linewidth. This is very likely due to the change of crystalline cell parameter of $ZnCr_2O_4$, brought about by the addition of increasing amounts of ZnO during coprecipitation. These effects are accompanied by a considerable change in reaction selectivity, with a peak value (e.g. 60% vs. 32-45 %) at Zn/Cr $\cong$ 3.

iv) The most important effect of the addition of Pd is the strong decrease in selectivity to acetone, as mentioned. Another interesting effect is once again the change in linewidth of the e.s.r. spectrum due to β-Cr^{3+} ions. Up to about 1 wt% Pd a $\approx$30% narrowing is observed, with respect to the Pd-free catalyst, followed by a strong ($\approx$280%) broadening for 1 < Pd wt% < 2 and again by a strong narrowing, down to the former value, for Pd > 2 wt%. A similar trend, although less pronounced, is observed for the catalytic yield vs. the same parameter.

All these observations point to the conclusion that the catalytic activity is very likely connected with the presence of a pseudo-amorphous or extremely microcrystalline structure possessing an expanded cell parameter with respect to the spinel-like Zn-chromite phase. This structure forms by calcination of the hydrotalcite-like phase, obtained after dehydration of the coprecipitated hydroxycarbonates, when an excess of ZnO is present, especially if the overall Zn/Cr atomic ratio is about 3/1. This particular structure improves the electrical conductivity of the oxide mixture, probably by favouring the mobility of the electrons, owing to the higher degree of disorder of the crystalline framework. The addition of Pd seems to have a similar effect. At least a part of the Pd probably penetrates into the crystal lattice of the spinel phase, again bringing about an expansion of the cell parameter, accompanied by an enhancement of the electron mobility.

MECHANISTIC STUDY

The mechanism of both the key-steps of the present process is still under study in our laboratory, principally by means of the TPD-TPR-MS technique. The aim is to individuate the most promising way for a possible further improvement of the catalytic performance. The information so far collected on the ammoxidation step[21] shows that all the reagents and products, except oxygen, adsorb competitively on at least two types of surface sites, characterised by a different energy of interaction with the adsorbed species. From the weaker sites all the species desorb unaltered, while the stronger sites are those onto which the reagents are activated for both the desired reaction to CP and the decomposition to byproducts. Ammonia adsorbs also on a third, very high-energy type of sites, able to activate the molecule for the oxidation to N_2 and NO_x. Oxygen does not compete in adsorption with any of the other species. Very likely it dissolves in the solid, rapidly diffusing through the bulk and it is involved in the reaction through a Mars-Van Krevelen mechanism. A Rideal-Eley type mechanism, with either oxygen or ammonia coming from the gas phase, to react with adsorbed MP, seems unsupported by our data.

As for the cyclysation step of the process, the reaction revealed much more complicated than it would appear from the simple stoichiometry

$$ED + PG \rightarrow MP + 2 H_2O + 3 H_2$$

Indeed, at least 30 different products could be detected in the reactor effluent under some reaction conditions, although most of them only in traces[17]. This is due not only to the relatively unstable nature of the reagents, especially PG, but also to the complex nature of the principal reaction. In fact, many different simultaneous or subsequent reactions were observed, promoted by our poly-functional Zn-Cr-O-Pd catalyst. Hence, several reaction intermediates are simultaneously present upon the catalyst surface during the reaction and each of them, in principle, can react in different ways, ending into different products. A good rationalisation of the matter has been attained[17], through a careful analysis of the effluent by GC-MS. This permitted to draw a general scheme of the reactions leading to the various products.

As for the mechanism of this first step of the process, a rate-determining step of the Rideal-Eley type, between adsorbed PG and ED coming from the gas phase seems the most probable one[17,22]. This step leads to the formation of the first, completely hydrogenated-ring intermediate, 2-methylpiperazine, which quickly and progressively dehydrogenates and aromatises to MP.

REFERENCES

1) Felder, E. and Pitre, D., in *Analytical Profiles of Drug Substances*, (K.Florey, Ed.) vol.12, Academic Press, New York, 1983, p.433.
2) Brit.Pat. 1016468, Jan.1966.
3) Felder, E., Pitre, D., Boveri, S. and Grabitz, E.B., *Chem.Ber.*, **100**, 555 (1967).
4) Swiss Pat. 458361, Aug.1968.
5) Okada, J. and Koichi, N., *Yakugaku Zasshi*, **19**, 416 (1971).
6) Jap.Kokai, 74 117480; Brit.Pat. 1565117, Sept.1977.
7) Okada, J., Morita, N., Miwa, Y. and Tashima, T., *Yakugaku Zasshi*, **98**, 1491 (1978).
8) Ger.Offen. 2722307, Mar.1978; Jap.Kokai 79 132588; Jap.Kokai 80 145672; U.S.Pat. 4284781, Aug.1981; Ger.Offen., DE 3107756 A1, Sept. 1982.
9) Foks, H. and Panchechowska, D., *Acta Pol.Pharm.*, **33**, 49 (1976).
10) Forni, L., *Appl.Catal.*, **20**, 219 (1986).
11) Forni, L., Stern, G. and Gatti, M., *Appl.Catal.*, **29**, 161 (1987).
12) Forni, L., *Appl.Catal.*, **37**, 305 (1988).
13) Forni, L., *J.Catal.*, **111**, 199 (1988).
14) Forni, L., Oliva, C. and Rebuscini, C., *J.C.S., Faraday I*, **84**, 2397 (1988).
15) Forni, L. and Oliva, C., *J.C.S., Faraday I*, **84**, 2477 (1988).
16) Forni, L. and Nestori, S., in *Heterogeneous Catalysis and Fine Chemicals*, (M.Guisnet *et al.*,Eds.), Elsevier, Amsterdam, 1988, p.291.
17) Forni. L. and Miglio, R., *Prepr. 2nd Intern. Symp. on Heterog. Catal. and Fine Chem.*, Poitiers, Sept.1990, p. C 171.

158

18) Krylov, O.V., *Catalysis by Non Metals*, Academic Press, New York, 1970.
19) Hucknall, D.J., *Selective Oxidation of Hydrocarbons*, Academic Press, New York, 1974.
20) Pascal, P., *Nouveau Traite de Chimie Minerale*, Masson, Paris, 1958, vol. IX, p.591.
21) Forni, L., Toscano, M. and Pollesel, P., *J.Catal.*, subm. for publ.
22) Forni, L., Miglio, R. and Pollesel, P., unpubl. results.

PERIODIC REGIMES IN A CATALYST PELLET WITH NARROW REGION OF ACTIVITY

Martin Barto, Jozef Markoš and Alena Brunovská

Department of Organic Technology, Slovak Institute of Technology, Radlinského 9, 812 37 Bratislava, ČSFR

1. ABSTRACT

The analysis of the dynamical behaviour of an isothermal continuous stirred tank reactor where the catalyst pellet with Dirac delta distributed activity is placed in the case of bimolecular Langmuir – Hinshelwood kinetics is presented. The bifurcation diagram in the plane active point location vs. parameter X is constructed. The existence of multiple periodic solutions is numerically established. The influence of the active point location, Thiele modulus and Damkoehler number is discussed.

2. INTRODUCTION

The dynamical behaviour of catalyst pellets has been the subject of vital interest of numerous experimental and theoretical studies during the past decades. It has been shown that even the isothermal catalytic reaction (described by Langmuir – Hinshelwood kinetic equation) is capable of performing quite complicated pellet dynamical behaviour[6]. The behaviour of catalyst pellets with uniformly distributed activity was investigated in most of these studies. The analysis of the dynamical behaviour of the catalyst pellets with nonuniformly distributed activity was published only recently in the papers of Brunovská [2] [3] in which the pellets with Dirac delta and step function activity distribution were studied. It was shown that the activity location considerably influences their dynamical behaviour. To investigate the dynamical behaviour of distributed parameter systems it is necessary to choose a reasonable discretization of differential operators. Several methods have been suggested and tested. In our recent paper[1] a novel method based on the results of the works of Michelsen[7] and Goyal[4] has been proposed. The orthogonal collocation method is applied on particular finite elements into which the catalyst pellet is divided. It is especially suitable for the dynamical simulation of catalyst pellets with nonuniformly distributed activity. The results in the paper[2], particularly the slow dumping of oscillations crossing the point C (Fig. 4), indicates the possibility of more complicated dynamic behaviour. This is why we were looking for a more effective method to extend these results.

3. METHOD

We shall assume a catalyst pellet with nonuniform activity distribution placed in a continuous stirred tank reactor and bimolecular catalytic reaction described by Langmuir - Hinshelwood kinetic equation. We will neglect external resistance to mass transport and we will assume isothermal conditions. The dimensionless balance equations and rate expression are as follows:

Pellet balances

$$\frac{\partial Y_A}{\partial \tau} = \nabla^2 Y_A - \Phi^2 R \tag{1}$$

$$\gamma \frac{\partial Y_B}{\partial \tau} = \nabla^2 Y_B - \beta \Phi^2 R \tag{2}$$

Reactor balances

$$\alpha \frac{\partial Y_{Af}}{\partial \tau} = 1 - Y_{Af} - Da_A \bar{R} \tag{3}$$

$$\alpha \frac{\partial Y_{Bf}}{\partial \tau} = 1 - Y_{Bf} - b\, Da_B \bar{R} \tag{4}$$

Pellet boundary condition

$$\tau > 0, \quad \varphi = 0: \quad \frac{\partial Y_A}{\partial \varphi} = \frac{\partial Y_B}{\partial \varphi} = 0$$

$$\varphi = 1: \quad Y_A = Y_{Af}, \quad Y_B = Y_{Bf} \tag{5}$$

Initial conditions

$$\tau = 0, \quad \varphi \in <0,1): \quad Y_A = Y_A^0, \quad Y_B = Y_B^0 \tag{6}$$

Reaction rate expression

$$R = a \frac{\omega^2 \, Y_A \, Y_B}{(1 + x_A Y_A + x_B Y_B)^2} \tag{7}$$

Pellet volume averaged reaction rate

$$\bar{R} = (n+1) \int_0^1 R \, \varphi^n \, d\varphi \tag{8}$$

The catalyst activity a is defined as the ratio of the local reaction rate constant to its volume averaged value and Dirac delta distribution at the point $\bar{\varphi}$ is given by

$$a(\varphi) = \frac{\delta(\varphi - \bar{\varphi})}{(n+1) \, \bar{\varphi}^n} \tag{9}$$

which satisfies the constraint

$$(n+1) \int_0^1 a \, \varphi^n \, d\varphi = 1 \tag{10}$$

In the case of Dirac delta activity distribution the pellet balances lead to two copies of the linear parabolic equations on the interval $<0,\bar{\varphi}) \cup (\bar{\varphi},1)$

$$\frac{\partial Y_A}{\partial \tau} = \nabla^2 Y_A \tag{11}$$

$$\gamma \frac{\partial Y_B}{\partial \tau} = \nabla^2 Y_B \tag{12}$$

which are coupled in $\bar{\varphi}$ by the interface conditions

$$\left. \frac{\partial Y_A}{\partial \varphi} \right|_{\varphi = \bar{\varphi}_-} - \left. \frac{\partial Y_A}{\partial \varphi} \right|_{\varphi = \bar{\varphi}_+} + \Phi^2 \, R(\bar{Y}_A, \bar{Y}_B) = 0 \tag{13}$$

$$\left.\frac{\partial Y_B}{\partial \varphi}\right|_{\varphi = \bar{\varphi}_-} - \left.\frac{\partial Y_B}{\partial \varphi}\right|_{\varphi = \bar{\varphi}_+} + \beta \, \Phi^2 \, R(\bar{Y}_A, \bar{Y}_B) = 0 \qquad (14)$$

The discretization procedure described in[1] transforms the system of ordinary and partial differential equations (3), (4), (11), (12) with interface conditions (13), (14) into the system of ordinary differential equations with nonlinear interface conditions and continuity conditions.

It has to be stressed that the system of ordinary differential equations is linear if $Da_A = Da_B = 0$ and the nonlinearity is then introduced only by the interface conditions. This is the case corresponding to that which was studied by Brunovská[3], i.e. the pellet with constant concentration on the outer surface.

As it was pointed out in the papers of Brunovská[2][3], the dynamical behaviour strongly depends on the active point location. To investigate this phenomenon the standard continuation procedure has been applied DERPAR[5] and the steady state branches have been obtained. The procedure involves the calculation of steady states and the eigenvalues of the corresponding Jacobi matrix. Eigenvalue calculations have been performed by means of routine EISYS[7]. The eigenvalue information was used for limit and Hopf bifurcation points estimation.

3.1. Steady State Branches

Under steady state conditions the solution of Eqs (1) – (10) transforms into the solution of one cubic equation for the unknown concentration of component A in the active point $\bar{\varphi}$[2]:

$$- \frac{n+1}{X}(1 - \bar{Y}_A) - R(\bar{Y}_A, \bar{Y}_B) = 0 \qquad (15)$$

where $\bar{Y}_B = 1 - \beta \, (1 - \bar{Y}_A)$.

The dependencies of $Y_A(\varphi)$, $Y_B(\varphi)$, Y_{Af} and Y_{Bf} on $\bar{Y}_A$ are linear. The region of multiplicity also results from the Eq. (15). If we choose X as the bifurcation parameter the maximal number of limit points on the solution diagram is 2. The multiplicity behaviour depends only on the parameter X , not on the active point location itself. For each value of X there exists the interval $I = \langle X_*, X^* \rangle$ such that Eq. (15) has 3 solutions if $X \in I$.

3.2. Hopf Bifurcation Points

Eq. (15) however is not capable of predicting Hopf bifurcation points and other dynamical bifurcations. These phenomena have been studied by means of steady state continuation and the corresponding Jacobi matrix eigenvalue calculation. The aforementioned discretization procedure has been adopted. The special character of the resulting set of discretized equations has been taken into account. The elements of the Jacobi matrix contain the term in which the interface conditions are incorporated. This is the way how the nonlinearity is introduced into the Jacobi matrix of the system of linear ordinary differential equations which are obtained by the discretization. Hopf bifurcation points have been found from known eigenvalues.

The character of periodic solutions originating in these points has been estimated by the dynamical simulation of balance equations for particular values of parameters X (or Thiele modulus Φ^2).

4. RESULTS

Numerical computations were performed for the set of fixed parameters $\varkappa_A, \varkappa_B, \beta$ and γ (see Table 1). These values are the same as in previous papers[1] [2] [6]. They correspond to considerably different adsorption constants and diffusion coefficients of components A and B.

Steady state branches with respect to parameter X have been computed for several active point locations $\bar{\varphi}$ and Damkoehler numbers Da. Limit and Hopf bifurcation points have been found on these branches. It has been pointed out that the shape of the diagram and the position of limit points do not depend on $\bar{\varphi}$. On the other hand, the position of Hopf bifurcation points differ for various values of $\bar{\varphi}$. This can be seen in Fig. 1 where the bifurcation diagram in the parameter plane $\bar{\varphi}$

vs. X is depicted. The branches of limit points (LP) are straight lines whereas Hopf point branches (HB_1, HB_2) draw nearer as $\bar\varphi$ increases but do not intersect. One unstable steady state exists inside the region O separated by the branches of Hopf bifurcation points ,i.e. for the parameters from this region O the stable periodic regime exists. Three unstable steady states and stable limit cycles have been found in the region OM. The curve SNP is the branch of saddle-node bifurcation of periodic solutions. In the region OS, between SNP and HB_1 curves, stable periodic solution coexists together with stable steady state. The only stable state is possible for the parameters outside the curves HB. The proposed method is unable to estimate the dynamic behaviour for the parameters from the region Q. In this case the collocation method produced very large collocation weights and therefore the discretized system is very "stiff".

The character of these periodic solutions and the curve SNP have been obtained by the simulation of the pellet balance equations. There is subcritical Hopf bifurcation on the upper branch HB_1 and $\bar\varphi < 0.8$, i.e. there exists the stable periodic solution together with the stable state. The periodic regime exists for all X ∈ (-0.918,-1.095) and $\bar\varphi$ = 0.5. The oscillations have a relaxation character for all parameter values. For $\bar\varphi$ ∈ <0.5 - 0.8> they are regular (Fig. 2) as it was shown in [1] [2]. The oscillation amplitude rapidly increases after X passes through its bifurcation value and it reaches a fixed value very soon. As the active point moves towards the pellet surface, their character changes and small spikes appear (Fig. 3). Their character changes even when X is changed for fixed $\bar\varphi$ (i.e. changing Thiele modulus).

Damkoehler number also influences the shape of the steady state branches and the position of bifurcation points. This is evident from Fig. 4 where they are depicted as the function of X and $Da_A = Da_B$. The pair of limit points vanish as $Da_A > 0.03$. The Hopf points are not influenced so strongly, they disappear for much higher Da_A values.

5. DISCUSSION

The results presented above illustrate complicated dynamical behaviour of the catalyst pellets with narrow active zone in the presence of the reaction with Langmuir - Hinshelwood kinetics. This behaviour strongly depends on the active zone location $\bar{\varphi}$. The region of periodic oscillations (i.e. interval of Thiele modulli) is broader as the active zone is moving towards the pellet center. This region becomes very narrow when the active zone is close the pellet surface. The amplitude of oscillations is not affected too much by the active zone location.

A new interesting phenomenon which has been found is the saddle-node bifurcation of periodic solutions; the coexistence of stable and unstable periodic solution with stable steady state, within the region OS, which is bounded by the upper branch of the Hopf bifurcation points HB_1 and the branch of the saddle-node bifurcation points SNP (Fig. 1).

6. CONCLUSIONS

Results presented in this paper are in coincidence with the previous ones[2] except of the Hopf bifurcation point branch HB_2. Using finite difference lumping method the periodic oscillation regime has not been observed for the values of X lower than that which corresponds to the limit point (i.e. in the region O_2). It is interesting to note that the disagreement in this region is also with the first work[6] where the authors used eigenfunction expansion based lumping procedure.

7. REFERENCES

1. Barto, M., Markoš, J. and Brunovská, A., Chem. Engng. Sci. 45, in press, (1990)

2. Brunovská, A., Chem. Engng. Sci. 42, 1969 - 1976, (1987)

3. Brunovská, A., Chem. Engng. Sci. 43, 2546 - 2548, (1988)

4. Goyal, S.K., Esmail, M.N. and Bakhsi, N.N., Can. Jour. Chem. Engng, 65, 833 - 844, (1987)

5. Kubíček M., ACM Trans. Math. Software 2, 98, (1975)

6. Uppal, A. and Ray, W.H., Chem. Engng. Sci. 32, 649 - 657, (1977)

7. Villadsen, J. and Michelsen, M.L., "Solution of Differential Equation Models by Polynomial Approximation", Prentice-Hall, Englewood Cliffs NJ, (1977)

8. NOTATION

a – catalyst activity distribution

b – stoichiometric coefficients ratio

c – concentration (mol/m^3)

D_e – effective diffusion coefficient (m^2/s)

Da – $Da = (1-\varepsilon)\ \xi_v^0\ V\ /\ (\dot{V}\ c_f^0)$, Damkoehler number

k – reaction rate constant $(mol\ m^{-3}s^{-1})$

K – adsorption constant (m^3/mol)

n – integer characteristic of pellet geometry

r – pellet space coordinate (m)

R – dimensionless reaction rate

R_p – pellet characteristic dimension (m)

t – time (s)

V – reactor volume (m^3)

$\dot{V}$ – volumetric flow rate (m^3/s)

V_p – pellet volume (m^3)

X – $X = \Phi^2 . \Psi(\bar{\varphi})$, $\Psi(\bar{\varphi}) = \bar{\varphi} - 1$ for $n = 0$ (slab)

$$\ln \bar{\varphi} \qquad 1 \text{ (infinite cylinder)}$$
$$1 - 1\ /\ \bar{\varphi} \qquad 2 \text{ (sphere)}$$

Y – dimensionless concentration

8.1 Greek

α – $\alpha = L\ D_{eA}\ \varepsilon\ /(R_p^2\ v)$, dimensionless parameter

β – $\beta = b.c_{Af}^0\ D_{eA}\ /(c_{Bf}^0\ D_{eA})$, dimensionless parameter

γ – $\gamma = D_{eA}\ /D_{eB}$, dimensionless parameter

δ – Dirac delta function

ε – bed void fraction

$\varkappa$ – $\varkappa = K\ c_f^0$, dimensionless parameter

τ – $\tau = t\ D_{eA}\ /\ R_p^2$, dimensionless time

φ $- \varphi = r / R_p$, dimensionless pellet coordinate

Φ $- \Phi^2 = R_p \xi_v^0 / (D_e c_{Af}^0)$, Thiele modulus

ω $- \omega = 1 + \varkappa_A + \varkappa_B$, dimensionless parameter

8.2 Subscripts   8.3 Superscripts

A   - component A $-$ - active point

B   - component B   o   - inlet

f   - fluid

TABLES

Table 1. Values of dimensionless parameters.

Parameter	Value
$\varkappa_A$	1
$\varkappa_B$	30
β	1.2
γ	0.12
α	0.12
n	1

FIGURES

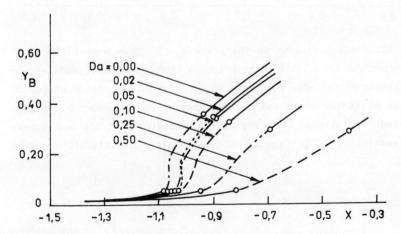

Fig. 4 Solution diagram for $\overline{\varphi} = 0.5$. $Da_A = Da_B = Da$ is the parameter of lines. ($\bullet$ - Hopf point)

168

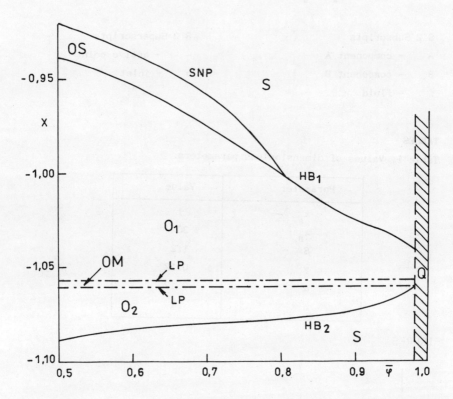

Fig. 1 Bifurcation diagram in the plane $\overline{\varphi}$ - X. HB - Hopf bifurcation point branches, LP - limit point branches, SNP - branch of saddle-node bifurcations of periodic solutions, S - region of one steady state, OS - region of steady state and periodic regime coexistence, O - region of periodic solutions, OM - region of periodic solutions and steady state multiplicity, Q - region of too "stiff" discretization. (Da_A = Da_B = 0)

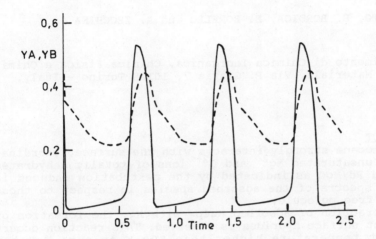

Fig. 2 Periodic solution from the region OS. (Da$_A$= Da$_B$= 0, $\bar{\varphi}$ = 0.5, X = -0.92)

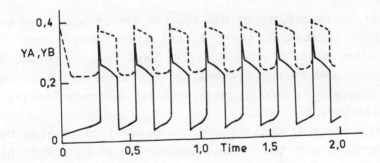

Fig. 3 Periodic solution from the region OM and for active point close to the pellet surface. (Da$_A$ = Da$_B$= 0, $\bar{\varphi}$ = 0.95, X = -1.05)

INTERACTION OF METALLOCENES WITH OXYDIC SURFACES: IR STUDY OF MAGNESIOCENE ON MgO AND Pd/MgO

G. SPOTO, S. BORDIGA, E. BORELLO and A. ZECCHINA

Dipartimento di Chimica Inorganica, Chimica Fisica e Chimica dei Materiali. Via P. Giuria 7, 10125 Torino - Italy.

ABSTRACT

Magnesiocene strongly interacts with the surface, coordinatively unsaturated Mg^{2+} and O^{2-} ions of totally dehydrated MgO and Pd/MgO as indicated by the pertubation induced in the IR spectra of the adsorbed species in respect to those of the free molecule.

On interaction of adsorbed $MgCp_2$ with H_2, the formation of abundant surface hydrides is observed. This reaction occurs only at temperature higher than 300 K on pure MgO but already at room temperature on the Pd/MgO system.

INTRODUCTION

The surface reactivity of MgO towards simple molecules has been investigated in great detail since many years. In particular, several studies (1-10) have been performed on the CO-MgO and NO-MgO systems, on the interaction of MgO with hydrocarbons (mainly unsaturated), heterocycles (Py), molecular hydrogen etc.

From all these investigations the general conclusion has been derived that the surface reactivity of MgO is mainly associated with highly coordinatively unsaturated (cus) Mg^{2+} and O^{2-} ions located on corner, edges and steps.

In particular the following reactions have been observed:

a) <u>reaction with CO</u>: basic O^{2-} ions on corner position display nucleophilic activity and give CO_2^{2-} (carbonite), $C_3O_4^{2-}$ and other oligomers $C_n O_{n+1}^{2-}$ These negative moieties are stabilized by coulombic interaction with Mg^{2+} ions in vicinal position (1-4);

b) <u>reaction with olephinic hydrocarbons RH</u>: the C-H in α-position are heterolitically splitted on coordinatively unsaturated $Mg^{2+}O^{2-}$ pairs giving OH^- and negatively charged R^-Mg^{2+} species. For instance, if the slightly acidic C_5H_6 (cyclopentadiene) is dosed on MgO, OH^- and $Mg^{2+}C_5H_5^-$ are readily formed (6). Successive reaction with H_2 at 473 K gives saturated hydrocarbons and surface H^- (hydrido) species. The surface coverage (θ) of the hydrido species which can be obtained in this way is ≈ 0.06 (which is a substantial fraction of the surface concentration of the ions in corner and edge position). The overall sequence of reactions can be represented as follows:

$$Mg^{2+}O^{2-}_{cus} \xrightarrow{\text{RH}} Mg^{2+}OH^- \underset{-RH_n}{\overset{+H_2}{\rightleftharpoons}} \overset{H^-}{Mg^{2+}OH^-} \qquad (1)$$

whereby the O^{2-}_{cus} ions are either three or fourfold coordinated;

c) <u>reaction with pyridine</u>: the C-H bonds in α-position are splitted, with formation of OH^- and $C_5NH_4^-$ which readily dimerizes giving highly colored, doubly charged dianions (8);

d) <u>reaction with metal carbonyls</u>: the O^{2-} ions in corner (or edge) position attack the terminal CO following the nucleophylic pathway schematized below:

$$M(CO)_6 + Mg^{2+}_{cus} \longrightarrow [\,(CO)_5M-C\overset{O}{\underset{O}{\diagdown}}\,]^{2-}Mg^{2+} \qquad (2)$$

The $[(CO)_5M-C\overset{\nearrow O}{\underset{\searrow O}{\big|}}]^{2-}Mg^{2+}$ species has been fully char-

acterized (10);

e) <u>reaction with hydrogen</u>: only very rare $Mg^{2+}O^{2-}$ pairs (presumably only those located at the corner position) are able to dissociate hydrogen following the reaction scheme:

$$Mg^{2+}_{cus} \ O^{2-}_{cus} \ \xrightarrow{\overset{H_2}{}} \ Mg^{2+}OH^- \qquad (3)$$

The sites able to dissociate hydrogen at room temperature represent less than 1 % of the total (i.e. approximately are one order of magnitude less than those giving hydrides <u>via</u> the reaction pathway 1) (9).

The comparison of the results illustrated at the points b) and e) demonstrates that the final population of the surface hydrides is strongly influenced by the preadsorption of molecules giving negatively charged hydrocarbon residues acting as promoters. This demonstrates that the absence of hydrogen dissociation on most of the surface Mg^{2+} O^{2-} pairs is more due to kinetic than to thermodynamic reasons.

Along this line, it is worth to recall the promoting effect of preformed negatively charged species at the surface of MgO on the formation of O_2^- species from gaseous O_2 (7). It has been demonstrated that while O_2^- are not formed on pure MgO, they are abundantly formed where the surface is previously saturated with suitable adsorbates (like hydrogen, pyridine, carbon monoxide etc.) which are known to give negatively charged moieties at the surface of MgO. There is a common feature involved in the two cases, which falls under the wide chapter of the promoting effect of coadsorbed species.

In view of the well documented ability of the adsorbed $(C_5H_5)^-$ anion to act as the precursor of the H^- hydride species following reaction 1), we report here on the result of:

a) adsorption of $Mg(Cp)_2$ on MgO;

a') reaction of adsorbed $Mg(Cp)_2$ with H_2 at increasing temperatures;

b) adsorption of $Mg(Cp)_2$ on Pd/MgO;

b') reaction of $Mg(Cp)_2$ adsorbed on Pd/MgO with H_2.

The final aim of this investigation is: i) to find the best and mildest conditions allowing the functionalization of the MgO surface with the H^- species; ii) to study in detail the vibrational characteristics of H^- species adsorbed on the surface of the structurally simple, highly ionic MgO.

EXPERIMENTAL

The procedures of preparation and thermal activation under high vacuum of the MgO samples have been fully described elsewhere (1-10).

Unless otherwise mentioned in the text, the standard out-gassing treatment was conducted at 1073 K for 2 hrs.: in this way the surface of the MgO sample (200 m^2 g^{-1}) was nearly completely free of residual hydroxyl groups (esti-mated concentration $\approx 0.1/100$ A^2).

The Pd/MgO samples were prepared following the procedure described below. $Mg(OH)_2$ was impregnated with a weighted amount of $Pd(NO_3)_2$ and then dried at 373 K. The powder was then compressed into a pellet, decomposed in vacuum at 523-573 K outgassed at 1073 K, reduced at the same tempera-ture in H_2 three times (total reduction time: 30 minutes) and then outgassed again at 1073 K to remove hydroxyl groups formed during the reduction procedure.

Magnesiocene, from Strem Chemicals, was directly dosed on

the samples through gas phase sublimation from a side arm attached to the suitably designed in situ IR cell.
The IR spectra were obtained by means of a Bruker IFS 113V FT spectrometer.

RESULT AND DICUSSION

1) Adsorption of $MgCp_2$ on MgO

The infrared spectra (background subtracted) of increasing doses of $Mg(Cp)_2$ adsorbed on MgO fully dehydroxylated at 1073 K are illustrated in Fig.1.

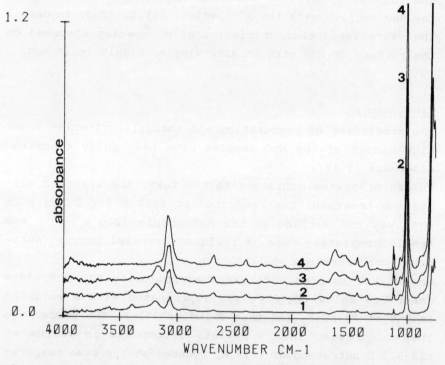

Fig.1: IR Spectra of $MgCp_2$ on MgO outgassed at 1073 K. Increasing coverages (1-4).

Most of the peaks closely correspond to those of $Mg(Cp)_2$ (11-15) and/or Cp^- (14-16) (table I).

Table I

Raman and IR spectra of $MgCp_2$ in the solid and adsorbed state.

melt Raman	KBR disc IR	ads. IR	
189			$Mg^{2+}Cp^-$ tilt. $\qquad$ E_{1g}
218			$Mg^{2+}Cp^-$ stretch. $\qquad$ E_{1g}
	441		asym. metal-ring stretch. A_{2u}
	524		
	}		asym. tilt.
	663		
750	758		CH bending $\qquad$ A_{2u}
778	779	762-781	CH bending (doublet) $\qquad$ A_{2u}
832			
	891	875 (broad)	CH bending ( ) $\qquad$ E_{1u}
	913		
	959		
1014	1004	1005	CH bending ($\parallel$) $\qquad$ E_{1u}
1063	1058	1056	CH bending $\qquad$ E_{2g}, E_{2u}
1113	1108	1116-1108	breathing A_{1g} (sym) A_{2u} (asym) (doublet)
1264	1257	1257	CH bending ($\parallel$) $\qquad$ A_{1u}
1342	1364	1348	C-C ring stretch. $\qquad$ E_{2g}, E_{2u}
	1428	1428	C-C ring stretch. $\qquad$ E_{1g}, E_{1u}
	1516	1546	
	1629	1621	
	1751	1746	
	2050	2059	
	--	2211-2191	overtones and
	2249	2263	combination
	2273	2399	
	--	2485	
	2658	2695-2680	
	--	2853	
	2913	2920	
3077	3063	3069-3062	
			CH str. A_{1u}, E_{1g}, E_{1u}, E_{2g}, E_{2u}
3105		3100 (sh)	
		3167	comb. 1428+1328+441=3197
		3392	comb. 1428+1328+441+189=3386
		3591	comb. 1428+1328+441+189+218=3604
		3932	comb. ?

176

A few bands however have a peculiar behavior as they are more prominent at low coverage (peaks at 3591, 3392 and 3167 cm^{-1}) and then simultaneously disappear around the monolayer completion. It is interesting to notice that most of these bands correspond to combination modes (see table I). The detailed comparison between the frequencies of Mg(Cp)$_2$ and Mg(Cp)$_2$ adsorbed on MgO reported in table I allows the following conclusion to be drawn:

i) the fundamental modes which are IR active in D$_{5d}$ symmetry are also among the strongest modes in the adsorbed state;

ii) those fundamental modes which are only Raman active in the D$_{5d}$ symmetry gain intensity in the adsorbed phase because of perturbation induced by the surface which reduces the symmetry;

iii) many intense overtones are observed in the 2400-1600 cm^{-1} interval: these overtones derive from summation of the internal modes of the cyclopentadienyl ring (14-16). Their frequency and intensity are not very much affected by the interaction with the surface;

iv) the broad peak at 3200-3160 cm^{-1} cannot be assigned in terms of overtones or combination modes only, because of its intensity, half width and complexity. We think that it is the overlap of several bands, some of which are coordination modes and one is a CH stretching mode of the Cp ring whose frequency has been shifted upward by some 80 ± 20 cm^{-1} with respect to the unperturbed molecule because of the interaction with the surface. A plausible general model for this interaction is represented below

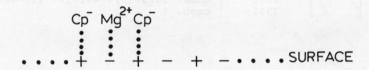

whereby the Mg(Cp)$_2$ (represented in its fully ionic form, for sake of simplicity) is interacting with the positive (Mg^{2+}) and negative (O^{2-}) ions of the surface to maximize the Madelung energy.

The interaction of the Cp$^-$ ring with the Mg^{2+} leads to localization of the negative charge on one of the carbon atoms as follows

The cyclopentadienyl group tends to become σ-bonded to the surface Mg^{2+} and π-bonded to the Mg atom of the molecule. One of the consequences of this interaction is that the four external CH groups becomes more similar to those found in sterically hindered olephins, which indeed are characterized by exceptionally high stretching frequencies;

v) the overtones and combination modes in the 3800-3000 cm^{-1} interval are clearly observable in the spectrum of adsorbed MgCp$_2$. To our knowledge, this is a rather exceptional fact and deserves a comment. As in the free molecule, the bands at frequencies higher than 3000 cm^{-1} can be explained only as combination between ring modes and modes involving the Cp$^-$-Mg^{2+} stretching and tilting vibrations (hereafter external modes) (189, 218 and 441 cm^{-1} in the neutral molecule). While the internal modes of the "robust" Cp$^-$ ring are substantially insensitive to the perturbation caused by the surface, this is not true for the external modes which are so the most natural "probes" of the adsorbent-adsorbate interaction. Unfortunately their direct observation in the adsorbed phase is prevented, because at these frequencies the MgO sample is not transparent at all. However the indirect evidence of their perturbation comes from the combination modes in the 3800-3000 cm^{-1} range. For instance the band at 3180 cm^{-1} can be assigned to 1428 + 1348 + 414 cm^{-1} summation ($Cp^- - Mg^{2+}$ stretching in the adsorbed phase), while the bands at 3392 and 3591 could be the simultaneous summation of a further frequency at 200 cm^{-1} (tilting). Of course the intensity of these bands is governed by the symmetry products of the involved modes, which in turn depend upon the arrangement of the $MgCp_2$ on the surface. In our opinion their simultaneous disappearance at the highest coverage, is associated with a change of the structure of the overlayer due to adsorbate-adsorbate interactions (phase transition) for instance as follows

$$\begin{array}{ccc} \overset{\delta^-}{Cp}\,\overset{\delta^+}{Mg}\,\overset{\delta^-}{Cp} & \overset{\delta^-}{Cp}\,\overset{\delta^+}{Mg}\,\overset{\delta^-}{Cp} & \overset{\delta^-}{Cp}\,\overset{\delta^+}{Mg}\,\overset{\delta^-}{Cp} \\ +\ -\ +\ -\ +\ -\ +\ -\ +\ -\ +\ - \end{array}$$

$$\downarrow MgCp_2$$

$$\begin{array}{cccccc} Cp & Cp & Cp & Cp & Cp & Cp \\ Mg & Mg & Mg & Mg & Mg & Mg \\ Cp & Cp & Cp & Cp & Cp & Cp \\ +\ - & +\ - & +\ - & +\ - & +\ - & +\ - \end{array}$$

It is most noticeable that in the more compact phase, the interaction of $MgCp_2$ with the surface occurs via one of the Cp^- rings only. The σ-polarizing effect described in scheme II is no more present: the abrupt disappearance of the 3180 cm^{-1} band is consequently readily explained. At the same time the local symmetry of the adsorbed species also changes: as a consequence the combination bands involving the external modes are critically affected and can become

IR silent (as in the free molecule).Due to heterogeneity of the surface, a more detailed discussion about the modes symmetry cannot be given without excess speculation;

vi) as shown in Fig.2, a minor fraction of MgCp$_2$ (1/5 of the total) can be removed by outgassing at room temperature.

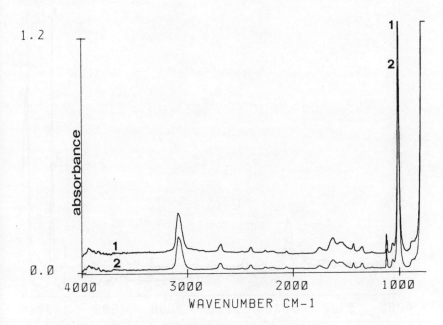

Fig. 2: IR Spectra of MgCp$_2$ on MgO outgassed at 1073 K: 1) last dosage, 2) pumping 10^r.

This reversible species is probably adsorbed in the second layer.

Due to the decreased interaction with the surface, the IR spectrum observed at high coverage becomes very similar to that of the MgCp$_2$ in the condensed phase.

2) Adsorption of MgCp$_2$ on Pd/MgO

The IR spectrum of MgCp$_2$ dosed on Pd/MgO is shown in Fig.3

(in the same figure the spectrum of MgCp$_2$ on pure MgO is also reported for sake of comparison).

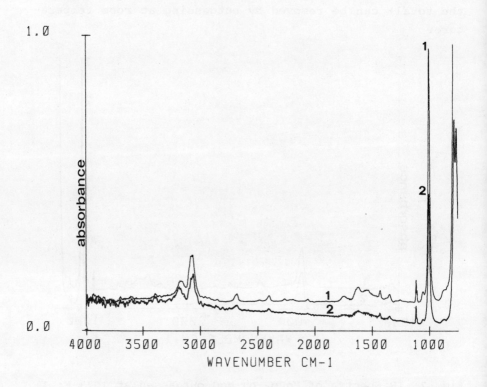

Fig. 3: IR Spectra of MgCp$_2$: 1) on MgO outgassed at 1073 K 2) on MgO-PdO outgassed at 1073 K.

It can be noticed that, beside the overall intensity decrement, there are no other substantial differences between the two spectra: this means that in the Pd/MgO system the MgCp$_2$ is mostly adsorbed on the surface of the MgO support. The smaller intensity found on the Pd/MgO system is only due to the decrease of the surface area of the MgO support caused by sintering during the high temperature reduction step.

3) <u>The reaction of adsorbed MgCp$_2$ with H$_2$ on pure MgO</u>

The interaction of adsorbed MgCp$_2$ with H$_2$ is illustrated in Fig.4.

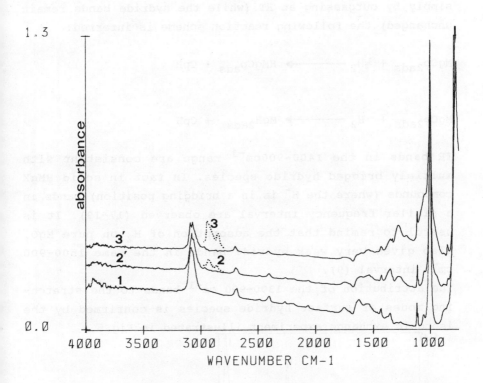

Fig. 4: 1) IR Spectra of MgCp$_2$ on MgO outgassed at 1073 K, 2) heated in H$_2$ for 30' at 373 K (....), 2') after pumping (——), 3) heated in H$_2$ for 30' at 473 K (.....), 3' after pumping (——).

The following can be commented:

i) at RT (spectrum not reported for sake of clarity) the effect of H$_2$ on preadsorbed MgCp$_2$ is very small (only a low intensity peak appears at 1270 cm^{-1} which is due to a hydrido species formed on the MgCp$_2$ free parts of the MgO surface). These species are formed also on pure MgO (9);

182

ii) at T = 373 - 473 K adsorbed $MgCp_2$ reacts with formation of broad bands due to hydrido species (1400-900 cm^{-1}) and other peaks associated with saturated hydrocarbons (2950-2850 cm^{-1}). As the latter species can be removed simply by outgassing at RT (while the hydride bands remain unchanged) the following reaction scheme is inferred:

$$MgCp_{2ads} + \tfrac{1}{2}H_2 \longrightarrow HMgCp_{ads} + CpH$$

$$MgCp_{2ads} + H_2 \longrightarrow MgH_{2ads} + CpH$$

IR bands in the 1400-900cm^{-1} range are consistent with multiply bridged hydrido species. In fact in solid HMgX compounds (where the H^- is in a bridging position) bands in a similar frequency interval are observed (17-19). It is useful to remind that the adsorption of H_2 on pure MgO, also gives very weak hydride bands in the same 1500-900 cm^{-1} interval (9).

The attribution of the 1300-900 cm^{-1} bands to the stretching modes of surface hydride species is confirmed by the isotopic exchange experiment illustrated in Fig.5.

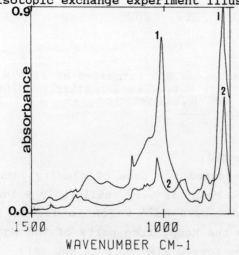

Fig. 5: IR Spectra of $MgCp_2$ on MgO outgassed at 1073 K: 1) after heating 30' in H_2, 2) after D_2 exchange.

In fact the effect of heating in D_2 is to decrease the intensity of the hydride bands (because they are shifted downwards by a factor of 1.34). Reexposure to H_2 at 473 K restores the initial situation. As observed for the hydrogenation rate of $MgCp_2$, the isotopic exchange rate is negligible for temperature lower than 473 K. It is most interesting that hydridic species with highest frequencies are the most reactive toward H_2-D_2 exchange.

3) The reaction of adsorbed $MgCp_2$ with H_2 on Pd/MgO

Unlike the pure H_2 on MgO-$MgCp_2$ system, on MgO-Pd the hydrogenation starts already at room temperature (although with slow rate) (Fig.6).

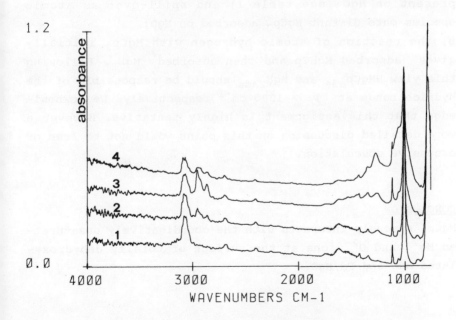

Fig. 6: 1) IR Spectra of $MgCp_2$ adsorbed on MgO-PdO out gassed at 1073 K, 2) H_2 at RT, 3) after three days of contact, 4) after heating 30'in H_2 at 473 K.

As usual, the Cp^- peaks are consumed and the hydrido bands develop. However, a substantial difference can be noticed: the spectrum of the hydrido species changes with the temperature.

In particular the relative intensity of the hydride peaks indicate that the high frequency bands at $\nu > 1200$ cm^{-1} are formed before those located at low ν (< 1200 cm^{-1}). At low hydrogenation temperature, a pronounced broad absorption in the 1600-1400 cm^{-1} interval is clearly visible. Heating in H_2 at 473 K gives the situation described in spectrum 4 in Fig.6 with disappearance of the broad feature at 1600-1400 cm^{-1} and a great increment of the intensity of the adsorption at $\nu < 1200$ cm^{-1}.

These facts can be interpreted as follows:

a) hydrogen dissociates on the large Pd^0 microcrystals present on MgO (see table I) and spill-over as atomic species onto distant $MgCp_2$ adsorbed on MgO;

b) the reaction of atomic hydrogen with $MgCp_2$ initially gives adsorbed MgHCp and then adsorbed MgH_2. Following this view $HMgCp_{ads}$ and MgH_{2ads} should be responsible of the hydride bands at $\nu > 1200$ cm^{-1} respectively. We acknowledge that this assignment is highly tentative. However a more detailed discussion on this point would not be free of excessive speculation.

CONCLUSION

$MgCp_2$ strongly interacts with the coordinatively unsaturated Mg^{2+} and O^{2-} ions at the surface of totally dehydroxylated MgO and Pd/MgO.

REFERENCES

1) A. Zecchina and F.S. Stone, J. Chem. Soc., Faraday Trans.1, **74** (1978) 2278.

2) E. Guglielminotti, S. Coluccia, E. Garrone and A. Zecchina, J. Chem. Soc., Faraday Trans.1, **75** (1979) 96.

3) E. Garrone, A. Zecchina and F.S. Stone, J. Chem. Soc., Faraday Trans.1, **84** (1988) 2843.

4) A. Zecchina, S. Coluccia, G. Spoto, D. Scarano and L. Marchese, J. Chem. Soc., Faraday Trans., **86** (1990) 703.

5) E. Escalona Platero, G. Spoto and A. Zecchina, J. Chem. Soc., Faraday Trans.1, **81** (1985) 1283.

6) G. Spoto, S. Bordiga and A. Zecchina, J. Mol. Catal., **49** (1988) 187.

7) E. Garrone, A. Zecchina and F.S. Stone, J. Catal., **62** (1980) 396.

8) A. Zecchina and F.S. Stone, J. Catal., **101** (1986) 227.

9) S. Coluccia, F. Boccuzzi, G. Ghiotti and C. Mirra, J. Phys.Chem. N.F., **131** (1980) 141.

10) E. Guglielminotti and A. Zecchina, J. Mol. Catal., **24** (1984) 331.

11) V.T. Aleksanyan, I.A. Garbuzova, V.V. Gavrilenko and L.I. Zokharkin, J. Organometal. Chem, **129** (1977) 139.

12) E.R. Lippincott, J. Xavier and D. Steele, J. Am. Chem. Soc.**83** (1961) 2262.

13) H.P. Fritz, Ber. Chem. Ges., **42** (1959) 780.

14) V.T. Aleksanyan and B.V. Lokshin, J. Organometal. Chem., **131** (1977) 113.

15) H.P. Fritz, Adv. Organometal. Chem, **1** (1964) 262.

16) H.P. Fritz and L. Schäfer, Chem. Ber., **97** (1964) 1829.

17) E.C. Ashby and A.B. Goel, Inorg. Chem., **16** (1977) 2082.

18) E.C. Ashby and A.B. Goel, Inorg. Chem., **16** (1977) 1441.

19) E.C. Ashby and A.B. Goel, Inorg. Chem., **16** (1977) 2941.

ANIONIC CLAYS WITH HYDROTALCITE-LIKE STRUCTURE AS PRECURSORS OF HYDROGENATION CATALYSTS

F. CAVANI, O. CLAUSE[*], F. TRIFIRO' AND A. VACCARI

Dipartimento di Chimica Industriale e dei Materiali, Viale Risorgimento 4, 40136 Bologna, Italy

[*] Institute Francais du Petrole, 1-4 av. de Bois-Preau, 92506 Rueil-Malmaison, France

ABSTRACT

The properties of some Cu and Ni containing hydrotalcite-type structures, examples of precursors of CO hydrogenation and steam reforming catalysts, have been examined, in order to evidence the influence of the nature of elements and precursor structure on the catalytic properties of the final catalysts.

INTRODUCTION

Hydrotalcite-type anionic clays (having general formula $[Me(II)_{1-x}Me(III)_x(OH)_2]^+[A^{n-}]_{x/n}.mH_2O$, where Me= metal, A= anion, usually carbonate) may be useful precursors of multicomponent catalysts; in these precursors all cations are randomly distributed in positively- charged brucite-like layers, connected through negatively-charged interlayers containing the anions and crystalline water. The thermal decomposition of the precursors leads to materials characterized by structural homogeneity and absence of chemical segregation, which are detrimental for the final catalyst performance.

Main examples of catalysts prepared from hydrotalcite-type precursors are: catalysts for aldol condensation from Mg-Al hydrotalcite- type precursors [1], hydrogenation catalysts, from Ni-Al, Zn-Cr, Cu-Zn- Al(Cr) and Cu-Co-Al(Cr) hydrotalcite-type precursors [2-5] and steam reforming catalysts from Ni-Al hydrotalcite-type precursors [6,7].

Aim of the present work is to compare the properties of some Cu- and Ni-containing hydrotalcite-type precursors, as examples of two important classes of catalysts (for hydrogenation of CO and for steam reforming, respectively); in particular, we focused the attention on the influence of the nature of either the elements or precursor structure on the chemical-physical and catalytic properties of the mixed oxides obtained by calcination.

EXPERIMENTAL

The hydrotalcite-type precursors were prepared by coprecipitation at pH 8.0 ± 1.0, by adding a solution of the metal nitrates into a solution of $NaHCO_3$, at 333 K (high supersaturation conditions); the resultant precipitates were filtered and washed with distilled water until a Na_2O content lower than 0.02 %; the precipitates were then dried at 363 K for 24 hours; a part of the dried precipitates were subjected to a further treatment in hydrothermal conditions(470 K,2.5 MPa,48h).

RESULTS AND DISCUSSION

Copper-containing mixed oxides

Copper-containing oxides are widely employed as catalysts in the synthesis at low temperature and pressure of methanol and methanol- higher alcohols mixtures from syngas [3,8,9]; the preservation of the hydrotalcite-type precursor homogeneity during its transformation allows to obtain a final catalyst characterized by the best performance.

It must be pointed out that in the presence of Al ions copper precipitates preferentially as malachite, and only when other bivalent elements (such as cobalt, zinc or magnesium) are added, copper is forced to enter into ternary hydrotalcite-like precursors, which can be obtained without side phases for Cu/Me(II) ≤ 1.0 and in the range Me(III)/(Me(II)+Me(III))= 0.24 to 0.31 [6,10]. However, it is worth noting that the presence of chromium as Me(III) leads to the formation, even if in small amounts, of a hydrotalcite-like phase. Table 1 shows some features of the synthetized hydrotalcite-like phases.

TABLE 1. Crystallographic parameters of synthetized compounds

Composition (at.ratios, %)	phases ident.	surf.area m^2/g	crystal size,nm	c (Å)	a (Å)	c/a
Cu/Cr 76/24	M >> HT	84				
Zn/Cr 76/24	HT	120	3.2	22.70	3.131	7.25
Co/Cr 76/24	HT	10				
Cu/Zn/Cr 38/38/24	HT	106	4.5	22.71	3.130	7.26
Cu/Mg/Cr 38/38/24	HT	55	4.5	23.01	3.109	7.40
Cu/Co/Cr 38/38/24	HT	58				
Cu/Zn/Al 38/38/24	HT	9	30.0	22.45	3.071	7.31
Hydrotalcite[a]				23.120	3.070	7.53

a) NBS 14-191; M= malachite-like phase; HT= hydrotalcite-like

The heating of the compounds leads to the disappearance of the hydrotalcite-like pattern, with the progressive appearance of the oxide and/or mixed oxides phases; at 623 K the total conversion is reached, with minimum crystal size, while at higher temperatures (up to 723 K) only a small amount of sintering is observed; a strong increase in the surface area is obtained, too. The scansion electron micrographs show a retention of the original laminar morphology.

The infrared spectra of the chromium-containing samples calcined at 573 K reveals the formation of amorphous chromates which at higher temperature give rise to spinel-type phases[11]. These redox steps reduce the specificity of the precursors nature.

Table 2 shows the catalytic activities and selectivities in methanol synthesis for some catalysts; the phases identified after the catalytic tests are also reported. The results show that, in determining the catalytic behavior, the relative stability of the mixed Cu/Me(II) phase in working conditions is more important than the nature of the precursor.

TABLE 2. Catalytic data for the synthesis of methanol

Compos.	select. mol. %	Rate of methanol form. a	b	phases identified after reaction
Cu/Cr	99.3	0.076	0.099	CuO, Cu_2O, $CuCrO_2$
Cu/Zn/Cr	99.7	0.166	0.423	CuO, ZnO, spinel
Cu/Mg/Cr	99.6	0.043	0.082	CuO, Cu_2O, MgO, $CuCr_2O$
Cu/Co/Cr	2.7	0.007	0.017	CuO, Cu_2O, spinel
Cu/Zn/Al	98.8	0.160	0.372	CuO, Cu, ZnO

a=Kg $(h\ Kg_{cat})^{-1}$ b=Kg h $(Kg_{Cu})^{-1}$; spinel= spinel-type phase

Ni-Al and Ni-Cr mixed oxides

The catalysts obtained by thermal decomposition of Ni-Al hydrotalcite-type precursors present very interesting properties, as, for istance, high thermal stability and metal dispersion also for high nickel contents. This behavior has been attributed by many authors to the particular structure of the hydrotalcite phase, and to the homogeneous distribution of the metals in the brucite-like sheets [6,7]. The formation of the spinel, occurring at very high temperature (1100 K), leads to an irreversible change in the mixed oxide structure.

Ni-Cr and Ni-Al hydrotalcite-type precursors were prepared at different supersaturation levels and with Ni/Me(III) ratios ranging from 2.0 to 3.0. Ni-Cr precipitates prepared at high supersaturation show the XRD patterns of quasi-amorphous compounds, independently from the composition (Fig. 1a). The hydrothermal treatment gives rise to the crystallization of these compounds, and typical XRD patterns of hydrotalcite-type phases may be observed (Fig.1b). On the other hand, the XRD analysis shows that at low supersaturation sufficiently crystallized phases are obtained yet after drying. In agreement with what previously reported the aluminium favours the formation of crystalline hydrotalcite-type phases, which are obtained with all the precipitation conditions (Fig. 1c). The differences in the values of the cell volume for Ni-Cr and Ni-Al phases are in good agreement with the dimensions of the trivalent element.

Further informations are obtained from the IR spectra; the splitting of the ν_3 frequency of the carbonate anion with formation of two intense bands in the 1450-1350 cm^{-1} region, and the presence of a shoulder at about 1050 cm^{-1}, corresponding to the ν_1 vibrational mode (inactive for fully symmetric carbonate anion) are evidences of a low symmetry site for the carbonate anions in the interlayers of the Ni-Cr samples after precipitation. After hydrothermal treatment the spectrum is modified, with increase of the simmetry of the carbonate ion, in agreement with the XRD analysis.

The XRD pattern of Ni-Al calcined samples do not exhibit significative differences as a function of composition or precipitation conditions; up to 1023 K only the pattern of NiO is present (Fig. 1d), whereas at 1173 K also the reflections of the spinel phase $NiAl_2O_4$ are observed (Fig. 1e),with dramatic increase of the NiO crystal size. However, the presence in the samples calcined at lowest temperature of amorphous spinel or alumina can not be excluded. IR spectra confirm XRD findings.

In the case of the Ni-Cr samples, the overlapping of the XRD patterns of NiO and $NiCr_2O_4$ is observed for the samples calcined at temperatures higher than 823 K (Fig. 1e); at lower T only the reflections relative to NiO are observed. The IR spectra shows the presence of $NiCrO_4$, beyond NiO, in samples calcined at 623 K. Increasing the temperature, the chromate amount decreases with an increase of the spinel-phase and of NiO.

The crystal size of NiO in the Ni-Cr samples is higher than that in Ni-Al ones. The lower values of lattice parameters of NiO for the Ni-Al samples calcined at 723 K in comparison with the values of unsupported NiO may be attributed to the presence of Al ions inside the NiO lattice [7]; the distortion becomes negligible on increasing the calcination temperature. No lattice distortion is instead observed for the Ni-Cr samples, whichever the calcination temperature.

Differences between the two classes of samples are also observed in the surface area values, as well as in the pore-size distribution curves. Furthermore, TPR tests reveal that the reducibility of NiO particles in

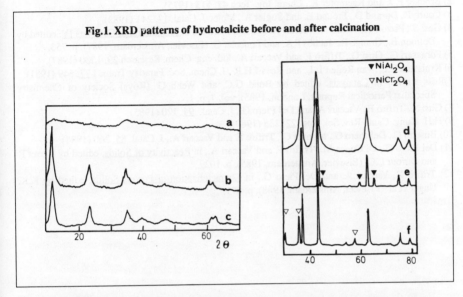

Fig.1. XRD patterns of hydrotalcite before and after calcination

Ni-Cr system is similar to the one of unsupported NiO, and much easier than for NiO in Ni-Al system.

In conclusion, the thermal stability of the NiO particles (smaller crystal size and lower reducibility in comparison to bulk oxide) obtained by decomposition of Ni-Al hydrotalcite-type precipitates seem to arise from the particular behavior of the alumina generated from hydrotalcite decomposition. The amorphous chromium oxide or the chromate obtained by decomposition of Ni- Cr hydrotalcite-type precursors are not able to stabilize the formed NiO particles, which show a behavior very similar to the one of unsupported NiO. In both cases, however, the formation of a spinel phase leads to a worsening of the thermal stability.

190

REFERENCES

1) Reichle W.T., J. Catal 94, 547 (1985).

2) Bröcker F. J. and Kaempfer K., Chem. Ing. Tech 47, 513 (1975).

3) CourtyP., Durand D., Freund E. and Sugier A., Molec J. Catal. 17, 241 (1982).

4) Gusi S., Pizzoli F., Trifirò F., Vaccari A. and Del Piero G., in Preparation of Catalysts IV, edited by Delmon B., Grange P., Jacobs P.A. and Poncelet G. (Elsevier, Amsterdam, 1987), p. 753.

5) Fornasari G., Gusi G., Trifirò F. and Vaccari A., Ind. eng. Chem. Research 29, 1500 (1987).

6) Kruissink E.C., van Reijen L.L. and Ross J.H.R., J. Chem. Soc. Faraday Trans. I 77, 649 (1981).

7)Ross J.R.H., in Catalysis, edited by Bond G.C. and Webb G. (Royal Society of Chemistry Specialist Periodical Reports, London, 1985), vol. 7, p. 1.

8) Gusi S., Trifirò F., Vaccari A. and Del Piero G., J. Catal. 94, 120 (1985).

9) H.H. Kung, Catal. Rev. Sci. Eng. 22, 235 (1980).

10) Busetto C., Del Piero G., Manara G., Trifirò F. and Vaccari A., J. Catal. 85, 260 (1984).

11) Del Piero G., Di Conca M., Trifirò F. and Vaccari A., in Reactivity of Solids, edited by Barret P. and Dufour L.C. (Elsevier, Amsterdam, 1985), p. 1029.

12) Trifirò F., Vaccari A. and Del Piero G., in Characterization of Porous Solids, edited by K.K. Unger et al. (Elsevier, Amsterdam, 1988), p. 571.

METAL CARBONYL CLUSTERS SUPPORTED ON INORGANIC OXIDES: A NEW APPROACH TO TAILORED HETEROGENEOUS CATALYSTS

R.Ugo, C. Dossi, A.Fusi
Dipartimento di Chimica Inorganica e Metallorganica
Via Venezian, 21 - 20133 Milano (Italy)

and

R. Psaro
Centro di studio sulla sintesi e struttura dei composti dei metalli di transizione nei bassi stati di ossidazione
Via Venezian, 21 - 20133 Milano (Italy)

ABSTRACT

When supported on the surface of inorganic oxides, metal carbonyl clusters give place to a series of surface reactions, which can be interpreted in terms of surface organometallic chemistry. According to the nature of the metal cluster and of the surface, weak or strong interaction can occur and different species can be generated and stabilized on the surface.
The full knowledge of this surface behavior is the necessary background for tailoring heterogeneous catalysts. Examples are given of surface species acting as heterogeneous molecular catalysts and of the specific preparation of bimetallic metal particles.

INTRODUCTION

The preparation of metal catalysts from molecular metal clusters could provide a new class of materials, in which the high reactivity of heterogeneous metal catalysts and the high selectivity of metal complexes in homogeneous solution are successfully combined.

In the last fifteen years, many groups have been involved in studying the anchoring process of molecular metal clusters to functionalized supports (e.g. phosphinated polymers [1] or phosphinated silica [2]). However, the low thermal stability of polymer supports and the negative effect of phosphorus on the activity of metal centers indicated that these materials cannot be considered as robust catalysts.

The alternative method of synthesis is the direct reaction between a metal cluster complex and an unfunctionalized oxide support [3]. Although the support is considered inert, there is often evidence of strong chemical interactions between the cluster and the support. This unexpected surface reactivity was interpreted in terms of reaction with the functional groups of the support [4].

In this way the chemical reactivity of molecular metal fragments supported onto the surface of high surface area inorganic oxides has been rationalized in a very elegant manner through the concept of "surface organometallic chemistry", the surface sites of the support being regarded as a rather rigid multidentate ligand [5].

Highly dispersed metal crystallites, as well as surface molecular complexes of specific nuclearity can be obtained by a chemical approach based on the reactivity of metal clusters and the surface properties (acidity/basicity, topology) of the inorganic supports.

With this in mind, the final goal was that of obtaining well-defined and tailored heterogeneous catalysts. This new approach has to answer to a more general question: do heterogeneous catalysts prepared from molecular clusters display special properties, such as activity and selectivity, compared to catalysts derived from mononuclear complexes or to traditional metal supported catalysts?

In principle, some advantages could be theoretically provided by heterogeneous catalysts prepared from molecular metal clusters such as a better control of selectivity, due to their uniformity, and a higher intrinsic and possibly unusual activity, due to the very small size of the metallic framework. Other advantages could be reached through the use of mixed metal clusters for the preparation of alloy catalysts of constant and well defined composition. In addition, metallic catalysts derived from supported molecular metal clusters can be made under rigorously clean conditions; no halides or other dopants are left on the surface, as it occurs in the traditional route of preparation using metal halides.

Most of the work, which is the subject of this paper, was devoted to transition metal carbonyl clusters supported on inorganic oxides.

CLUSTER REACTIVITY AT THE METAL-OXIDE INTERFACE

A new concept of supported metal clusters as precursors of "cluster-derived" heterogeneous catalysts is proposed. New catalysts are obtained, whose properties can be "tuned" at a some extent on the basis of the chemical reactivity of the original cluster precursor and of the physico-chemical properties of the surface. In particular, metal particles are best obtained by mild thermal decarbonylation of the supported molecular cluster in the absence of strong chemical interactions with the support. Such chemical interactions lead, on the contrary, to oxidized surface-grafted metal complexes, often showing high stability and low reducibility. The nature of the chemical interaction can be determined by a series of spectroscopic techniques such as FT-IR, XPS and EXAFS.

Thermoanalytical methods, mainly Temperature Programmed Decomposition (TPDE) [6], have been successfully applied as dynamic methodology.

Very recently we proposed [7] the combined use of Differential Thermal Gravimetry (DTG) and Thermal Programmed Oxidative Decomposition (TPOD) techniques for studying cluster-support interactions. The use of an oxidizing environment is a necessary requirement, in order to minimize reactions of cluster aggregation onto the surface. These reactions would tend to mask the chemical interactions with the active sites of the support.

Silica supported $Ir_4(CO)_{12}$ and $Os_3(CO)_{12}$ are typical examples of the two possible surface interactions. In the case of $Ir_4(CO)_{12}/SiO_2$ samples, the TPOD showed a very intense and narrow peak at 428 K corresponding to a complete decarbonylation to metal. By comparison of TPOD profile with that observed in DTG of pure $Ir_4(CO)_{12}$, it is clear that the same decomposition pathway occurs for the pure and the supported iridium cluster. Consequently, the absence of strong interactions between $Ir_4(CO)_{12}$ and the silica surface is inferred. In fact, the TPDE in helium atmosphere showed a single decomposition peak around 453 K (Fig.1), corresponding to the complete evolution of CO and formation of Ir metal particles :

$$Ir_4(CO)_{12}/SiO_2 \longrightarrow 4/x\ Ir_x/SiO_2 + 12\ CO \tag{1}$$

The high dispersion of the iridium particles has been demonstrated by chemisorption studies [8] and TEM investigations.

Fig. 1 - *TPDE profiles of $Ir_4(CO)_{12}$ / SiO_2 in a flow of Helium.*

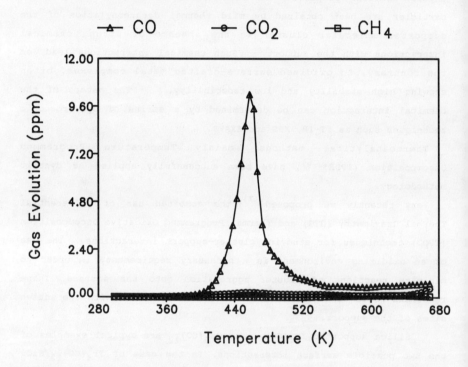

On the contrary, strong chemical interactions are involved between the more reactive $Os_3(CO)_{12}$ cluster and the $\geqslant Si-OH$ groups of the silica surface. It is well known that the surface anchored cluster $HOs_3(CO)_{10}(OSi\leqslant)$ is formed in a first step below 423 K, and subsequently decomposes to mononuclear surface-grafted Os(II) carbonyls, $[Os(CO)_x(OSi\leqslant)_2]_n$ (x=2,3), of high thermal stability [9]. Osmium metal particles start to be formed at much higher temperature, above 600K, as evidenced by methane formation in TPDE (Fig.2).

Fig. 2 - *TPDE profiles of $Os_3(CO)_{12}/SiO_2$ in a flow of helium.*

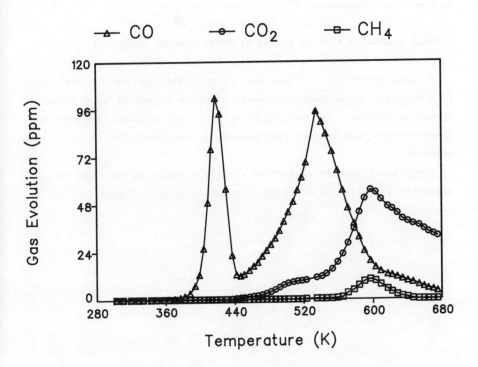

The detailed investigation of the chemical reactivity of the molecular carbonyl metal cluster with the surface of the inorganic oxide is the first necessary step towards a molecular approach to tailored catalysts. It can provide information on the nature of surface species, on their stability and reactivity, and finally on their transformation into metallic particles.

Catalytic reactions can thus be carried out under conditions where well-characterized surface metallic species (either as molecular species or metallic particles) are formed and stabilized.

This kind of investigation is now an important segment of the relatively new field of "surface organometallic chemistry" which is governed by the rules of molecular chemistry.

The detailed analysis of this particular subject is, however, outside of the scope of this work; anyway, it was thoroughly reviewed in the recent literature [10].

SURFACE MOLECULAR SPECIES ACTING AS HETEROGENEOUS CATALYSTS

A large amount of work was carried out with catalysts derived from $Os_3(CO)_{12}$ and other Osmium carbonyl clusters supported on a series of inorganic oxides, in particular silica and alumina, because well characterized and rather stable surface organometallic species were obtained.

The overall pattern of surface reactions occurring when $Os_3(CO)_{12}$ is supported on silica is depicted in Scheme 1 :

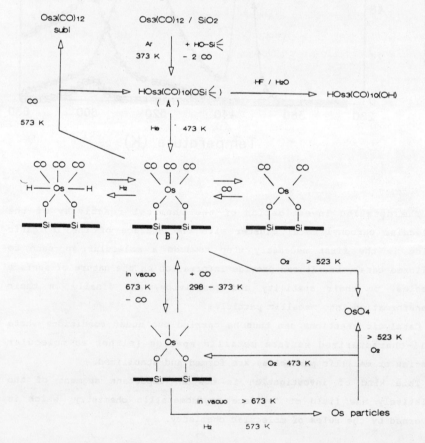

A step-by step oxidative addition of surface $>$Si-OH groups leads initially to the formation of the grafted $HOs_3(CO)_{10}(OSi<)$ cluster, (A), which is later decomposed to oxidized Os(II) surface carbonyls $[Os(CO)_x(OSi<)_2]_n$ (x=2,3), (B). Reconstruction of the triosmium framework is then possible by reductive carbonylation of the mononuclear $[Os(CO)_x(OSi<)_2]_n$ species in CO atmosphere at 523K. However, this surface aggregation process is the major responsible for the serious limitations of such catalysts in CO-involving catalytic reactions. Nevertheless, in the absence of CO, these molecular osmium surface species are stable enough in well-defined temperature ranges, so that they can be used as heterogeneous molecular catalysts under specific reaction conditions.

A large fraction of the reactions known to be catalyzed by osmium clusters in solution are alkene conversions [11], and, not surprisingly, most of the catalytic reactions occurring in the presence of the supported analogues also involve alkenes.

The air stable grafted cluster (A) efficiently catalyzes the hydrogenation of ethylene under mild reaction conditions (363 K and atmospheric pressure) [12].

Basset et al. [12] proposed a catalytic cycle involving the intact triosmium framework in all the elementary steps (Scheme 2).

Volumetric measurements are consistent with the IR spectroscopic observations and indicate that an ethylene adduct is formed, as the first step according to the equilibrium:

$$Os_3(CO)_{10}(\mu-H)(\mu-OSi{\lessdot}) + C_2H_4 \rightleftharpoons Os_3(CO)_{10}(C_2H_4)(\mu-H)(-OSi{\lessdot}) \qquad (2)$$

The driving force of the process is the reversible opening of an Os-O-Os bond, in which the surface oxygen atom of silica behaves as a 3- or 1-electron ligand.

The grafted cluster (A) is also catalytically active for isomerization of 1-butene to give 2-butene at 1 atm between 323 K and 363 K [13]. The catalytic activity increased slowly with time on stream, to reach a maximum and then it remained constant. Infrared spectra of the catalyst, under reaction conditions, indicated that the activity increase was accompanied by a reversible loss of CO ligands from the cluster, with parallel coordination of 1-butene:

$$Os_3(CO)_{10}(\mu-H)(\mu-OSi{\lessdot}) \underset{CO}{\overset{C_4H_8}{\rightleftharpoons}} Os_3(CO)_9(C_4H_8)(\mu-H)(\mu-OSi{\lessdot}) \qquad (3)$$

In fact, when CO was introduced into the feed stream, the catalytic activity ceased. The IR spectra indicated that the grafted cluster (A) was maintained intact under reaction conditions and itself provided the catalytic sites.

Working at a higher reaction temperature, viz. 388 K [14], the low (6.9%) initial conversion continuously increased with time on stream, until a final, steady state value of about 36 % was obtained only after 14 h. In the mean time, the cis/trans ratio decreased from 0.9 to 0.72;

the observed steady state values were found constant for over 100 h on stream. The long induction period and the change in the cis/trans ratio suggest a slow transformation of the starting cluster precursor into new, more active species identified by FT-IR and XPS as the oxidized $[Os(CO)_x(OSi{<})_2]_n$ species (B).

Since the grafted cluster (A) is thermally stable at 388 K in argon flow [14], its transformation into species (B) must be promoted by the presence of 1-butene, via the formation of an intermediate adduct with butene.

Two different reaction pathways have been proposed to explain the interaction of olefin with $Os_3(CO)_{10}(\mu-H)(\mu-OSi{<})$: (i) the reversible opening of an Os-O-Os bond (eq. 2) and (ii) the reversible dissociation of CO (eq. 3). No significant differences in the infrared spectra have been observed in both cases, even if two different olefin adducts are involved.

The infrared investigation (Fig. 3) suggests that, under our experimental conditions [14], either the original $Os_3(CO)_{10}(\mu-H)(\mu-OSi{<})$ (Fig.3-A) and the intermediate olefin adduct(Fig. 3-B) are simultaneously present.

Accordingly, in the reaction with ethylene at 353 K (eq. 2) the equilibrium is shifted to the formation of the adduct for only 20% [12].

We were therefore able to obtain the IR spectrum of the pure butene adduct (Fig.3-C) by subtracting the spectrum of the original catalyst from that obtained after olefin chemisorption. However, from the simple IR spectrum it is not possible to unequivocally identify which butene adduct has been formed. The butene adduct is not stable at 388 K and a complete decomposition to oxidized osmium species occurred [14].

Inhibition of the isomerization activity by carbon monoxide was also observed at 388 K. Under such conditions, carbon monoxide does not act as a simple catalyst inhibitor, by preferential saturation of the free coordination sites of the osmium centers in competition with 1-butene, but it causes significant structural modifications on the osmium surface species. *In-situ* IR investigation gives evidence of a partial reconstruction of the original triosmium cluster moiety via reductive carbonylation of the oxidized species [14].

Fig.3   *IR spectra in the ν(CO) region of Os$_3$(CO)$_{10}$(μ-H)(μ-OSi≺)*
         in flow of 1-butene/nitrogen mixture:
         (A) at 298 K for 16 h, ν(CO) = 2115, 2079, 2066, 2032,
         *   2014 cm^{-1};*
         (B) after 45 min at 388 K, ν(CO) = 2106, 2079, 2068,
         *   2030 cm^{-1};*
         (C) difference spectrum obtained by subtraction of A
         *   from B, ν(CO) = 2106, 2068, 2028 cm^{-1}.*

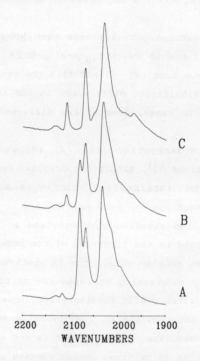

The catalytic behavior of the oxidized species (B), prepared by different routes, indicates that a significant role is played by the presence of surface hydrido carbonyl species (see Scheme 1), generated under catalytic conditions. The existence of these unstable surface molecular osmium hydrides is further confirmed by the effect of hydrogen addition to the reaction mixture, which significantly increases the total catalytic activity.

On the contrary, silica-supported metallic osmium not only shows different activity and selectivity, but also the addition of CO or H_2 does not produce any relevant change on the catalytic properties.

These results strongly support the "molecular nature" of the catalytic process of 1-butene isomerization involving oxidized osmium surface species as heterogeneous catalysts.

We have also studied the heterogeneous reduction of ketones catalyzed by the grafted cluster (A) [15,16] using propan-2-ol as the hydrogen source, on the basis of the known ability of transition metal complexes to catalyze hydrogen transfer from alcohols to ketones [17].

The catalytic behavior of the heterogeneous system is strongly influenced by the temperature and by the nature of the organic reactant.

In the presence of saturated ketones, the grafted cluster (A) is quite stable between 383 and 423 K. A catalytic cycle involving coordination of the ketone on the intact molecular grafted cluster could be proposed on the basis of *in situ* IR investigation. This hypothesis of molecular cluster catalysis in the reduction of hexan-2-one [15] has been supported by the completely different catalytic behavior shown by the preformed surface species (B), (Table 1) under the same reaction conditions [16].

A remarkably different behavior is observed in the reduction of unsaturated ketones (t-4-hexen-3-one or 5-hexen-2-one): the carbon-carbon double bond is selectively hydrogenated, whilst we could not detect any reduction of the ketonic group .

With 5-hexen-2-one, a stepwise isomerization of the terminal carbon-carbon double bond to internal position is also observed (Table, run 3). In the meantime, the thermal stability of the grafted cluster (A) noticeably decreases, because significant changes in the $\nu(CO)$ region of the IR spectrum are already observed at 383 K. These structural modifications become more evident upon increasing the temperature. A similar reactivity is reported in homogeneous conditions. Triosmium clusters such as $Os_3(CO)_{10}(CH_3CN)_2$ and $H_2Os_3(CO)_{10}$ easily coordinate unsaturated ketones, e.g. 5-hexen-2-one [18]. These clusters easily interact with the organic molecule, via coordination of the double bond followed by chelation through the organic carbonyl ligand. The subsequent isomerization of the C=C double bond leads to a product having the α,β-unsaturated ketone coordinated to the cluster cage. On heating in n-hexane solution, cleavage of the osmium-osmium bond is observed, with loss of one $Os(CO)_4$ unit.

Table – *Transfer reduction of saturated and unsaturated ketones using $[Os_3(\mu\text{-}H)(CO)_{10}(\mu\text{-}O\text{-}Si{<})]$ and $[Os(CO)_x(OSi{<})_2]_n$ (x=2,3) as catalysts precursors.* [a]

| Run | Substrate [b] | Reaction Temperature (K) | | | |
	Products [b]	383	403	423	443
	Precursor = $[Os_3(\mu\text{-}H)(CO)_{10}(\mu\text{-}O\text{-}Si{<})]$				
1.	**hexan-2-one**	100	87	27	40
	hexan-2-ol	0	13	73	60
2.	**4-hexen-3-one**	93	87	79	68
	hexan-3-one	0	5	15	27
3.	**5-hexen-2-one**	25	8	4	3
	isomers [c]	74	88	80	60
	hexan-2-one	1	4	16	37
	Precursors = $[Os(CO)_x(OSi{<})_2]_n$ (x=2,3)				
4.	**hexan-2-one**	86	72	41	26
	hexan-2-ol	14	28	59	74
5.	**4-hexen-3-one**	93	90	85	66
	hexan-3-one	1	3	9	31

a. reaction conditions: W/F_{tot} = 0.11 g ml min^{-1}, $P_{propan-2-ol}$ = 7 kPa, $P_{substrate}$ = 1.6 kPa, P_{argon} = 92.7 kPa. All the measurements were performed after 5 hours of reaction in steady state conditions.
b. % moles.
c. sum of % of internal isomers of 5-hexen-2-one.

A similar break-up of the surface cluster (A) by coordination of the olefinic group of the unsaturated ketones is likely to take place in the heterogeneous process. In fact, an extensive isomerization was observed and, at the same time, the grafted cluster (A) breaks apart into the oxidized species, which are the catalytically active species for double bond hydrogenation and isomerization.

The hydrogenation of the organic carbonyl group requires its prior coordination to the osmium metal cage, a process which is hindered with unsaturated ketones by the strong coordination of the olefinic bond leading to preferential cluster break-up.

Ethylene hydroformylation was then tested as model reaction, since the observed effect of C=C double bonds on cluster stability could be counterbalanced by the presence of the reducing atmosphere of CO +H_2, which promotes surface reaggregation of metal fragments. This reaction was studied under flow conditions at 1 atm and 453 K using as catalyst precursors either the hydrido cluster (A) or the oxidized surface species (B). No formation of oxygenated products (aldehyde and/or alcohols) was observed, but only a very moderate activity for hydrogenation to ethane, falling off to zero within 1-2 hours. At the same time, a yellow material appeared as long needles on the cold walls of the reactor, and was further characterized as a mixture of $Os_3(CO)_{12}$ and $H_4Os_4(CO)_{12}$ by IR and MS analyses. The transformation of the starting surface-grafted osmium carbonyls into the two volatile clusters was quantitative, since no osmium was left on the catalyst.

The reported CO hydrogenation in batch conditions, to give mainly methane [19], is, on the contrary, probably related to a stoichiometric reaction with surface water and parallel formation of metallic osmium.

The use of basic surfaces, such as magnesium oxide, effectively prevents the removal of metal as volatile carbonyls, since anionic carbonyl clusters, of very low volatility, are formed and stabilized by the basic nature of the surface [20]. It is, however, essential to have a careful control on the presence of surface modifiers, e.g. chlorine, since they accelerate metal losses, via preferential labilization of the grafting bonds at the metal-oxide interface, as we have previously shown [21].

By adsorption of $H_2Os(CO)_4$ onto the surface of basic magnesia, a deprotonation occurs leading to $[HOs(CO)_4]^-$ anion strongly held to the surface. In the CO hydrogenation at 548 K under 10 atm of a mixture of CO/H_2 (1:1) it behaves as the precursor of surface cluster anionic species [22]. According to the authors, the only surface species detected under catalytic conditions by infrared spectroscopy are the anions $[H_3Os_4(CO)_{12}]^-$ and $[Os_{10}C(CO)_{24}]^{2-}$. These molecular species were extracted from the surface and chemically characterized.

Another reported example of molecular heterogeneous catalysis is the water gas shift reaction catalyzed by $Os_3(CO)_{12}$ supported on the acid form of a 13 X-type zeolite [23]. The initial catalyst is the anchored species $Os_3(CO)_{10}(\mu-H)(\mu-Z)$ (where Z means the zeolite surface) similar to the anchored species (A) formed on silica surface. This surface species, which is active at temperatures higher than 413 K, evolves during the reaction into the oxidized Os(II) species, which are reported to be firmly bonded to the zeolite structure, even under CO pressure. In the meanwhile the catalytic activity reaches steady values.

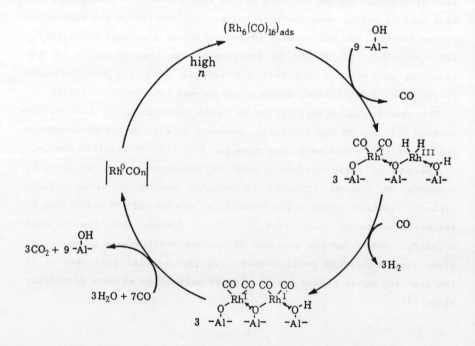

It is also reported that Rh(I) carbonyl surface species grafted to the surface of alumina or of a zeolite catalyse the WGSR under mild conditions [24]. The catalytic cycle is based on a continuous destruction and recostruction of the cluster frame.

Finally, an area which still deserves more detailed investigations involves the formation on the surface of high nuclearity metal carbonyl clusters, which could act as molecular heterogeneous catalysts.

For instance, catalysts containing high nuclearity clusters (12 metal atoms) derived from $Os_3(CO)_{12}$ and $Os_6(CO)_{18}$ physisorbed on silica [25] were studied in ethylene hydrogenation (325-535 K), CO hydrogenation (455-665 K) and ethane hydrogenolysis (395-665 K) [26]. Each reaction has been also compared with results obtained from conventionally prepared catalysts [27].

The hydrogenation of ethylene requires a significantly higher temperature than that required over a conventional osmium catalyst; the activation energies are also higher.

Carbon monoxide hydrogenation is, for the most part, similar to that of conventional catalysts. The behavior of cluster-derived catalysts have been studied under high pressure of CO and H_2 by *in-situ* infrared spectroscopy [28]. The surface species are found to sinter to polycrystalline metallic osmium at 523 K under 10 atm of CO or H_2 ; however, under 10 atm of CO + H_2 mixture (1:1), they are converted quantitatively to $Os_3(CO)_{12}$ at 473 K and to $H_4Os_4(CO)_{12}$ at 523 K[28]. In agreement with our findings, these observations demonstrate again the serious limitations of these materials as catalysts for the hydrogenation of CO under the typical conditions of industrial processing.

The most relevant results have been obtained in the hydrogenolysis of ethane to methane. The cluster-derived catalysts show exceptional activity, some apparent turnover numbers being 2 orders of magnitude higher than those displayed by conventionally prepared osmium catalysts. The reason for this enhanced activity is not clear. Much work is still to be done in order to identify the real molecular osmium species acting as catalysts and the mechanistic reasons for the different behavior from conventional osmium metallic catalysts.

MONOMETALLLIC AND BIMETALLIC HETEROGENEOUS CATALYSTS

Thermal decomposition of supported metal carbonyl clusters leads to the formation of highly dispersed metal particles. The knowledge of this particular area, which was deeeply reviewed in the case of both monometallic [29] and bimetallic clusters [30] is far to be satisfactory from the point of view of obtaining tailor-made catalysts.

It is now quite clear that monometallic metal particles of very small size and high dipsersion can be obtained, but they are usually poorly characterized and often unstable, because nucleation to larger size particles easily occurs under catalytic conditions [31]. In addition, supported bimetallic clusters show the tendency to phase separation and segregation, particulary on highly acidic surface [32].

However, few fundamental concepts are now clear and can be of help in tailoring cluster-derived catalysts.

The formation of small metallic particles from supported clusters is best achieved in the absence of strong cluster-support interactions; high-temperature reduction treatments would be otherwise needed, consequently leading to very large particles.   Therefore, if highly unreactive metal precursors, such as $Ir_4(CO)_{12}$, are not available, the complete removal of all the reactive surface sites of the support should be performed. This is easily accomplished with large-pore zeolites, since all reactive framework protons can be completely ion-exchanged against alkaline (Na^+ or K^+) cations.

Low-nuclearity (up to 4-atom) carbonyl clusters can be conveniently introduced into the supercages of Na^+ zeolites by sublimation, where simple physisorption occurs.   Metal particles are subsequently generated by mild thermal treatment [33].

This new approach has thus opened tailor-made pathways to the preparation of bi- or poly-metallic catalysts by "step-by-step deposition". Small particles of a second metal, previously prepared inside zeolite cages, serve as nucleation sites for the anchoring and the decarbonylation to metal of the molecular carbonyl precursor [33], mimicking the reactivity observed in solution [35].

Unusual alloys, as well as cherry crystallites, can be obtained *via* this route. For example, zeolite-supported PtRe catalysts are not conveniently prepared by conventional technique because of the difficulty of introducing the anionic Re precursor into the zeolite framework. Bimetallic PtRe particles are instead generated by sublimation and further decarbonylation of $Re_2(CO)_{10}$ onto prereduced Pt particles inside the cages of NaY zeolite. TPRD and catalytic studies have confirmed the specific and highly efficient formation of metal alloys via this route [34]. PtRe alloy particles are in fact unambiguously characterized by a high selectivity for deep hydrogenolysis of alkanes to methane in the absence of sulfur [36]. Heptane conversion at 773 K and 5 atm was thus chosen as model reaction [37]. The selectivity for CH_4 formation (>90%) is accordingly much higher than that of the two pure metals(Fig. 4).

Fig. 4 – *Product selectivity in n-heptane conversion at 773 K and 5 atm for a series of NaY-supported catalysts.*

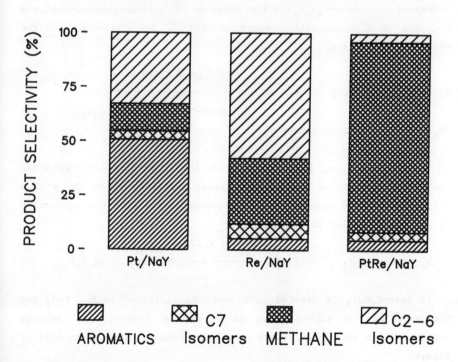

The bimetallic $PtRe_2(CO)_{12}$ cluster has also been used as catalyst precursor. This complex is, however, too big to easily enter the windows interconnecting the supercages. Most is thus left at the external surface of the zeolite crystal, where phase separation and Re segregation occur, due to the low strength of metal-metal bonds and to the different reactivity of the external surface compared to the Na-exchanged cages. The typical product selectivity of conventional Pt catalysts supported on amorphous alumina is thus observed.

The reaction of organometallic compounds with supported metal particles is still a rather unknown area, but it appears to be a very promising aspect of surface organometallic chemistry, in particular for the preparation of tailored bimetallic heterogeneous catalysts.

Basset and his group started the investigation of the reaction on the reactivity of volatile alkyl-tin derivatives with supported group VII transition metals [38].

When silica-supported particles of rhodium or ruthenium are contacted with $Sn(n-C_4H_9)_4$ in the presence of hydrogen, hydrogenolysis of two Sn-C bonds still occurs at 398 K. The following surface reaction takes place:

$$M_s \ + \ x \ Sn(n-C_4H_9)_4 \ + \ x/2 \ H_2 \ \xrightarrow{\text{398 K}< \text{T} < \text{473 K}} \ M_s \ [Sn(n-C_4H_9)_2]_x \ + \ 2x \ C_4H_{10} \quad (4)$$

(M_s= Rh or Ru surface atoms)

The species $M_s \ [Sn(n-C_4H_9)_2]_x$ is a real surface organometallic fragment bound at the surface of a metal particle. Above 473 K this fragment starts to undergo complete hydrogenolysis with the production of an intermetallic alloy:

$$M_s \ [Sn(n-C_4H_9)_2]_x \ + \ x \ H_2 \ \xrightarrow{\text{473 K}< \text{T} < \text{673 K}} \ MSn_x \ + \ 2x \ C_4H_{10} \quad (5)$$

If $Sn(n-C_4H_9)_4$ is reacted with small particles of Rh_2O_3, RuO_2 and NiO supported on silica there is first the formation of surface organometallic complexes, which are then reduced into intermetallic alloys.

The composition of the final alloy is mostly determined by the SnR_4 / metal ratio. The supported alloys have been characterized: their particle size is much larger than those of the original monometallic surface species and the X-ray emission pattern clearly show that the particles are bimetallic [38].

The EXAFS data indicate that in the case of Rh/Sn bimetallic particles the average number of Rh-Rh nearest neighbors decreases considerably after alloying; the XPS spectra confirm that rhodium and tin are in zerovalent oxidation state.

The presence of an organometallic fragment $Sn(n-C_4H_9)$ at the surface of a rhodium metal particle enhances the selectivity of the catalytic system.

In contrast to monometallic catalysts, which are unselective for the hydrogenation of citral, the tin-modified catalysts become selective for the hydrogenation of citral (cis + trans) to geraniol and nerol [39].

The selectivity varies with the Sn/Rh ratio: at low ratios, the catalyst is selective for the hydrogenation of the double bond, whereas at a ratio of unity a selectivity of 96% towards carbonyl reduction is observed.

Alloys of various compositions associating Rh, Ru, Ni and Sn have a tendency to be inert towards the cleavage of C-C and C-H bonds of hydrocarbons. On the contrary, they are active and selective for the hydrogenolysis of esthers to alcohols [40].

CONCLUSIONS

The surface organometallic chemistry let us know the reactivity of molecular metals carbonyl clusters with the surface of amorphous metal oxides and, by extension, of zeolites.

It is difficult to decide whether this area belongs more to surface science or to inorganic and organometallic chemistry. However, the strategy followed to develop this field has privileged the molecular aspect, but using many typical surface techniques.

Dazzlingly simple and understandable IR, XPS, and EXAFS investigations are now available, making us confident on the structures

210

of the molecular surface species.   This is not, however, true for
metal particles (mono- and bimetallic) generated by thermal treatment
or by chemical reduction of supported metal carbonyl clusters.   In
addition, the preparation and use of such catalysts requires great care
in finding suitable experimental conditions.

Despite these limitations, we now have information for a chemical
and molecular approach to the tailoring of heterogeneous catalysts and
a better understanding of some elementary steps in the transformation
and poisoning of catalysts under reaction conditions.

Acknowledgment

The work was supported by National Research Council (grant Progetto
Finalizzato Chimica Fine II) and by the Ministry of University and
Scientific and Technological Research. One of us, C. D., is indebted
to prof. W.H.M. Sachtler, Northwestern University, for a postdoctoral
position and fruitful discussions.

REFERENCES

1. Pierantozzi, R., McQuade, K. J., Gates, B. C., Wolf, M., Knözinger, H. and Ruhmann, W., J. Am. Chem. Soc. 101, 5436 (1979).

2. Brown, S. C. and Evans, J., J. Mol. Catal. 11, 143 (1981).

3. Ugo, R., Psaro, R., Zanderighi, G. M., Basset, J. M., Theolier, A. and Smith, A.K., in M. Tsutsui (Ed.), Fundamental Research in Homogeneous Catalysis, Plenum, New York, 1979, p. 579.

4. Psaro, R. and Ugo, R., in B. C. Gates, L. Guczi and H. Knözinger (Eds.), Metal Clusters in Catalysis, Elsevier, Amsterdam, 1986, pp. 451-462.

5. Basset, J. M. and Choplin, A., J. Mol. Catal. 21, 95 (1983).

6. Brenner, A., in M.Moskovitz (Ed.), Metal Clusters, Wiley, New York, 1986, p.249.

7. Dossi, C., Fusi, A., Psaro, R. and Roberto, D., Thermochim. Acta, in the press.

8. Anderson, J. R., and Howe, R. F., Nature 268, 129 (1977).

9. Dossi, C., Fusi, A., Psaro, R., and Zanderighi, G. M., App.Catal. 46, 145 (1989).

10. Lamb, H. H., Gates, B. C. and Knözinger, H., Angew. Chem. Int. Ed. Engl. 27, 1127 (1989); Basset, J. M., Candy, J. P., Choplin, A., Santini, C. and Theolier, A., Catal. Today 6, 1 (1989); Basset, J. M., Gates, B. C., Candy, J. P., Choplin, A., Quignard, F., Leconte, M. and Santini, C. (Eds.), Surface Organometallic Chemistry: a Molecular Appproach to Surface Catalysis, Kluver, Dordrecht, 1988.

11. Keister, J.B. and Shapley, J.R., J.Am.Chem. Soc. 98, 1056 (1976) .

12. Choplin, A., Besson, B., D'Ornelas, L., Sanchez-Delgado, R. and Basset, J. M., J. Am. Chem. Soc. 110, 2783 (1988).

13. Barth, R., Gates, B. C., Zhao, Y., Knözinger, H. and Hulse, J. Catal. 82, 147 (1983).

14. Dossi, C., Fusi, A., Grilli, E., Psaro, R., Ugo, R. and Zanoni, R., J. Catal. 123, 181 (1990).

15. Kaspar, J., Trovarelli, A., Graziani, M., Dossi, C., Psaro, R., Ugo, R., Zanderighi, G. M., Lenarda, M. and Ganzerla, R., J. Mol. Catal. 44, 183 (1988).

16. Kaspar, J., Trovarelli, A., Graziani, M., Dossi, C., Fusi, A.,

Psaro, R., Ugo, R., Lenarda, M. and Ganzerla, R., J. Mol. Catal. 51, 181 (1989).

17. Kaspar, J., Spogliarich, R. and Graziani, M., J. Organomet. Chem. 281 229 (1985).

18. Arce, A. J., Boyar, E. and Deeming, A. J., J. Organomet. Chem. 320, 385 (1987).

19. Psaro, R., Ugo, R., Zanderighi, G. M., Besson, B., Smith, A.K. and Basset, J. M., J. Organomet. Chem. 213, 215 (1981).

20. Lamb, H. H., Fung, A. S., Tooley, P. A., Puga, J., Krause, T. R., Kelley, M. J. and Gates, B. C., J.Am.Chem.Soc.111, 8367 (1989).

21. Dossi, C., Psaro, R. and Ugo, R., J.Organomet.Chem. 359, 105 (1989).

22. Lamb, H. H. and Gates, B.C., J.Am.Chem.Soc. 108, 81 (1986).

23. Lenarda, M., Kaspar, J., Ganzerla, R., Trovarelli, A. and Graziani, M., J. Catal. 112, 1 (1988).

24. Basset, J. M., Theolier, A., Commereuc, D. and Chauvin, Y.,J. Organomet. Chem. 279, 147 (1985). 25. Collier, G., Hunt, D. J., Jackson, S. D., Moyes, R. B., Pickering, I. A. and Wells, P. B., J. Catal. 80, 154 (1983).

26. Jackson, S. D., Moyes, R. B., Wells, P. B. and Whyman, R., J. Catal. 86, 342 (1984).

27. Jackson, S. D. and Wells, P. B., Platinum Met. Rev. 30, 14 (1986).

28. Whyman, R. in Basset, J.M., Gates, B. C., Candy, J. P., Choplin, A., Quignard, F., Leconte, M. and Santini, C. (Eds.), Surface Organometallic Chemistry: A Molecular Approach to Surface Catalysis, Kluver, Dordrecht, 1988, pp. 82-89.

29. Bailey, D. and Langer, S. H., Chem. Rev. 81, 110 (1981); Phillips, J. and Dumesic, J. A., Appl. Catal. 9, 1 (1984).

30. Huang, L., Choplin, A., Basset, J. M., Siriwadarne, U., Shore, S. G. and Mathieu, R., J. Mol. Catal. 56, 1 (1989).

31. Commereuc, D., Chauvin, Y., Hugues, F., Basset, J. M. and Olivier, D., J. Chem Soc. Chem. Commun., 154 (1980).

32. Choplin, A., Leconte, M., Basset, J. M., Shore, S., and Hsu, W. L., J. Mol. Catal. 21, 389 (1983).

33. Tsang, C. M., Augustine, S. M.. Butt, J. B., and Sachtler, W. 46,45 (1989).

34. Dossi, C., Schaefer, J. and Sachtler, W. H. M., J. Mol. Catal. **52**, 193 (1989).

35. Shapley, J.R., Pearson, G.A., Tachikawa, M., Schmidt, G.E., Churchill, M. R., and Hollander, F.J., J.Am.Chem.Soc. **99**, 8064 (1977).

36. Haining, I H. B., Kemball, C., Whan, D. A., J.Chem.Res. (S), 2056-2077 (1977) .

37. Dossi C., Tsang, C. M., Sachtler, W. H. M., Psaro, R. and Ugo, R., Energy and Fuel **3**, 468 (1989).

38. Agnelli, M., Candy, J. P., Bournoville, Ferretti, O. A., Mabilon, G. and Basset, J. M., Catalysis Today **6**, 63 (1989).

39. Basset, J. M., Candy, J. P., Leconte, M. and Theolier, A., in R. Ugo (ed.), Aspects of Homogeneous Catalysis, Vol. 7, Kluver, Dordrecht, pp.105-112.

40. El Mansour, A., Candy, J. p., Bournoville, J. P., Ferretti, O. A., Mabilon, G. and Basset, J. M., Angew. Chem. **28**, 347 (1989).

Molecular Analogues of Surface Species in Hydrodesulfurization (HDS) Catalysis: Metal Complexes of Thiophene and Related Ligands, and the Mechanism of Hydrogenation of Benzothiophene

Roberto Sánchez-Delgado
Chemistry Center
Instituto Venezolano de Investigaciones Científicas,
I.V.I.C., Caracas, VENEZUELA

ABSTRACT

We present an account of our recent research concerning some aspects of the coordination chemistry, theoretical calculations, and homogeneous catalysis pertinent to the HDS reaction. In particular, we describe the synthesis and characterization of rhodium thiophene and benzothiophene complexes, as well as a theoretical study of molybdenum-thiophene complexes, as models for the chemisorption of such compounds on active metal sites of solid catalysts. Also, we report a kinetic and mechanistic study of the selective hydrogenation of benzothiophene to dihydrobenzothiophene, carried out in order to gain some insight into the hydrogenation step of the HDS of such heterocycles.

INTRODUCTION

Venezuela is one of the largest oil producers and exporters, current production levels been in the order of 2 million barrels/day; the developement of an important refining and petrochemical industry, and the vast proven reserves of light and heavy oil, particularly in the eastern part of the country, north of the Orinoco river, have stimulated fundamental and applied research in all branches of chemistry related to the petroleum industry.

One of the most important processes in refining technology is the set of reactions known as **hydroprocessing**, the catalytic interaction of petroleum components with hydrogen. Within this process, the most important reaction is **hydrodesulfurization (HDS)**, which involves the removal of sulfur from petroleum compounds through their conversion into hydrocarbons and H_2S (Equation 1):[1]

$$[R\text{-}S] + H_2 \xrightarrow{\text{Cat}} R\text{-}H + H_2S \quad (1)$$

Petroleum feedstocks contain a series of organosulfur compounds, the main types been listed in Fig. 1, in approximate order of decreasing reactivity in HDS. These compounds have to be removed, since they are strong poisons for catalysts used in further steps of refining, like cracking and reforming, and also, because combustion of sulfur compounds present in fuels produce highly polluting sulfur oxides. Thiols, sulfides and disulfides are very reactive and therefore relatively easy to remove. Thiophenes are very refractary and constitute the most difficult task in HDS chemistry.

The catalysts used for industrial applications are generally composed of combinations of metal sulfides (e.g. Co-Mo, Ni-W) supported on inorganic solids (e.g. Al_2O_3, SiO_2), the most widely used and perhaps more studied system been Co-Mo/Al_2O_3. Many other metal sulfides in bulk, or dispersed on a support, have proved to be active in HDS.[2] Approximate reaction conditions for this process are 300-400ºC and 35-170 bar .

SOME SULFUR-CONTAINING COMPOUNDS IN PETROLEUM

RSH

RSR´

RSSR´

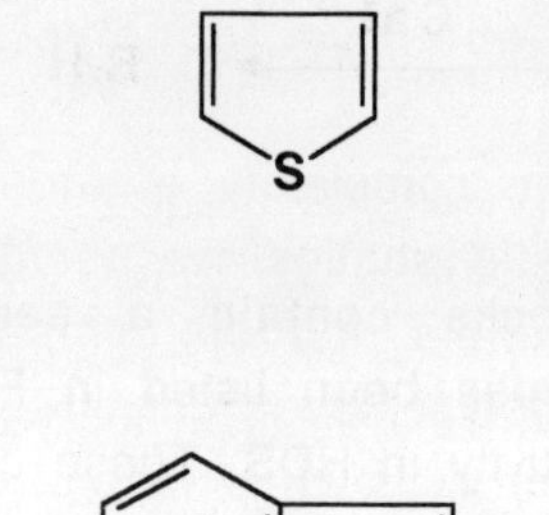

Fig. 1

Despite this industrial impact and numerous studies devoted to this reactions, a fundamental understanding of the catalytic sites, reaction intermediates, and the elementary steps involved in the catalytic cycles is far from complete.[1] It is agreed, however, that the HDS mechanism consists of four main steps, which are:

-**Formation of the active sites on the catalyst surface**

-**Chemisorption of the organosulfur compound on active sites of the catalyst**

-**Dissociative chemisorption of hydrogen on the surface**

-**Reactions of the adsorbates with hydrogen (hydrogenation and hydrogenolysis)**

Because of the high complexity of the chemistry involved in hydrotreatment, mechanistic studies frequently use thiophene and benzothiophene as simple model compounds for petroleum constituents. The catalyst itself is frequently simplified in fundamental surface chemistry studies to pure MoS_2.

An alternative approach which we and others have developed is the use of molecular chemistry as a model of interactions on solid catalysts.[3-8] The use of metal complexes allows a detailed knowledge of structures and modes of reaction which may be considered analogous to those occurring in heterogeneous catalysis; this provides information complementary to that obtained by the usual methods of surface chemistry.

In this paper we present an account of our recent research on some aspects of the coordination chemistry, theoretical calculations, and homogeneous catalysis related to the chemisorption and the hydrogenation of sulfur-containing aromatic compounds, as organometallic models of interactions on catalytic surfaces in HDS.

MODELLING CHEMISORPTION IN HDS

One of the most debated points of the HDS mechanism is the mode of bonding of thiophene and benzothiophene type molecules to active metal centers on the catalyst. Some of the most frequently proposed modes of adsorption are shown in Fig. 2.

Although a growing number of metal-thiophene complexes is appearing in the literature, their occurrence is still somewhat uncommon. A special mention must be made of the work of Angelici and his coworkers, who have developed a great deal of the available knowledge on the synthesis and reactivity of metal-thiophene and related species.[7] Complexes with S-coordinated,[9] and η^2-coordinated[10] thiophene have been reported, and examples of η^{4}[11] and η^5-bonding[3] have been characterized by X-ray diffraction.

In our work, we have found that cationic Rh complexes react according to Equation 2 to produce species containing coordinated thiophene or benzothiophene:

$$[Rh(COD)(PPh_3)_2]^+ + H_2 + L \longrightarrow [Rh(L)(PPh_3)_2]^+ \qquad (2)$$

(L= cyclo octadiene; L= thiophene, benzothiophene)

For L= thiophene the complex was characterized by X-ray diffraction, through a collaboration with Prof. A. Tirippichio at the University of Parma, showing a η^5-coordination:

POSSIBLE MODES OF CHEMISORPTION

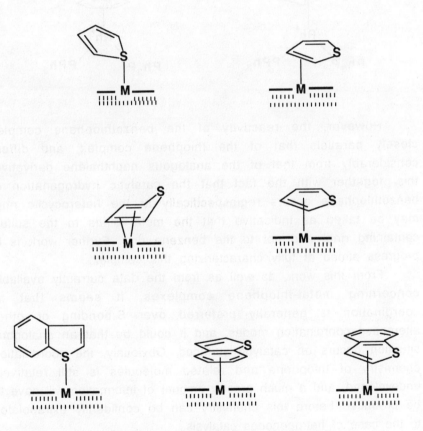

Fig. 2

In the case of benzothiophene, the analogous reaction takes place leading to a complex [Rh(BT)(PPh$_3$)$_2$]$^+$, whose analytical and spectroscopic data do not allow to unambiguously distinguish between the η^5- and the η^6-bonding modes:

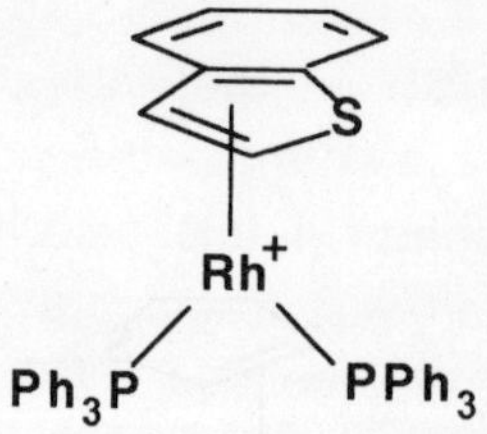

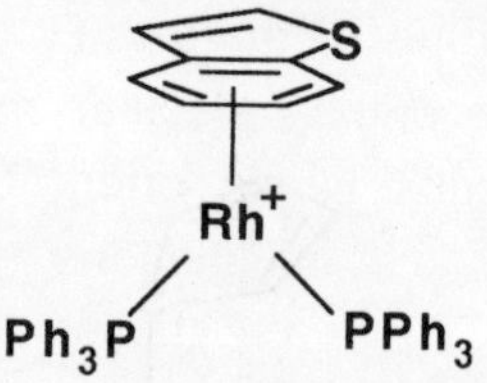

However, the reactivity of the benzothiophene complex closely parallels that of the thiophene complex, and differs considerably from that of the analogous naphthalene derivative; this, together with the fact that the catalytic hydrogenation of benzothiophene occurs regiospecifically at the heterocyclic ring, may be taken as indicative that the metal binds to the sulfur-containing ring, and not to the benzene ring. Further work is in progress aimed at fully characterizing this complex.

From this work, as well as from the data currently available concerning metal-thiophene complexes, it seems that π-coordination is generally preferred over S-bonding or other alternative coordination modes, and it could be that an analogous situation occurs on catalytic surfaces. Obviously, the coordination chemistry of thiophene and related molecules is still relatively undeveloped, and a much greater amount of information will have to be produced before this chemistry can be confidently extrapolated to the case of hetrogeneous catalysis.

One obvious limitation of these models is that they involve metals (Rh, Ru, Ir) that are not used in the real catalysts in commercial operation; however, it has been shown that these metals are precisely the most active of all d-block elements (in the form of the sulfide) for the HDS reaction.[2)]

A very interesting area of work is the synthesis of Mo-thiophene complexes, which are presently unknown, but would represent a closer model to real systems. Our own efforts in this direction have so far met with no success. For this reason it seemed appropriate to carry out a theoretical study (in collaboration with Dr. F. Ruette of IVIC) of the interaction of thiophene with molecular molybdenum fragments, in the hope that such results would orient future experiments in this field.[4)]

For our calculations (**CNDO**) the carbonyl fragments $Mo(CO)_5$ and $Mo(CO)_3$ were chosen as models of the S-bonded and π-bonded structures:

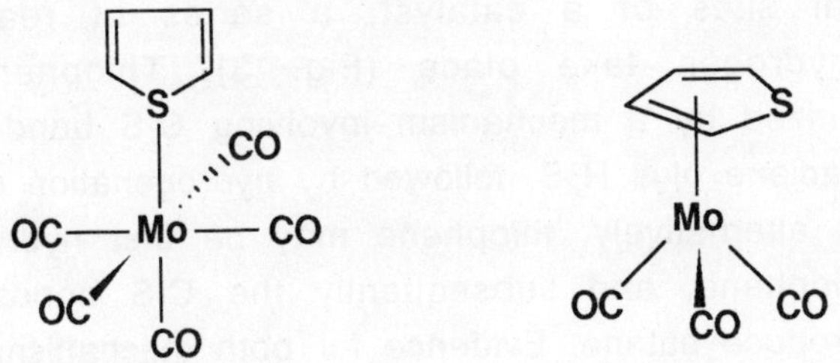

Our results[4)] suggest that although the complexes $Mo(\eta^1S\text{-}$ thiophene$)(CO)_5$ and $Mo(\eta^5\text{-}$thiophene$)(CO)_3$ have not yet been synthesized, their formation is possible. The nature of the metal-thiophene bond is mainly sp-sp, with some d-d and sp-d contributions; the binding energy of thiophene in the tricarbonyl complex is greater than in the pentacarbonyl derivative, which correlates well with surface chemistry results. Finally, a closer look at the molecular orbital diagrams indicates that activation of the C-S bond toward nucleophilic attack at C_1 or C_4 is expected in the case of $Mo(\eta^5\text{-thiophene})(CO)_3$, whereas no such activation is apparent for $Mo(\eta^1\text{-thiophene})(CO)_5$.

In conclusion, the η^5 structure is also favored in our theoretical study over the S-bonded form, and the predicted reactivity also correlates well with the chemisorption and further reactivity of thiophene on catalytic surfaces.

We are currently directing our efforts to analogous calculations involving $Mo(SR)_4$ complexes, which are even closer to the real situation, both in the oxidation state of the molybdenum, and in the coordination sphere of sulfur atoms surrounding molybdenum.

MODELLING THE HYDROGENATION STEP IN HDS

Once thiophene or benzothiophene has been adsorbed onto active metal sites of a catalyst, a series of reactions with activated hydrogen take place (Fig. 3). Thiophene can be hydrodesulfurized by a mechanism involving C-S bond scission to produce butadiene plus H_2S, followed by hydrogenation of butadiene into butane; alternatively, thiophene may be first hydrogenated to tetrahydrothiophene, and subsequently the C-S bonds would be broken to produce butane. Evidence for both mechanisms has been provided in the literature, but the former seems to be better substantiated.

For benzothiophene the situation is more clear, and there is a general agreement in that benzothiophene first undergoes a reversible and very rapid hydrogenation to 2,3-dihydrobenzothiophene, followed by the stepwise breaking of the C-S bonds to finally yield ethylbenzene plus H_2S; ethylbenzene may be further hydrogenated under HDS conditions to produce ethylcyclohexane.

We have investigated the homogeneous, hydrogenation of these ... one-molecular, using a series of metal complexes, capable of reducing, either thiophenes. Our results are summarized in Fig. 4

REACTIONS OF ADSORBATES WITH H₂

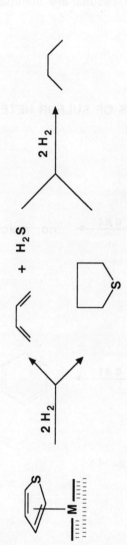

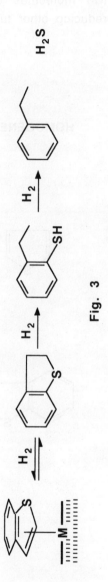

Fig. 3

224

We have investigated the homogeneous hydrogenation of these two molecules using a series of metal complexes capable of reducing other functionalities. Our results are summarized in Fig. 4:

HOMOGENEOUS REACTIONS OF SULFUR HETEROCYCLES

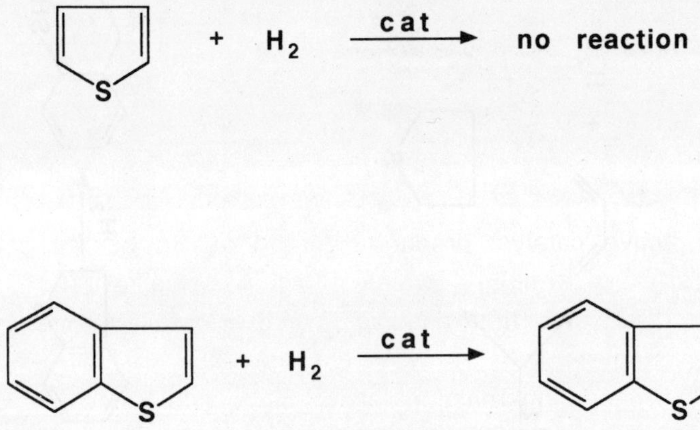

Fig. 4

We note that thiophene is never hydrogenated under our reaction condititons (100-170°C, 70 bar H_2) using as catalyst precursors the complexes $[Rh(COD)(PPh_3)_2]PF_6$, $RhCl(PPh_3)_3$, $RuCl_2(PPh_3)_3$, $RuHCl(CO)(PPh_3)_3$, and $OsHCl(CO)(PPh_3)_3$. This could favor the mechanism that proposes that C-S bonds are broken without prior hydrogenation of the ring.

For benzothiophene, however, all the complexes showed catalytic activity for the regiospecific hydrogenation of the heterocyclic ring (Equation 3):

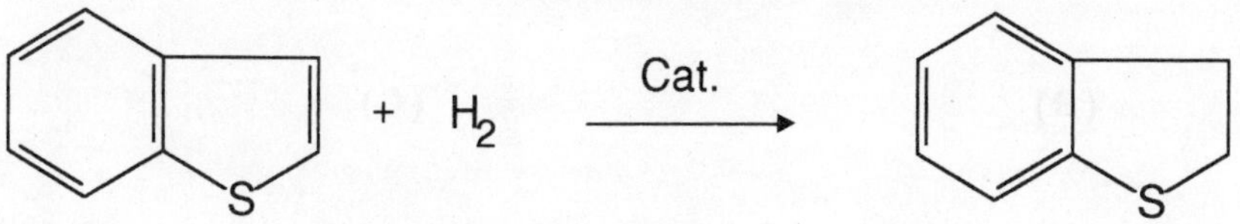

The most active catalyst precursor turned out to be the cationic complex $[Rh(COD)(PPh_3)_2]^+$, which functions also at 150°C and atmospheric pressure; this allowed a more detailed kinetic and mechanistic study.

The hydrogenation reaction follows an overall rate law :

$$-[BT]/dt = k_{cat}[Rh][H_2]$$

where $k_{cat} = 0.75 \pm 0.01$ $M^{-1}s^{-1}$; $\Delta H^{\neq} = 20.1 \pm 0.9$ Kcal mol^{-1}; $\Delta S^{\neq} = -9.4 \pm 0.8$ e.u.

The catalyst precursor is transformed during the reaction into $[Rh(BT)(PPh_3)]_2^+$, where presumably the benzothiophene is bound through the hetrocyclic ring. This is probably the active species implicated in the catalysis.

The kinetic data, together with the coordination chemistry described above allow us to deduce a mechanism for the reaction, represented by Scheme 1:

$$[Rh(BT)(PPh_3)_2]^+ \; + \; H_2 \xrightarrow{\; k_1 \;} [RhH_2(BT)(PPh_3)_2]^+$$

(A)   (B)

$$[RhH_2(BT)(PPh_3)_2]^+ \xrightarrow{\; k_2 \;} [Rh(PPh_3)_2S_2]^+ \; + \; DHBT$$

(B)   (C)

$$[Rh(PPh_3)_2S_2]^+ \; + \; BT \xrightarrow{\; k_3 \;} [Rh(BT)(PPh_3)_2]^+$$

(C)   (A)

BT = **benzothiophene**

DHBT = **2,3-dihydrobenzothiophene**

S = **solvent**

Scheme 1

If the oxidative addition of hydrogen (k_1) is assumed to be the rate determining step, then

$$\frac{d[DHBT]}{dt} = k_1[A][H_2]$$

where $k_{cat} = k_1$

An alternative mechanism in agreement with the experimentally determined rate law can be envisaged, in which the oxidative addition of hydrogen is rapid and reversible, and the transfer of hydrides to the substrate is the rate determining step (Scheme 2):

$$[Rh(BT)(PPh_3)_2]^+ \quad + \quad H_2 \underset{k_2}{\overset{k_1}{\rightleftharpoons}} [RhH_2(BT)(PPh_3)_2]^+$$
$$(A) \qquad\qquad\qquad\qquad\qquad\qquad (B)$$

$$[RhH_2(BT)(PPh_3)_2]^+ \xrightarrow{k_3} [Rh(PPh_3)_2S_2]^+ \quad + \quad DHBT$$
$$(B) \qquad\qquad\qquad\qquad (C)$$

$$[Rh(PPh_3)_2S_2]^+ \quad + \quad BT \xrightarrow{k_4} [Rh(BT)(PPh_3)_2]^+$$
$$(C) \qquad\qquad\qquad\qquad\qquad (A)$$

$$\frac{d[B]}{dt} = k_1[A][H_2] - k_2[B] - k_3[B] = 0$$

Scheme 2

In this case,

$$\frac{d[DHBT]}{dt} = k_3 \left[\frac{k_1}{k_2 + k_3} \right] [A][H_2]$$

if $k_2 \gg k_3$

$$\frac{d[DHBT]}{dt} = k_3 \ K \ [A][H2]$$

where $k_{cat} = k_3 \ K$

Although the intimate details of each step in this mechanism have not been elucidated, they can be visualized in the cycle proposed in Scheme 3.

It is possible that the hydrogenation step in the HDS reaction of benzothiophene over solid catalysts involves a mechanism analogous to those described for the homogeneous rhodium system.

FINAL REMARKS

In this paper we have illustrated some of the ways in which molecular chemistry may be of help in understanding surface phenomena. As in any modelling work, this approach, on the one hand, has the advantage of its simplicity which allows us to establish structures and mechanisms with a reasonable precision; on the other hand, it suffers from its been far from the real systems, ignoring cooperative effects between several metal centers, promoter and support effects, as well as other important parameters in surface chemistry.

It is not intended that the study of metal complexes provide

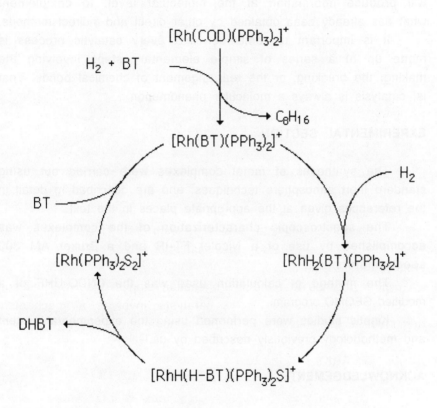

Scheme 3

complete mechanistic answers to the problems of heterogeneous reactions nor that it substitute the methods of solid state and surface chemistry. We beleive, nevertheless, that this type of study will produce information at the molecular level, to complement what has already been obtained by other direct and indirect methods.

It is important to remember that every catalytic process is made up of a series of simple elementary steps involving the making, the breaking, or the rearrangement of chemical bonds. That is, catalysis is always a molecular phenomenon.

EXPERIMENTAL SECTION

The syntheses of metal complexes were carried out using standard inert atmosphere techniques, and are described in detail in the references given at the appropriate places in the text.

The spectroscopic characterization of the complexes was accomplished by use of a Nicolet FT-IR and a Bruker AM 300 spectrometers.

The method of calculation used was the CNDO-UHF of a modified GEOMO program.

Kinetic studies were performed using the experimental system and methodology previously described by us.[12]

ACKNOWLEDGEMENTS

First of all I want to thank the following students who very efficiently performed the experiments described: **Antida Andriollo, Rosa-Linda Marquez-Silva, Norma Valencia, Edgar Gonzalez y Verónica Herrera**. The crystal structure mentioned was determined by Prof. A. Tirippichio in Parma, the theoretical studies were carried out in collaboration with Dr. F. Ruette and the kinetic studies with Dr. G. Martín, both of IVIC.

Finally, generous financial support from CONICIT is acknowledged.

REFERENCES

1.) See, for instance, Gates, B. C.; Katzer, J. R.; Schuit, G. C. A., *The Chemistry of Catalytic Processes*, McGraw-Hill, New York, 1979

2.)Pecoraro, T. A.; Chianelli, R. R., *J. Catal. 67*, 430 (**1981**); Harris, S.; Chianelli, R. R., *J. Catal. 86*, 400 (**1987**); Harris, S., *Polyhedron 5*, 151 (**1986**); Vissers, J. P. R.; Groot, C. K.; Van Oers, E. M.; De Beer, V. H. J.; Prins, R., *Bull. Soc. Chim. Belg. 93*, 813 (**1984**)

3.) Sanchez-Delgado, R. A.; Marquez-Silva, R. L.; Puga, J.; Tirippichio, A.; Tirippichio-Camellini, M. *J. Organomet. Chem. 316*, C35 (**1986**)

4.) Ruette, F.; Valencia, N.; Sanchez-Delgado, R. A. *J. Am. Chem. Soc. 111*, 40 (**1989**)

5.) Sanchez-Delgado, R. A.; Gonzalez, E. *Polyhedron 8*, 1431 (**1989**); Andriollo, A; Herrera, V; Sanchez-Delgado, R. A., to be published

6.) Chaudret, B.; Jalon, F.; Perez-Manrique, M.; Lahoz, F.; Plou, F. J.; Sanchez-Delgado, R. A., *New J. Chem. 14*, 38 (**1990**)

7.) Angelici, R. J., *Acc. Chem. Res. 21*, 387 (**1988**)

8.) Draganjac, M.; Ruffing, C. J.; Rauchfuss, T. B., *Organometallics 4*, 1909 (**1985**)

9.) Choi, M.G.; Angelici, R. J., *J. Am. Chem. Soc. 111*, 8753 (**1989**)

10.) Cordone, R.; Harman, W. D.; Taube, H., *J. Am. Chem. Soc. 111*, 5969 (**1989**)

11.) Chen, J.; Angelici, R. J., *Organometallics 8*, 2277 (**1989**)

12.) Sanchez-Delgado, R. A.; Andriollo, A.; Puga, J.; Martin, G. *Inorg. Chem. 26*, 1867 (**1987**)

Homogeneous Catalysis in the Synthesis of Fine Chemicals : Heterocycles by Deoxygenation of Aromatic Nitro Compounds

by Corrado Crotti and Sergio Cenini

Dipartimento di Chimica Inorganica e Metallorganica and C.N.R. Center, Via Venezian 21, 20133 Milano, Italy.

ABSTRACT. Transition metal complexes are able to promote the deoxygenation of aromatic nitro compounds to give several classes of organic compounds, and among them, nitrogen containing heterocycles. We have found that $Ru_3(CO)_{12}$ at high temperature and CO pressure (200 °C and 50 bar) is a very efficient catalyst for this reaction. Starting from *ortho*-substituted aromatic nitro compounds, it is possible to synthesize, sometimes in good yields, carbazole, indoles, benzimidazoles and triazoles. Some limits of this reaction and the detailed mechanism are discussed.

1.   INTRODUCTION

The use of transition metal complexes to promote the deoxygenation and/or carbonylation of aromatic nitro compounds is well known and studied[1], particularly for the production of isocyanates, carbamates and ureas. Isocyanates are very important derivatives, since they are fundamental intermediates for the synthesis of polyurethanes and pesticides (Eq. 1).

$$ArNO_2 + 3\ CO \xrightarrow[\text{T}]{[M]} ArN=C=O + 2\ CO_2 \qquad (1)$$

Nowadays these compounds are producted by a classic organic synthesis, i.e. hydrogenation of the nitro compound and subsequent reaction of the obtained amine with phosgene to get the isocyanate (Eq. 2 and 3).

It is of obvious and practical interest for the industrial companies to find alternative routes to produce isocyanates without the

$$ArNO_2 + 3 H_2 \xrightarrow{[M]} ArNH_2 \qquad (2)$$

$$ArNH_2 + COCl_2 \longrightarrow ArN=C=O \qquad (3)$$

use of phosgene, a very dangerous, toxic and energy-intensive material.

However, the deoxygenation of nitro groups can be a very useful route to obtain many other products, even not carbonylated, depending on the co-reagent and the catalytic system used in the reaction. Some examples of these possibilities are reported in Scheme 1, like the formation of the corresponding amines, azo compounds, Schiff bases, amides, oximes, and last but not least, nitrogen containing heterocycles.

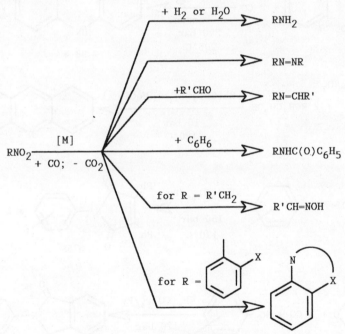

Scheme 1

It is noteworthy that all the reactions reported in Scheme 1 imply as first step the deoxygenation of the nitro group to a nitrene or imido species, generally coordinated to the metal, followed by subsequent reaction with the co-reagent.

2. SYNTHESIS OF HETEROCYCLES FROM AROMATIC NITRO COMPOUNDS

2.1   Already Known Examples

Few papers concerning the synthesis of heterocycles from nitro compounds are reported in literature; among the most significant we can cite Kmiecik's synthesis of carbazole from *ortho*-nitrobiphenyl[2] (Eq. 4), the synthesis of substituted quinolines[3] from aromatic nitro compounds (Eq. 5) and the synthesis of cyclic imides by reaction of aromatic nitro compounds in the presence of alkynes[4] or anhydrides[5] (Eq. 6 and 7).

$$\text{(biphenyl-NO}_2) + 2\ CO \xrightarrow[\substack{\text{in benzene} \\ 200\ \text{bar} \\ 205°C}]{Fe(CO)_5} \text{(carbazole, HN)} + 4\ CO_2 \qquad \sim 38\ \% \qquad (4)$$

$$\text{(}C_6H_5\text{-}NO_2) + 2\ RCH_2CH_2OH \xrightarrow[\substack{10\ \text{bar} \\ 180°C}]{[Rh(CO)_2Cl]_2\ -\ MoCl_5} \text{(quinoline, R, N, }CH_2R) \qquad \approx 80\% \qquad (5)$$

$$\underset{Ph}{\overset{Ph}{\|}} + 4\ CO + NO_2\text{-}R \xrightarrow[\substack{150\ \text{bar} \\ 170°C}]{Rh_6(CO)_{16}/Py} \text{(Ph, Ph, N-R imide)} + 4\ CO_2 \qquad >75\% \qquad (6)$$

$$\text{(phthalic anhydride, O)} + 3\ CO + NO_2\text{-}R \xrightarrow[\substack{120\ \text{bar} \\ 170°C}]{Rh_6(CO)_{16}/Py} \text{(phthalimide N-R)} + 3\ CO_2 \qquad (7) \qquad \approx 90\%$$

It appears that all these reactions proceed according to very different mechanisms : reaction **4** implies an insertion of a nitrene species into an aromatic C-H bond. On the other hand, it has been demonstrated that the mechanism of reaction **5** corresponds to a hydrogen transfer from the alcohol to the nitro group to give the aldehyde and the amine, and subsequent condensation as in the usual Skraup's synthesis of quinolines; finally, mechanisms of reactions 6 and 7 are probably based on the deoxygenation of the nitro group to a nitrene intermediate, followed by attack on the co-reagent.

The aim of our researches is to explore a more general route to obtain heterocycles from aromatic nitro compounds and we have choosen as approach the deoxygenation of ortho-substituted nitro compound, where the intermediate nitrene can attack the ortho-substituent to give the corresponding heterocycle.

2.2 Heterocycles From Ortho-Subtituted Aromatic Nitro Compounds

We have used $Ru_3(CO)_{12}$ as catalyst at high CO pressure and temperature, since it is known that this complex promotes the carbonylation of aromatic nitro compounds to isocyanates and carbamates[6].

This catalytic system is able to catalyze reaction 4, giving carbazole by deoxygenation of ortho-nitrobiphenyl, in MeCN, at 220 °C and 50 bar of CO[7]. The yields in carbazole are quite low, about 35%, with 2-aminobiphenyl as the main product (60%); since the yields in carbazole do not increase under careful anhydrous conditions, it is very likely that the hydrogen atoms necessary for the formation of 2-aminobiphenyl are abstracted from the solvent. Although the yield in carbazole are low, this reaction is important, since the formation of carbazole from ortho-nitrobiphenyl is considered an indication of the presence of an intermediate nitrene complex in the mechanism. Actually, it is known that $Ru_3(CO)_{12}$ reacts with aromatic nitro compounds to give a complex where the nitro group has been completely deoxygenated and the nitrogen atom coordinates to the three ruthenium atoms[8]. The ability of $Ru_3(CO)_{12}$ to promote the formation of carbazole, suggests the intermediate formation of this type of nitrene complex, which could then generate the heterocycle.

This ability is confirmed and improved changing the ortho-substituent from phenyl to a C=C double bond, to get indoles from ortho-nitrostirenes[9] (Eq. 8).

In this case, the yields in indoles are much higher, between 50

$$\text{[styrene with }NO_2\text{]} + 2\ CO \xrightarrow[\substack{200\text{-}220\ ^\circ C;\ 60\ bar \\ \text{in Toluene}}]{Ru_3(CO)_{12}} \text{[indole, }NH, R\text{]} + 2\ CO_2 \tag{8}$$

and 70%, depending on the substituent on the double bond, with the corresponding amino compounds, 2-aminostirenes, as side products. Reaction **8** seems to be a convenient route to synthesize 2-subtituted indoles, since the starting materials are easily available by a Wittig synthesis, and many substituents R are not involved in the reaction (high chemoselectivity).

To explore the best performances obtainable, reaction **8** has been optimized by chemometric methods, obtaining the relationship between the per cent Conversion of the reaction and four independent variables, i.e. Temperature, CO Pressure, Catalyst Amount and Substrate Amount[101].

The per cent Conversion of the reaction, i.e. the activity of the catalytic system, turned out to increase by increasing the Temperature, and by decreasing the CO Pressure. Unfortunately, an analogous study on the influence of the four independent variables on the selectivity of the system gave few meaningful results, but on the other hand, the results on the conversion gave us important information about the mechanism of the reaction. Among all, the most important result is the evidence of two different pathways, based respectively on the mononuclear complex, $Ru(CO)_5$, and on the trinuclear cluster, $Ru_3(CO)_{12}$, which are in equilibrium in the conditions used for Reaction **8**; the mechanism based on $Ru(CO)_5$ is predominant when low amounts of $Ru_3(CO)_{12}$ are used as catalyst, and viceversa (Scheme **2**).

Moreover, when the active catalyst is $Ru_3(CO)_{12}$, the rate determining step should be the dissociation of a carbonyl to give the unsaturated species $Ru_3(CO)_{11}$, whereas when the active species is $Ru(CO)_5$, the rate determining step seems to be the attack of the nitro group on the unsaturated species $Ru(CO)_4$.

Other nitrogen containing heterocycles can be obtained by this

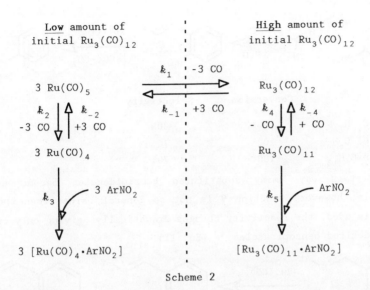

Low amount of
initial $Ru_3(CO)_{12}$

High amount of
initial $Ru_3(CO)_{12}$

Scheme 2

route. When the *ortho*-substituent is a Schiff base, benzimidazoles are produced in very good yields with the same catalytic system of reaction 8 (Eq. 9)[11].

(9)

Ar	Conversion	Selectivity	
C_6H_5	100%	94%	4%
$4-Cl-C_6H_4$	100%	86%	9%
$2-Py$	85%	80%	5%

$ArNO_2$ / cat. = 25; T = 220 °C; P_{CO} = 50 bar; solvent = Toluene.

Unfortunately, few Schiff bases of this kind are stable and suitable as starting materials, but the same catalytic system is able to promote the formation of benzimidazoles also from *ortho*-nitroaniline and an aldehyde (Eq. 10).

$$(10)$$

R	Conversion	Selectivity
$1\text{-}C_{10}H_7$	100%	80%
$4\text{-}Cl\text{-}C_6H_4$	100%	70%
$1\text{-}n\text{-}C_6H_{13}$	100%	70%

By this way, many substituted benzimidazoles become easily available; however, reaction **9** is not so general, since when the C=N isomer is used, the reactivity changes dramatically, giving only traces of the desired benzopirazoles[11] (Eq. **11**).

$$(11)$$

Ar	Conversion	Selectivities	
C_6H_5	100%	30%	9%
$4\text{-}Me\text{-}C_6H_4$	100%	34%	10%
$4\text{-}Br\text{-}C_6H_4$	100%	18%	7%

In this case, the main products are the corresponding amino and amido compounds, formed respectively by abstraction of hydrogen atoms from the solvent, and by insertion of the intermediate isocyanate into the aroamtic C-H bond of the benzene used as solvent.

Another interesting application of this route is the synthesis of benzotriazoles (useful compounds as U.V. protecting agents) from nitro compounds with an azo group as *ortho*-substituents[12] (Eq. **12**).

For this synthesis, $Ru_3(CO)_{12}$ by itself is not very active and a tertiary amine is necessary as co-catalyst to promote the reaction; works are in progress to clarify the role of the amine.

Reactions **4**, **8**, **9**, **10** and **12** demonstrate that the deoxygenation of *ortho*-substituted aromatic nitro compounds can be a general route to

$$(12)$$

ArNO$_2$ / cat. = 50; T = 200 °C; P$_{CO}$ = 70 bar; solvent = 1,2-Cl$_2$-C$_6$H$_4$.

synthesize nitrogen containing heterocycles, and Ru$_3$(CO)$_{12}$ is a catalyst able to promote such reactivity. However, all the reactions reported need rather drastic conditions to give reasonable yields, and particularly the high temperature (never lower than 170 °C) can be a serious problem, when reactive groups are present on the aromatic ring.

This is the case of Reaction **13**, where the substituent is an allylic group[13].

$$(13)$$

On this substrate, it is possible to observe the isomerization of the allylic double bond, the allylic cleavage to give nitrophenol, the Claisen rearrangement to give the substituted nitrophenol and some products by further reactions of these three compounds, but no traces of the desired benzoxazines were found.

What can we say about the mechanism of all the reactions here reported ? Clearly, there has to be a common step, that is the deoxygenation of the nitro group to the intermediate nitrene. We have already mentioned that $Ru_3(CO)_{12}$ reacts with aromatic nitro compounds to give nitrene complexes[8]; by the chemometric study, we know that also $Ru(CO)_5$ can act as catalyst[10], but we suppose that the mechanism should not be too different. Nitrene ligands are known to be rather inert, particularly when they are triply bound to a metal or to more metal centres[14], but it is possible to make them more reactive by the addition of an appropriate ligand that, coordinating to the metal atom, force the nitrene to be doubly bound to the metal (Scheme 3).

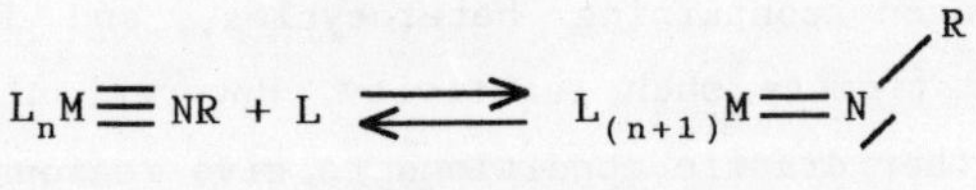

$$L_nM \equiv NR + L \rightleftharpoons L_{(n+1)}M = N \backslash^R$$

Scheme 3

In the bent, double bonding coordination, the nitrogen atom has a lone pair available to undergo nucleophilic attack[15].

In our case, the substituent by itself can interact with a ruthenium atom, breaking a nitrogen-ruthenium bond and making available the lone pair on the nitrogen (Scheme 4).

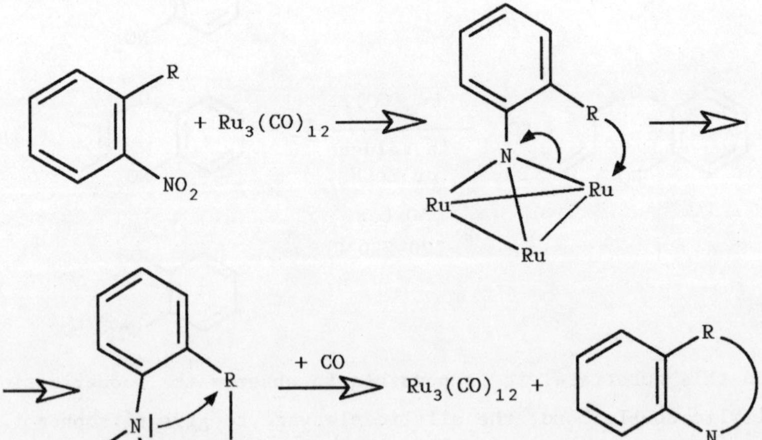

Scheme 4 (Carbonyls on ruthenium atoms omitted for clarity)

Moreover, the interaction between the substituent and the metal modifies the reactivity of the same substituent, making it more available to the attack from the lone pair of the nitrogen atom. A result confirming this hypothesis of mechanism comes from the reactivity of the bis-nitrene complex $Ru_3(CO)_9(o\text{-}C_6H_5\text{-}NC_6H_4)_2$, synthesized from *ortho*-nitrosobiphenyl and $Ru_3(CO)_{12}$ (Scheme 5)[71].

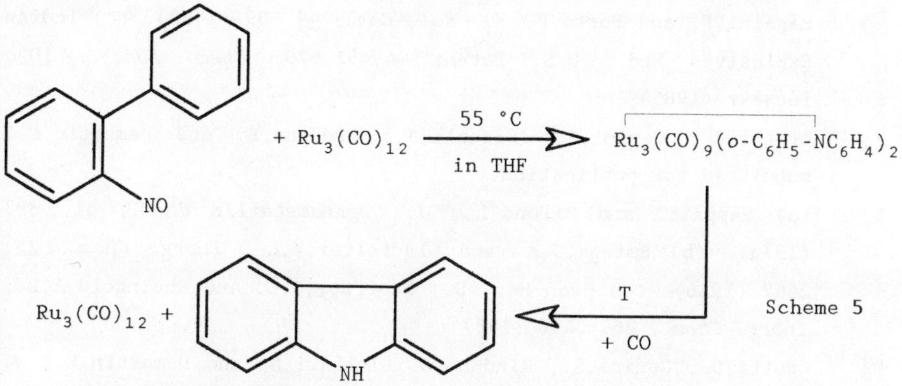

Scheme 5

This complex, in the same conditions of the catalytic system used for Reaction 4, at 220 °C and 50 bar CO, gives $Ru_3(CO)_{12}$ and carbazole, confirming to be a potential intermediate in the synthesis of carbazole from *ortho*-nitrobiphenyl.

According to the present hypothesis, the high selectivity in the synthesis of the heterocycles is the consequence of an easy reactivity between the substituent and the metal atom. Thus, in order to obtain good yields, it is necessary to use appropriate substituent groups, keeping in mind the shape of the heterocycle we are building and the interaction between the functional group and the metal center. In other words, the present synthesis is a case of *substrate design*, more than *catalyst design*.

3. REFERENCES

1] Cenini,S.; Pizzotti,M. and Crotti,C., in *Aspects of Homogeneous Catalysis*; Ugo,R. Ed.; D.Reidel Publishing Company, Dordrecht (NL); Vol. 6, 97 (1988).

2] Kmiecik,J.E., *J. Org. Chem.*, 30, 2014 (1965).

242

3]   Boyle,W.J. and Mares,F., *Organometallics*, $\underline{1}$, 1003 (1982).

4]   Iqbal,A.F.M., *Angew. Chem.*, *I.E.*, $\underline{11}$, 634 (1972).

5]   Iqbal,A.F.M., *Chemtech*, 566 (1974).

6]   (a) Cenini,S.; Crotti,C.; Pizzotti,M. and Porta,F., *J. Org. Chem.*, $\underline{53}$, 1243 (1988). (b) Cenini,S.; Pizzotti,M.; Crotti,C.; Ragaini,F. and Porta,F., *J. Mol. Cat.*, $\underline{49}$, 59 (1988). (c) Indian Explosives Ltd., U.S. Patent, 4,491,670; *Chem. Abstr.*, $\underline{102}$, 166489r (1985).

7]   Crotti,C.; Cenini,S.; Bassoli,A.; Rindone,B. and Demartin,F., submitted for publication.

8]   (a) Sappa,E. and Milone,L., *J. Organometallic Chem.*, $\underline{61}$, 383 (1973). (b) Smieja,J.A. and Gladfelter,W.L., *Inorg. Chem.*, $\underline{25}$, 2667 (1986). (c) Hwan Han, S.; Geoffroy,G.L. and Rheingold,A.L., *Inorg. Chem.*, $\underline{26}$, 3426 (1987).

9]   Crotti,C.; Cenini,S.; Rindone,B.; Tollari,S. and Demartin,F., *J. Chem. Soc., Chem. Commun.*, 784 (1986).

10]   Crotti,C.; Cenini,S.; Todeschini,R. and Tollari,S., submitted for publication.

11]   Crotti,C.; Tollari,S.; Cenini,S. and Ragaini,F., manuscript in preparation.

12]   Pizzotti,M.; Cenini,S.; Psaro,R. and Costanzi,S., *J. Mol. Cat.*, in press.

13]   Bassoli,A.; Rindone,B.; Tollari,S.; Cenini,S. and Crotti,C., *J. Mol. Cat.*, $\underline{52}$, L45 (1989).

14]   (a) Cenini,S. and La Monica,G., *Inorg.Chim. Acta, Rev.*, $\underline{18}$, 279 (1976). (b) Nugent,W.A. and Haymore,B.L., *Metal-ligand Multiple Bond*, Wiley-Interscience Publication, New York, 1988.

15]   (a) Hwan Han,S. and Geoffroy,G.L., *Polyhedron*, $\underline{7}$, 2331 (1988). (b) Hwan Han,S.; Song,J.S.; Macklin,P.D.; (c) Nguyen,S.T.; Geoffroy,G.L. and Rheingold,A.L., *Organometallics*, $\underline{8}$, 2127 (1989).

CHANGING SELECTIVITY IN PALLADIUM–CATALYZED REACTIONS INVOLVING OXIDATION STATE IV.

Marta Catellani and Gian Paolo Chiusoli

Istituto di Chimica Organica, Università, Viale delle Scienze, 43100 Parma, Italy.

ABSTRACT. The selectivity of palladium–catalyzed reactions, involving changes in oxidation state from O to IV, can be controlled by the appropriate choice of ligands.

It is well known that transition metal complexes can activate aromatic C–H bonds, in particular through formation of metallacycles [1]. The ortho–palladation reaction, for example, shows a strong tendency for these species to form five membered rings.

Some years ago we found [2] that intramolecular activation of an inert aromatic C–H bond could be achieved catalytically using palladium complexes according to equation 1:

$$+ \quad Br\!\!-\!\!\bigcirc \quad \xrightarrow{\text{Pd cat.}} \quad \text{(1)}$$

The reaction occurs under mild conditions at $105°C$ for 24 h in anisole as solvent in the presence of a palladium complex such as $Pd(PPh_3)_4$ and hindered phenoxides. The product, obtained in more than 90% yield, is the exo isomer of benzocyclobutene and its formation clearly implies aromatic C–H activation. The reaction consists of the initial oxidative addition of bromobenzene to palladium(O), followed by norbornene coordination and insertion, which lead to a phenylnorbornylpalladium complex (eq. 2):

$$\text{(2)}$$

In the latter complex, palladium then attacks the aromatic nucleus (we shall see later which kind of activation is at work) giving a five-membered palladacycle. Reductive elimination finally leads to benzocyclobutene.

The palladacycle proposed as intermediate in the previous reaction was isolated in a stabilized form, using phenanthroline as ligand [3] (eq. 3):

$$\text{(3)}$$

The new complex was obtained starting from dimeric phenylnorbornylpalladium chloride [4] in dichloromethane solution by addition at room temperature of potassium phenoxide and phenanthroline (62% yield). It was isolated as an orange microcrystalline solid and was characterized by NMR spectroscopy and chemical methods. Particularly informative was the reaction of the complex with NaBD$_4$, which selectively gave phenylnorbornane, dideuterated at the <u>exo</u> position of the norbornyl unit and in the aromatic ring ortho to the substituted carbon, thus indicating that palladium was previously bonded to these two positions.

The complex is square planar, as clearly indicated by the strong nOe effects observed in the proton NMR spectrum within the palladium-coordinated groups. Particularly significant are those shown by a) the two aromatic protons, one on the phenanthroline and the other one on the carbon atom ortho to the palladium-bonded carbon (ca. 19%) and b) the bridgehead proton of the norbornyl ring and the facing phenanthroline proton (ca. 10%). These nOes indicate that the mentioned protons are opposite to each other and this is possible only in a square planar arrangement of the ligands.

To elucidate the nature of the intramolecular aromatic substitution process, which gives good results both with electron-withdrawing and electron-releasing substituents in the aromatic ring, the course of the reaction was followed in the NMR tube at low temperature using chloroform as solvent. Arylnorbornylpalladium complexes, bearing different substituents in the aromatic rings, were prepared and their reactivity was studied [5]. For this purpose, pyridine as ligand was used, because it offered a simpler way to study the NMR spectrum (eq. 4):

$$Y = OMe, H, NO_2$$

$$OMe > H > NO_2$$

On addition of potassium phenoxide to a dichloromethane or chloroform solution of the arylnorbornylpalladium complex, at -10°C, a new species was detected before cyclization. This new species probably corresponds to a complex containing phenoxide in place of chloride as ligand.

A large difference was observed in the behaviour of the unsubstituted phenyl group, compared with the p-methoxy and the p-nitrophenyl groups, so that there is no doubt on the reactivity sequence: OMe > H > NO_2, which corresponds to an electrophilic substitution process. This could not be appreciated from the isolation of organic products, deriving from further reaction of the intermediate metallacycle, because of the different stabilities and reactivities of these intermediates.

When we studied the reactivity of the palladacycle with phenanthroline as ligand, we found that the latter was readily attacked by reactive organic halides [3]. Iodomethane, for example, reacted with the complex at low temperature (-20°C), giving a new species, which was isolated and characterized as the palladium(IV) complex shown in equation 5.

$$(5)$$

This reaction is quite general and it has been extended to the oxidative addition of allyl and benzyl halides, which give much more stable palladium(IV) species [6]. Though palladium(IV) complexes have been previously proposed as intermediates in several reactions [7,8], (see also other references [3]) only recently they have been prepared and fully characterized by X-ray methods [9]. The palladium(IV) complex shown in equation 5 is, however, the first alkylaromatic species containing an arylpalladium bond. Moreover, it has been proved to be involved in catalysis [8]. The solution structure was determined by ^{1}H NMR spectrocopy [6]. NMR data indicate that the phenylnorbornyl ligand essentially is unchanged. In addition to the signals of the coordinated phenanthroline, other signals are present due to the coordinated methyl group or to the coordinated group derived from the organic halide used (allyl or benzyl). Chemical shifts, nOe effects and the presence of steric interactions led us to discard all the other nine possible structures resulting from different arrangement of ligands.

The structure shown in equation 5 derives from a <u>cis</u> oxidative addition of the organic halide to the palladacycle, which is attacked from the less sterically hindered side. One nitrogen of the phenanthroline ligand is shifted to the axial position. As a consequence a six-coordinated intermediate is formed, in which phenanthroline lies in a plane perpendicular to that containing the phenylnorbornyl group and also is <u>cis</u> to the norbornyl unit.

So we can conclude that, under these conditions, in the presence of phenanthroline as ligand, we obtain only one structure out of the ten possible ones. The phenanthroline ligand apparently directs the attack of the organic halide to the palladium(II) metallacycle so that only one isomer of the palladium(IV) metallacycle is obtained.

When a solution of the palladium(IV) complex, obtained by oxidative addition of iodomethane to the palladium(II) metallacycle at -20°C, is allowed to warm to room temperature a new species is formed (eq. 6). It derives from selective migration of the methyl group to the phenyl ring. Subsequent treatment with sodium borohydride gives o-tolylnorbornane (66% yield).

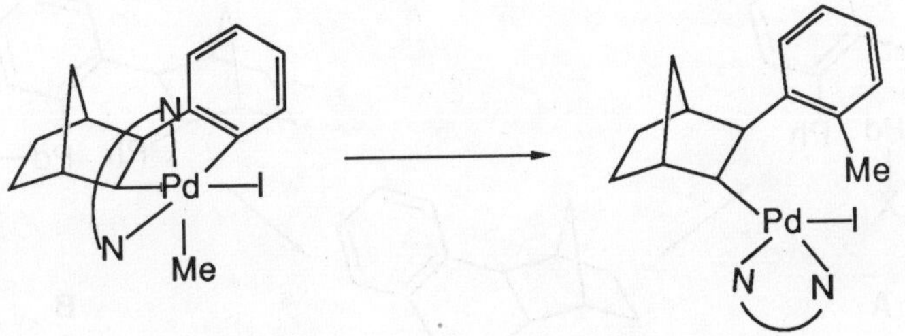

This result suggests that selective alkylation at an inert position of an aromatic ring can be achieved through metallacycle formation and ligand-controlled reaction of the latter with alkylating agents.

We shall now see other examples which remarkably adds to the synthetic potential offered by metallacycle formation.

In fact, the same palladacycles must also be involved in the catalytic reaction of aryl bromides with norbornene, which leads to the formation of a methanotriphenylene derivative [8] (eq. 7).

$$(7)$$

The reaction was carried out under nitrogen in the presence of $Pd(PPh_3)_4$ as catalyst, t-butoxide as base and anisole as solvent at $105°C$ for 20 h. The proposed mechanism is the following (eq. 8, X=Br):

$$(8)$$

By analogy with the reactions described above we assume that the palladium(II) metallacycle undergoes oxidative addition of another molecule of bromobenzene leading to the formation of a palladium(IV) species. The latter undergoes reductive elimination to two palladium(II) complexes (A and B), which derive from migration of the phenyl ring either to the norbornyl or to the aryl group. The methanotriphenylene derivative is then formed by ring closure. In equation 8 ligands are omitted for simplicity and drawings do not imply a stereochemical arrangement.

That methanotriphenylene derives from both the two palladium(II) species, one containing the norbornyl-Pd bond (A) and the other one the phenyl-Pd bond (B), was proved by placing a substituent <u>para</u> to the bromine on the aromatic ring [8]. Two isomers, deriving from the two proposed pathways for ring formation were isolated when a substituent such as F was present in the aromatic nucleus. The ratio (1:3) corresponds to that between intermediates A and B.

It is worth recalling at this point what we observed with the phenantroline-containing palladacycle. Only one out of many possible isomers was formed. The present case shows that two palladium(II) isomers are formed probably either because of ligand control of formation of the palladium(IV) intermediate is not as strict as with phenanthroline, or because isomerization of the first formed palladium(IV) intermediate occurs. In any case two palladium(II) intermediates are formed and we can wonder at this point whether they can be caused to react selectively to obtain different reactions.

German authors [10] have recently reported that under different conditions (Pd(OOCMe)$_2$, K$_2$CO$_3$, Bu$_4$NBr, DMF, 60°C) the reaction between norbornene and bromo or iodobenzene follows a different pathway (eq. 9).

$$\text{(9)}$$

As shown in equation 10, the formation of this compound is likely to imply the same palladium(IV) species previously reported, but under the conditions adopted only the alkyl palladium intermediate containing the norbornyl-Pd bond is formed, due to selective migration of the phenyl group to the aromatic ring. Again intramolecular aromatic substitution leads to the formation of the seven-membered ring. A new oxidative addition of iodobenzene to the seven-membered metallacycle is followed once again by selective migration of the phenyl group to the aromatic ring, before final ring closure to the substituted methanotriphenylene derivative.

(10)

Thus working under the conditions reported (without triphenylphosphine as ligand), only the intermediate A (eq. 8), containing the norbornyl-palladium bond, is formed or reacts in preference to the one containing the aryl-palladium bond (B).

In the attempt to understand the reason for selectivity towards a compound derived from intermediate A we caused palladium(0) complexes to react without and with triphenylphosphine as ligand [11]. With $Pd(dba)_2$ and K_2CO_3 in DMF at 80°C we observed the predominant formation of the A-derived compound, while in the presence of triphenylphosphine as ligand ($Pd(PPh_3)_4$, K_2CO_3, 80°C, 22 h, DMF) we obtained a different compound in satisfactory yield (52%) (eq. 11).

The structure of this compound clearly derives from the arylpalladium intermediate B (eq. 12).

The reaction follows the same pathway as in equation 10 until a palladium(IV) is formed. The phenyl group then migrates selectively on the norbornane ring, thus forming the arylpalladium bond of B. In place of giving an intramolecular aromatic substitution the arylpalladium complex thus formed prefers the insertion of a new molecule of norbornene before the final four-membered ring closure.

We think that the origin of this drastic change in selectivity is connected with the use of triphenylphosphine, which makes easier the formation of the arylpalladium intermediate B. The latter is rather reluctant to electrophilic aromatic substitution and prefers the insertion of a new molecule of norbornene.

In conclusion different selectivities can be obtained through control of the stereochemical evolution of palladium(IV) intermediates by appropriately chosen ligands.

REFERENCES

1. Parshall, G.W., "Intramolecular Aromatic Substitution in Transition Metal Complexes", Acc. Chem. Res. 3, 139-144 (1970); Jones, W.D. and Feher, F.J., "Comparative Reactivities of Hydrocarbon C-H Bonds with a Transition Metal Complex", Acc. Chem. Res. 22, 91-100 (1989).

2. Catellani, M., Chiusoli, G.P. and Ricotti, S., "A New Palladium-catalyzed Synthesis of 1,2,3,4,4a,8b-Hexahydro-1,4-methanobiphenylenes and 2-Phenylbicyclo[2.2.1]hept-2-enes", J. Organomet Chem. 296, C11-C15 (1985).

3. Catellani, M. and Chiusoli, G.P., "Palladium-(II) and -(IV) Complexes as Intermediates in Catalytic C-C Bond-forming Reactions", J. Organomet. Chem. 346, C27-C30 (1988).

4. Horino, H., Arai, M. and Inoue, N., "Reaction of Norbornene with Phenylpalladium Chloride", Tetrahedron Lett. 647-650 (1974).

5. Catellani, M. and Chiusoli, G.P., results to be published.

6. Catellani M. and Mann, B.E., "Conformational Effects in Elementary Steps in Catalytic Reactions. Oxidative Addition of

3-Bromoprop-1-ene to a Palladium(II) Metallacyclic Complex", J. Organomet. Chem. 390, 251-255 (1990).

7. Stille, J.K. and Lau, K.S.Y., "Oxidative Addition of Alkyl Halides to Zero-Valent Palladium Complexes. Mechanisms", J. Am. Chem. Soc. 98, 5841-5849 (1976).

8. Catellani, M. and Chiusoli, G.P., "Palladium-catalyzed Synthesis of 1,2,3,4,,4a,12b-Hexahydro-1,4-methanotri-phenylenes", J. Organomet. Chem. 286, C13-C16 (1985).

9. Byers, P.K., Canty, A.J., Skelton, B.W. and White, A.H., "The Oxidative Addition of Iodomethane to [PdMe$_2$(bpy)] and the X-ray Structure of the Organopalladium(IV) Product fac-[PdMe$_3$bpy)I] (bpy=2,2'-bipyridyl)", J. Chem. Soc., Chem. Commun. 1722-1724 (1986).

10. Reiser, O., Weber, M. and de Meijere, A., "Selective 1:3 Coupling of Norbornene and Iodobenzene: a Facile Synthesis of Benzo[e]pyrenes with Annelated Cycloaliphatic Moieties", Angew. Chem. Int. Ed. Engl. 28, 1037-1038 (1989).

11. Catellani, M., Chiusoli, G.P. and Castagnoli, C., results to be published.

CATALYTIC HYDROGENATION OF BIOLOGICAL MEMBRANES

Ferenc Joó[+] and László Vígh[++]

[+]Institute of Physical Chemistry, Kossuth Lajos University, P.O.Box 7, H-4010 Debrecen, Hungary, and [++]Institute of Biochemistry, Biological Research Center of the Hungarian Academy of Sciences, P.O.Box 521, H-6701 Szeged, Hungary

ABSTRACT

Hydrogenation of biological membranes containing unsaturated fatty acid residues was studied using soluble transition metal complex catalysts, as well as a heterogeneous, supported palladium catalyst. It is demonstrated, that in hydrogenation of living cells -in addition to chemo- and regioselectivity- spatial selectivity can be observed, due to the different accessibility of the various membrane regions. The actual physical state of the lipid bilayers greatly influences the rate and selectivity of such hydrogenations.

INTRODUCTION

Many functions and phenomena of the living state are directly or indirectly influenced by the composition and organization of the membranes of the respective cells. One factor, which crucially contributes to the "optimum functional state" of the membranes is a particular distribution of saturated and unsaturated fatty acids esterified in the lipid constituenst. Under environmental stress the cells strive to maintain this particular distribution by several means (<u>de novo</u> synthesis of fatty acids, modification of existing ones, retailoring the lipids by fatty acid interchange). The regulation of this adaptation is virtually unknown, and what is most intriguing is that the cells may respond very much the same way to seemingly unrelated environmental effects, like sudden change in temperature, pH or salinity. Moreover, in several organisms, some "odd" <u>trans</u>-fatty acids are found, but what is their precise role, and why specifically the particular <u>trans</u>-acids are suitable to play that role, is still to be understood.

We have developed a method to selectively try the role of unsaturated acids in the membranes, without changing the dietary conditions of the cells, the composition, pH and temperature of their medium. For this purpose we hydrogenate the cells <u>in vivo</u>, or the isolated membrane fractions, by using water-soluble or heterogeneous transition metal catalysts.

MATERIALS AND METHODS

Monosulfonated triphenylphosphine (m-sulfophenyldiphenylphosphine, $mSPPh_2$) was synthetized according to Ahrland et al.[1]. For reviews on water soluble phosphine complexes of transition metals see [2] and [3]. Preparation of $Pd(QS)_2$ is published in [4] (details of preparation and use in [5]). The preparation of liposomes and the gas-chromatographic determination of fatty acids after transmethylation of lipids can be found in [6]. Culture and isolation of biological material (chloroplasts[7], mitochondria[8], protozoae[9], and platelets[10]) is described in the references.

Colloidal Pd supported on polyvinylpolypyrrolidone

(Pd-PVPP) was prepared as follows. 100 mg of the water insoluble PVPP (Fluka Cat.No. 81385, Plasdone XL) was stirred in 10 ml of 20 mM Na-phosphate buffer (pH=7.0) for 30 min. After letting it to settle the supernatant was discarded, and 20 mg of $(NH_4)_2PdCl_4$ (Johnson Matthey) in 10 ml of the same buffer was added to the washed PVPP. The suspension was placed under H_2, stirred in this atmosphere until it became dark grey, and finally settled. The supernatant was siphoned off and the remaining wet solid was taken up in 10 ml of fresh buffer. This suspension was ready to use for hydrogenation, or could be stored for a few hours without loss of activity.

RESULTS AND DISCUSSION

General Properties of Lipid Membranes Relevant to Catalytic Hydrogenation

Biological membranes are major constituents of a cell, and they either surround the cytoplasm (plasmamembrane) or comprise an organisation form of different organelles (chloroplast, mitochondrium, etc). They are built up mainly of lipids and proteins. There is a constant motion inside the membrane, _i.e._ trans-membrane and lateral transport of material. The more _fluid_ is a membrane, the less hindered is this motion. Fluidity (or its inverse, microviscosity) of the membranes can be treated quantitatively by determining motion parameters of labelled molecules (so-called probes), the most frequently used such parameters being the e.s.r. rotational correlation time of spin-labelled fatty acids[11] and the fluorescence anisotropy[12'] of suitable probes.

For several purposes biomembranes can be modelled by fine aqueous dispersions of polar lipids, termed liposomes.

Very fine dispersions can be prepared with ultrasound devices (sonication). The vesicules formed this way have unilamellar boundary membranes, into which neutral lipids (e.g. sterols) and proteins can be built in by co-sonication with the polar lipids. Very often liposomes are prepared from lipids of natural origin (soybean, sunflower, or fish) which contain different proportions of different lipid classes (phospholipids, galactolipids, etc) and of different molecular species (e.g. phosphatidylcholine, phosphatidyletanolamine, etc). All these different lipids contain two long-chain fatty acids (like stearic, 18:0, oleic, 18:1, linoleic, 18:2, linolenic, 18:3, etc acids) esterified to glycerol.

Fluidity of the membrane is determined by a delicate balance of all this features (head-group and tail of polar lipids, relative amount of neutral lipids and proteins) and Nature has efficient ways of keeping up this balance. Adaptation to environmental stress (e.g. temperature acclimation) brings about changes of all these characteristics, therefore selective modification of only one parameter: the average unsaturation of fatty acids, may have potential in biochemical investigations. It was Chapman and Quinn, who first suggested such a modification by catalytic hydrogenation[13], and their pioneering work was later taken up in our research groups.

Conditions and Catalysts for Membrane Hydrogenations

The natural environment for cells and liposomes is an aqueous suspension. Consequently, for hydrogenation studies water-soluble catalysts should be applied. Indeed, the first attempts to use $RhCl(PPh_3)_3$ showed, that the non-polar catalyst was incorporated to the lipid bilayers and could not be removed without damage to the membranes[14]. In some special cases it can be advantageous to use <u>heterogeneous</u> catalysts.

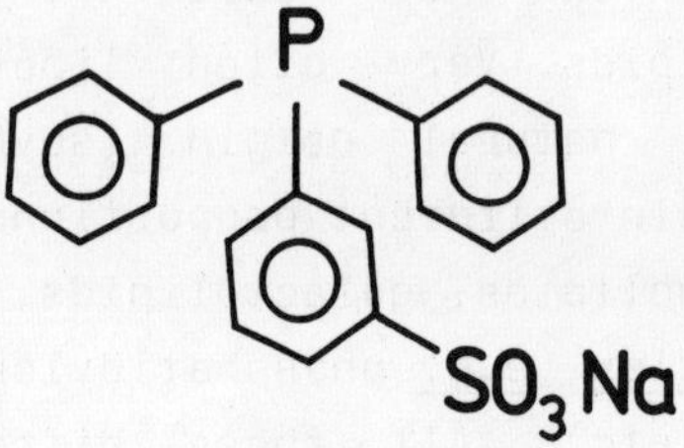

$$CH_3-(CH_2)_{17}-O-CH_2$$
$$CH_3-(CH_2)_{17}-O-CH$$

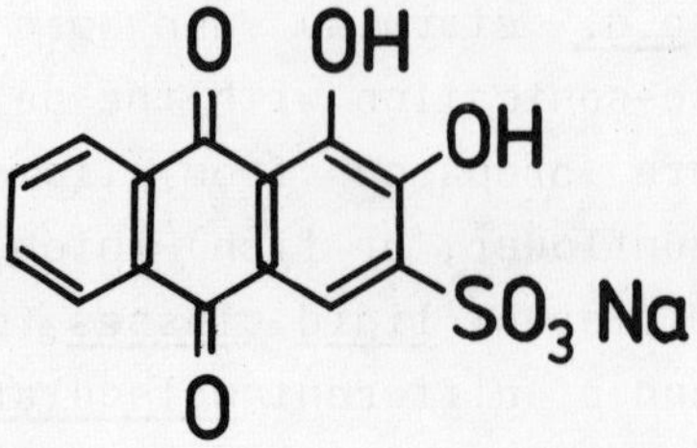

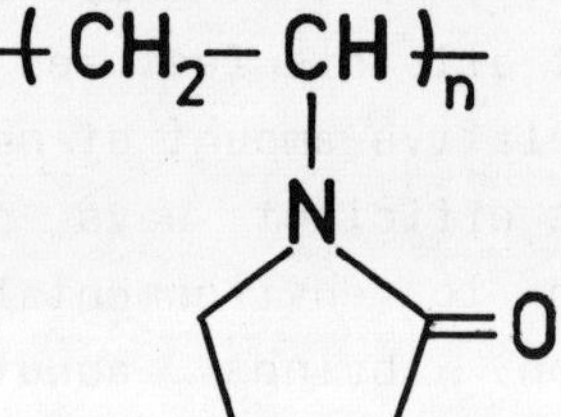

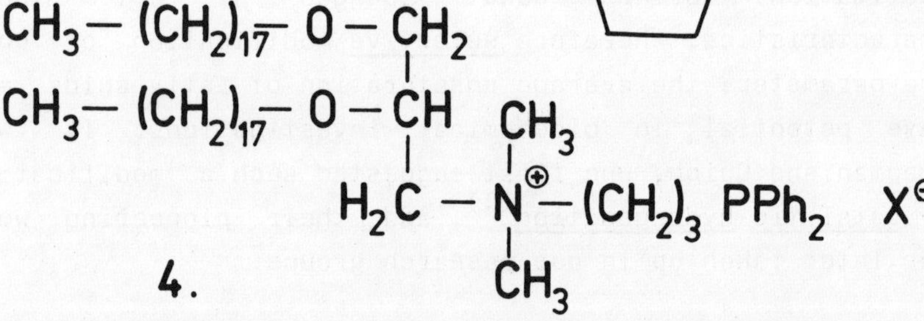

Fig. 1 Ligands of catalysts for hydrogenations in aqueous systems.

There is a rapidly increasing number of water-soluble transition metal catalysts[2),3),14)]. Fig. 1 shows ligands of the most frequently used catalysts, among them the mono-sulfonated triphenylphosphine ($mSPPh_2$, or TPPMS, 1) and Alizarin Red, 2). (Complexes of tris-m-sulfonated triphenylphosphine, TPPTS, outstandingly successful in industrial catalysis[15),16)], have not yet been used for biomembrane hydrogenation.)

Selectivity in Hydrogenation of Biomembranes

As in many other branches of catalysis, <u>selectivity</u> is the most important feature in hydrogenation of biological

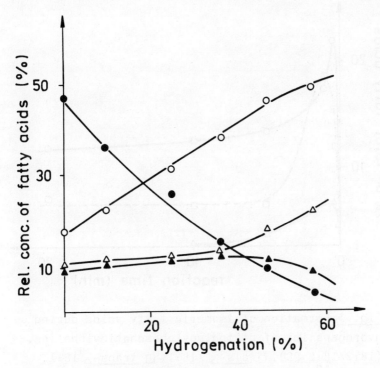

<u>Fig. 2</u> Relative proportions of fatty acids during hydrogenation of pea chloroplast. Catalyst: $Pd(QS)_2$ (80 µg/ml), $p(H_2)=0.3$ MPa, $T=25°C$.
18:3 (●); 18:2 (▲); 18:1 (○); 18:0 (△)

membranes. In many respect, under hydrogenation conditions membrane lipids behave like simple esters of unsaturated

acids. For example, polyunsaturated lipids react faster
than those containing fatty acyl residues with only one
double bond, 18:1 or 16:1 (Fig. 2). Also, cis-double bonds
are saturated faster than their trans-counterparts.
Consequently, unnatural lipids containing isomeric
trans-fatty acids may accumulate, when hydrogenation is
accompanied by relatively fast isomerization. As is shown
on Fig. 3, not only geometric, but positional isomers

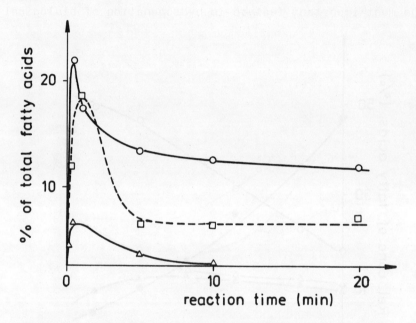

Fig. 3 Formation of isomeric fatty acids during
hydrogenation of dilinoleoylphosphatidylcholine,
(18:2/18:2 PC). ○ cis-Δ^9-18:1, □ trans-$\Delta^9$18:1,
△ cis-Δ^{12}-18:1. Catalyst: Pd(QS)$_2$ (0.1 mg/ml), 20°C.

(e.g. cis-Δ^{12}-18:1) can be formed. In the literature on
homogeneous hydrogenation with water soluble catalysts
there is only one example, when a trans-acid (fumaric acid)
was hydrogenated preferentially over its cis-isomer (maleic

acid)[17], and it is still unknown whether this selectivity is displayed in lipid dispersions, as well.

It is very important to realize, that liposomes and cells are <u>microheterogeneous</u> systems, in which <u>mass transport</u> as opposed to inherent chemical reactivity may be rate determining in hydrogenation reactions. Therefore hydrogenation rates are influenced by the actual physical state of the membrane, the latter being determined by its chemical composition, and temperature. As seen on <u>Fig. 4</u>, the rate of hydrogenation of soybean lecithin decreased

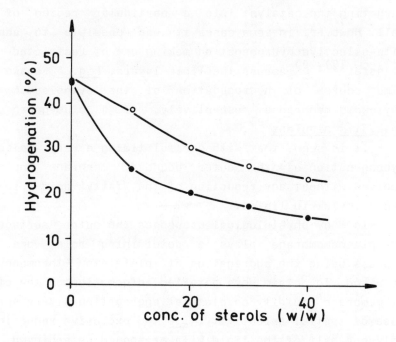

<u>Fig. 4</u> Hydrogenation of soybean lecithin liposomes containing stigmasterol (o) and cholesterol (●). Catalyst: $RuCl_2(mSPPh_2)_2$, $T=20^oC$, $p(H_2)=0.1$ MPa, [Ru]/ lipid =0.06

with increasing sterol content, as a result of the increase in microviscosity of the membrane[18]. We have also found[6], that dispersions of dioleoylphosphatidylethanolamine were reduced slower by Pd(QS)$_2$, than those of dioleoylphosphatidylcholine, because 18:1/18:1 PE forms close-packed hexagonal$_{II}$ liothropic liquid crystalline phases in contrast to the less dense bilayers of 18:1/18:1 PC.

Living cells are characterized by a sophisticated spatial organization of their functions, and therefore site-selectivity of the hydrogenation catalyst is a most desired feature. Up till now, there is no general method of targeting the catalyst into a particular region of the cell. However, in some cases it was possible to achieve site-selective hydrogenation making use of restricted mass transfer[19],[20] across the lipid layers. Fig. 5 shows the time course of hydrogenation of the cytoplasmic and thylakoid membranes, respectively, of a blue-green alga, Anacystis nidulans[19].

It is seen, that with careful timing a very selective hydrogenation of the outer boundary membrane could be achived without any reduction of the fatty acids in the inner thylakoid lipids.

In many physiological processes the outer "surface" of the plasmamembrane plays a determining role, one such process being the aggregation of platelets (thrombocytes) in blood. To obtain more detailed information on the effect of membrane fluidity on platelet aggregation a very special case of spatial selectivity, i.e the exclusive reduction of only one half of the lipid bilayer should be achieved. The water soluble catalyst, Pd(QS)$_2$ can not be used in this system[20], because the catalyst itself completely blocks aggregation, presumably due to its strong binding to proteins[9], abundant in the plasmamembrane of platelets. This is the case when a heterogeneous catalyst is beneficial. We have demonstrated[20], that colloidal Pd precipitated onto the surface of the biocompatible support, polyvinylpolypyrrolidone, PVPP (<u>3</u> on <u>Fig. 1</u>), was "surface-selective" in the hydrogenation of thrombocytes with no considerable self-effect on aggregation.

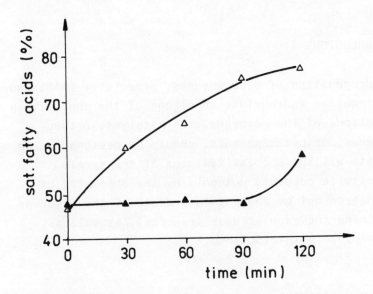

<u>Fig. 5</u> Changes in the relative proportion of saturated fatty acids in the lipids of cyto-plasmic (△) and thylakoid (▲) membranes during hydrogenation of <u>Anacystis</u> <u>n.</u>. Catalyst: $Pd(QS)_2$ (0.6 mg/ml), $p(H_2)=0.3$ MPa, $T=28^{\circ}C$.

A very important question is the partition of the catalyst among the bulk aqueous phase of lipid or cell dispersions and the rather hydrophobic membrane regions. The catalyst should -to some extent- be able to partition into hydrophobic regions or to cross membrane boundaries. Therefore complexes of tris(m-sulfophenylphosphine), TPPTS, carrying high overall ionic charge, do not seem very promising for endomembrane hydrogenations. On the other hand, complexes of the lipid-like phosphines ($\underline{4}$ on $\underline{\text{Fig. 1}}$) can be incorporated and strongly held inside the membrane, and what is perhaps gained in higher hydrogenation rates, is lost when it comes to the removal of the catalyst.

CONCLUSIONS

Hydrogenation of biomembranes, especially in living cells, requires appropriate knowledge of the composition and functions of the membrane. The catalyst, either homogeneous, or heterogeneous, should be designed as to accomodate all the special features of the sample. Selectivity is governed not only by the chemistry of hydrogenation but by the physical state of the membrane (determining the ease of mass transfer), as well as catalyst/protein interactions.

ACKNOWLEDGEMENT

This work was supported by the Hungarian National Research Council (OTKA) through grants No. 133/86 (to F.J.) and No. 543/86 (to L.V.). The loan of $RuCl_3.3H_2O$ and $(NH_4)_2PdCl_4$ by Johnson Matthey P.L.C. is also gratefully acknowledged.

REFERENCES

1. Ahrland, S., Chatt, J., Davies, N.R., and
   Williams, A.A., J. Chem. Soc. 276 (1958)

2. Joó, F., and Tóth, Z., J. Molec. Catal. 8
   369 (1980)

3. Sinou, D., Bull. Soc. Chim. France 480 (1987)

4. Bulatov, A.V., Izakovich, E.N., Karklin, L.N., and
   Khidekel, M.L., Izv. Akad. Nauk. SSSR, Ser. Khim.
   2032 (1981)

5. Joó, F., Balogh, N., Horváth, L.I., Filep, Gy.,
   Horváth, I., and Vígh, L., Anal. Biochem.
   submitted for publication

6. Vígh, L., Horváth, I., Joó, F., and Thompson, G.A.Jr.
   Biochim. Biophys. Acta 921 167 (1987)

7. Vígh, L., Joó, F., Droppa, M., Horváth, L.I., and
   Horváth, G., Eur. J. Biochem. 147 477 (1985)

8. Schlame, M., Horváth, I., Török, Zs., Horváth, L.I.,
   and Vígh, L., Biochim. Biophys. Acta 1045 1 (1990)

9. Pak, Y., Joó, F., Vígh. L., Kathó, Á., and
   Thompson, G.A., Jr., Biochim. Biophys. Acta
   1023 230 (1990)

10. Piche, L.A., and Mahadevappa, V.G., Biochem. J.
    263 143 (1989)

11. Horváth, G., Droppa, M., Szitó, T., Mustárdy, L.A., Horváth, L.I., and Vígh, L., Biochim. Biophys. Acta **849** 325 (1986)

12. Bergelson, L.D., Molotkovsky, J., and Manevich, Y.M., Chem. Phys. Lipids **37** 165 (1985)

13. Chapman, D., and Quinn, P.J., Proc. Nat. Acad. Sci. USA **73** 3971 (1976)

14. Chapman, D., and Quinn, P.J., Chem. Phys. Lipids **17** 363 (1976)

15. Herrmann, W.A., Kellner, J., and Riepl, H., J. Organometal. Chem. **389** 103 (1990)

16. Kuntz, E., CHEMTECH **17** 570 (1987)

17. Joó, F., Somsák, L., and Beck, M.T., J. Molec. Catal. **24** 71 (1984)

18. Vígh, L., Joó, F., van Hasselt, P.R., and Kuiper, P.J.C., J. Molec. Catal. **22** 15 (1983)

19. Vígh, L., Gombos, Z., and Joó, F., FEBS Let. **191** 200 (1985)

20. Benkő, S., Horváth, I., Török, Zs., Joó, F., and Vígh, L., in preparation for Biochim. Biophys. Acta

MOLECULAR HYDROGEN COMPLEXES IN HOMOGENEOUS CATALYSIS. SELECTIVE HYDROGENATION OF 1-ALKYNES TO ALKENES CATALYZED BY AN IRON(II) *CIS*-HYDRIDE(η^2-DIHYDROGEN) COMPLEX

Claudio Bianchini, Andrea Meli and Maurizio Peruzzini

Istituto per lo Studio della Stereochimica ed Energetica dei Composti di Coordinazione, CNR Via J. Nardi 39, 50132 Firenze, Italy

Piero Frediani

Dipartimento di Chimica Organica, Università di Firenze, 50121, Italy

Cristina Bohanna, Miguel A. Esteruelas and Luis A. Oro

Departamento de Quimica Inorganica, Instituto de Ciencias de Materiales de Aragon, Universidad de Zaragoza-C.S.I.C., 5009 Zaragoza, Spain

ABSTRACT

Terminal alkynes are selectively and catalytically hydrogenated to alkenes by the iron(II) η^2-H_2 complex [(PP$_3$)Fe(H)(H$_2$)]BPh$_4$ [PP$_3$ = P(CH$_2$CH$_2$PPh$_2$)$_3$] in THF under very mild conditions. A detailed experimental study on the hydrogenation reaction of HC≡CPh has shown that i) the dihydrogen ligand does not leave the metal prior to alkyne coordination and ii) the reduction of the substrate occurs *via* an intramolecular acid/base reaction involving η^2-H_2 and σ-vinyl ligands mutually *cis* disposed.

In comparison with the abundance of η^2-H_2 compounds in number and variety,[1] not much is known on their chemistry. The η^2-H_2 ligand is a good leaving group,[2] and may exhibit acidic character with pKa values ranging from 7.1 to 10.[3]

Recently, η^2-H_2 metal complexes have begun to attract interest because of their potential as catalysts in several homogeneous reactions.[4] All the mechanistic interpretations of these reactions center on the ability of H_2 to be readily displaced by the substrate.

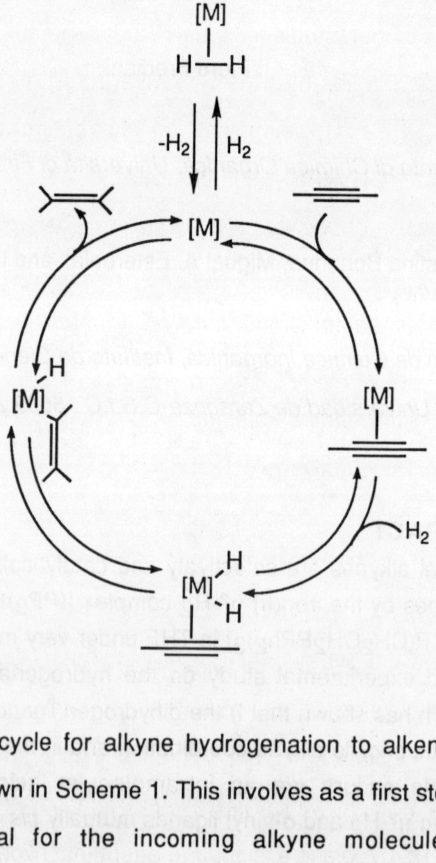

Scheme 1

A typical catalysis cycle for alkyne hydrogenation to alkenes assisted by η^2-H_2 complexes is shown in Scheme 1. This involves as a first step, creation of a free site at the metal for the incoming alkyne molecule through H_2 decoordination. After alkyne bonding in π fashion, dihydrogen reenters the metal coordination sphere whereupon it undergoes oxidative cleavage to give a classical dihydride. Finally, through migration of hydride from metal to π-alkyne (or alkyne insertion across one of the two M-H bonds), followed by a reductive elimination step, the substrate is reduced to alkene. According to the reaction sequence shown in Scheme 1, η^2-H_2 complexes are only precursors to the catalysts that, actually, are coordinatively unsaturated species.

Inspection of Scheme 1 reveals that dihydrogen plays a dual role: as a weakly bound molecular ligand, it contributes to generate the catalyst, and then, in the classical dihydride form, it reduces the alkyne.

In the course of our studies on dihydrogen metal compounds, we have recently synthesized a cis-hydride(η^2-dihydrogen) Fe(II) complex, namely $[(PP_3)Fe(H)(H_2)]BPh_4$ (1),[5] exhibiting an exceptional thermal and chemical stability [PP_3 = $P(CH_2CH_2PPh_2)_3$]. In particular, 1 is fairly stable in refluxing THF under argon and does not undergo H/D exchange when treated for 3 h with D_2 or D_2O. Intrigued by the remarkable stability of the H_2 ligand, we decided to investigate the potential of 1 as catalyst in homogeneous hydrogenation reactions of unsaturated substrates.

Here, we report the results obtained on the homogeneous hydrogenation of 1-alkynes by using 1 as catalyst precursor.

THE FLUXIONAL BEHAVIOUR OF 1 IN SOLUTION

Compound 1 can be obtained, as yellow crystals, by reaction of $[(PP_3)FeCl]BPh_4$ (2) in THF with an excess of $NaBH_4$ under 1 atm of H_2.[5] It is highly fluxional in solution as shown by variable-temperature ^1H and $^{31}P\{^1H\}$ NMR spectra. The ^1H NMR spectrum (300 MHz) in acetone-d_6 at 233 K exhibits a broad singlet at -7.21 ppm, which is typical of an η^2-H_2 ligand. A well-resolved multiplet (tdd) at -12.47 ppm is assigned to a terminal hydride which is coupled to two equivalent and two non-equivalent phosphorus nuclei. As the temperature is increased, the two resonances become broader and broader, and finally collapse at *ca.* 293 K. At higher temperature, the intramolecular exchange of the hydride and dihydrogen ligands become faster, and a single resonance appears at -9.13 ppm. In a similar way, below 260 K, the ^{31}P NMR spectrum (acetone-d_6, 121.42 MHz) consists of an AMQ$_2$ splitting pattern typical of octahedral PP$_3$ metal complexes.[6] When the temperature is raised, a dynamic process takes place and, at *ca.* 273 K, this makes equivalent the three terminal phosphorus atoms of PP$_3$, as is the case when the (PP$_3$)M fragment adopts a C_{3v} symmetry (trigonal bipyramidal geometry). Interestingly, both the chemical shift and the multiplicity of the bridgehead phosphorus of PP$_3$ remain practically unchanged over the temperature range 193-313 K. In conclusion, on the NMR time scale and in ambient temperature solutions, compound **1** appears as a trigonal bipyramidal species with three equivalent hydrogen atoms *trans* to the bridgehead phosphorus of PP$_3$.

The mutual exchange mechanism responsible of the equivalence of the terminal P donors has been studied by DNMR3 spectroscopy assuming exchange between the three configurations $P_AP_MP_QP_Q \Leftrightarrow P_AP_QP_MP_Q \Leftrightarrow P_AP_QP_QP_Q$. Provided the validity of this model system, the following activation parameters can be calculated: $\Delta G^{\dagger}$ (298 K) = 13 ± 1 kcal mol^{-1}; $\Delta H^{\dagger}$ = 9.7 ± 0.5 kcal mol^{-1}, $\Delta S^{\dagger}$ = -9 ± 2 cal K^{-1} mol^{-1}, E_a = 10.3 ± 0.5 kcal mol^{-1}. These data point to a relatively endothermic and ordered transition state. In light of the activation parameters, of the NMR and chemical results, a reasonable mechanistic interpretation for the dynamic behavior of **1** is the one shown in Scheme 2. This involves interaction between *cis* dihydrogen and hydride ligands, decoordination of a phosphine arm and, finally, reformation of a H$_2$ ligand invariably *trans* to the bridgehead phosphorus of PP$_3$. By so doing, all of the terminal phosphorus and hydrogen atoms can exchange their position thus accounting for the ^{31}P and ^{1}H NMR spectra.

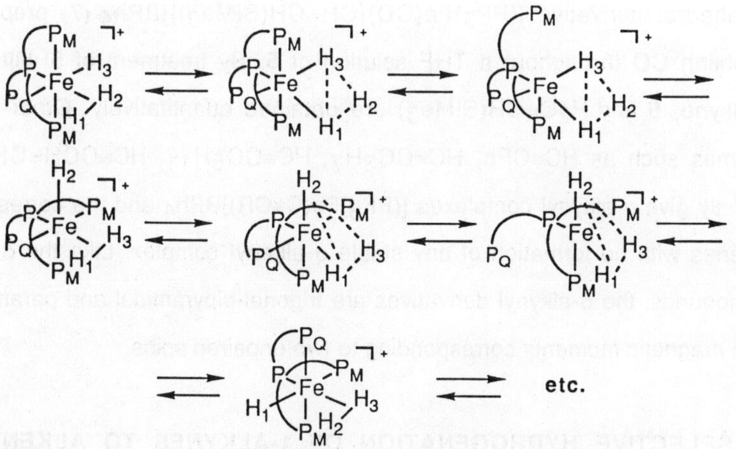

Scheme 2

REACTIONS OF 1 WITH 1-ALKYNES

As previously mentioned, **1** is exceedingly stable, especially when compared to all of the other η^2-H_2 complexes reported in the literature.[1] Replacement of H_2 with N_2 or MeCN is a feasible reaction pathway but quite long times are required for appreciable formation of the corresponding $[(PP_3)Fe(H)(N_2)]BPh_4$ (**3**) and $[(PP_3)Fe(H)(MeCN))]BPh_4$ (**4**) derivatives at room temperature (75 % conversion to **3** in 3 days, THF, 1 atm of N_2; 40 % conversion to **4** in 2 h, neat MeCN).[5] In contrast, the regeneration of **1** from **3** or **4** is a very fast reaction, complete within ca. 30 min.

Compound **1** reacts with 1-alkynes to give trigonal-bipyramidal, paramagnetic σ-alkenyl complexes which may or may not be isolated depending on the alkyne substituent.[7] An alkenyl derivative, $[(PP_3)Fe\{CH=CH(SiMe_3)\}]BPh_4$ (**5**), is obtained, as the predominant product, by reaction of **1** with $HC\equiv CSiMe_3$ together with some σ-alkynyl complex $[(PP_3)Fe(C\equiv CSiMe_3)]BPh_4$ (**6**) and free vinyltrimethylsilane (10-15%). The trans insertion of the alkyne across the Fe-H bond has been established by ^{1}H NMR spectroscopy on the diamagnetic octahedral derivative $[(PP_3)Fe(CO)\{CH=CH(SiMe_3)\}]BPh_4$ (**7**) prepared by bubbling CO throughout a THF solution of **5**. By treatment of **5** with further 1-alkyne, **6** and $H_2C=CH(SiMe_3)$ are obtained quantitatively. Other terminal alkynes such as $HC\equiv CPh$, $HC\equiv CC_3H_7$, $HC\equiv CC_5H_{11}$, $HC\equiv CCH=CH(OMe)$ directly give σ-alkynyl complexes $[(PP_3)Fe(C\equiv CR)]BPh_4$ and the corresponding alkenes with no formation of any stable σ-alkenyl complex. Like the σ-alkenyl compounds, the σ-alkynyl derivatives are trigonal-bipyramidal and paramagnetic with magnetic moments corresponding to two unpaired spins.

SELECTIVE HYDROGENATION OF 1-ALKYNES TO ALKENES

Under 1 atm H_2, the reactions between **1** and excess 1-alkynes in THF are catalytic and produce only alkenes regardless of the temperature, except for $HC\equiv CSiMe_3$ which is prevalently converted to 1,4-bis(trimethylsilyl)butadiene at high temperature [7] (Table 1).

Table 1. Catalytic Hydrogenation of Terminal Alkynes in the Presence of **1**[a].

Substrate	T	Product (t.o.f. [b])	
RC≡CH	°C	RCH=CH₂	RCH=CHCH=CHR
Ph	20	3.2	
	66	19.2	
SiMe₃	20	3.2	
	66	2.2	9.8
n-C₃H₇	20	3.1	
	66	14.7	
n-C₅H₁₁	20	2.7	
	66	9.5	
CH=CH(OMe)	20	1.2	
	66	8.2	

[a] Reaction conditions: Alkyne 0.9 mmol; Catalyst 0.03 mmol; H_2 pressure 1 atm; Time 3 h; THF (solvent) 10 ml. [b] T.o.f.: Moles of substrate transformed per mole of catalyst per hour.

A detailed kinetic study has been carried out for the selective reduction of phenylacetylene to styrene at H_2 pressures in the range from 0.5 to 1 atm and in the temperature range from 293 to 333 K. The reactions invariably exhibit a first-order dependence on both substrate and **1** concentrations and, surprisingly, a zero-order in hydrogen pressure. Plotting log K against $1/T$ results in a straight line from which the activation parameters $\Delta G^{\dagger}$, $\Delta H^{\dagger}$ and $\Delta S^{\dagger}$ can be calculated. The largely negative value for $\Delta S^{\dagger}$ indicates that the transition state for the rate determining step is ordered.

$$-\frac{d\,[PhC{\equiv}CH]}{dt} = [Cat]\,[PhC{\equiv}CH]$$

$\Delta H^{\dagger} = 11.2 \pm 0.8\ \text{kcal mol}^{-1}$ $\Delta G^{\dagger}\ (298\ K) = 19 \pm 2\ \text{kcal mol}^{-1}$

$E_a = 11.8 \pm 0.8\ \text{kcal mol}^{-1}$ $\Delta S^{\dagger} = -27 \pm 3\ \text{cal K}^{-1}\ \text{mol}^{-1}$

The non-dependence of the reaction rate on the hydrogen pressure holds also in the range from 5 to 100 atm (Table 2).

Table 2. Hydrogenation of Phenylacetylene in the Presence of **1**[a].

Hydrogen pressure atm	$PhCH{=}CH_2$ %	$PhC{\equiv}CH$ %
5	7.6	92.4
15	9.3	90.7
28	8.7	91.3
105	6.1	93.9

[a] Reaction conditions: Catalyst 0.02 mmol, Substrate 20 mmol, THF (solvent) 50 ml, T 60°C, Time 3 h.

Monitoring the reactions by either $^{31}P\{^1H\}$ NMR or X-band ESR spectroscopy at regular intervals from the beginning to the total consumption of the alkyne substrate shows that i) the starting hydride(η^2-dihydrogen) complex **1** is the only NMR active species during the catalysis cycle and the termination product as well, and ii) no ESR active compound forms in the course of the reaction. In contrast, when the reactions are carried out by using more alkyne than dihydrogen, the paramagnetic σ-alkynyl $[(PP_3)Fe(C{\equiv}CPh)]BPh_4$ is found as the termination product.

According to the commonly accepted role of η^2-H_2 complexes in hydrogenation reactions, *i. e.* the H_2 ligand is easily displaced by the substrate, a catalysis cycle which takes into account some of the experimental observables is the one reported in Scheme 3. This involves a number of steps which are not detectable on the NMR time scale. The non-dependence of the reaction rate on the H_2 pressure tells us that both the elimination of H_2 from **1** (step **a**) and the H_2 uptake by the coordinatively unsaturated alkenyl intermediate (step **d**) should be much faster than either alkyne insertion across the Fe-H bond (step **c**) or alkene elimination from the *cis*-$(H_2)(\sigma$-vinyl) intermediate (step **e**). Step **e** might proceed *via* either oxidative addition of H_2 to iron(II) to give an iron(IV) classical dihydride, followed by reductive elimination of alkene, or an intramolecular acid/base reaction involving the mutually *cis* H_2 (acidic character) and vinyl (basic character) ligands. The former reaction sequence is less likely than the latter one, particularly as one considers that iron(II) has not a great tendency to be oxidized to iron(IV). Also, such a complicated reaction sequence would reasonably constitute the rate determining step and this is ruled out by the $\Delta H^\dagger$ and $\Delta S^\dagger$ values which are consistent with an ordered transition state as well as an endothermic process of scarce entity. Both these requirements are fulfilled by steps **c** and **e**, each of which might be the rate determining step *via* four-centered transition states.

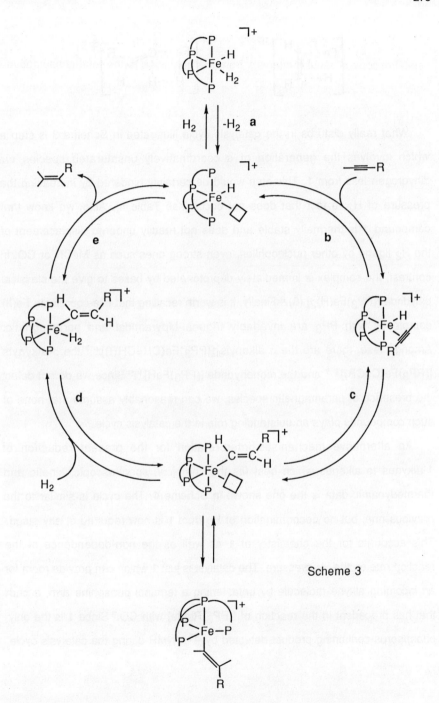

Scheme 3

What really disturbs in the catalysis cycle illustrated in Scheme 3 is step **a** which involves the generation of a coordinatively unsaturated species *via* dihydrogen loss from **1**. This step would be certainly hindered by increasing the pressure of H_2, a fact that does not occur (see Table II). Also, we know that compound **1** is thermally stable and does not readily undergo displacement of the H_2 ligand by other nucleophiles, even strong ones such as MeCN or CO. In contrast, the complex is immediately deprotonated by bases to give the classical dihydride $[(PP_3)Fe(H)_2]$ **(8)**.[8] Finally, it is worth recalling that five-coordinate Fe(II) complexes with PP_3 are invariably trigonal-bipyramidal and paramagnetic. Among these, there are the σ-alkenyls $[(PP_3)Fe(CH=CHR)]^+$,[7] the σ-alkynyls $[(PP_3)Fe(C≡CR)]^+$ [7] and the monohydride $[(PP_3)FeH]^+$.[8] Since we do not detect the presence of paramagnetic species, we can reasonably assume that none of such compounds plays an outstanding role in the catalysis cycle.

An alternative mechanistic interpretation for the present reduction of 1-alkynes to alkenes which best fits the chemical, spectroscopic, kinetic and thermodynamic data is the one shown in Scheme 4. The cycle is similar to the previous one, but no decoordination of H_2 from **1** is now required at any stage. This accounts for the chemistry of **1** as well as the non-dependence of the reaction rate on the H_2 pressure. The catalyst is just **1** which can provide room for an incoming alkyne molecule by unfastening a terminal phosphine arm, a path that has precedent in the reaction of $[(PP_3)RhMe]$ with CO.[9] Since **1** is the only phosphorus-containing product detected by ^{31}P NMR during the catalysis cycle,

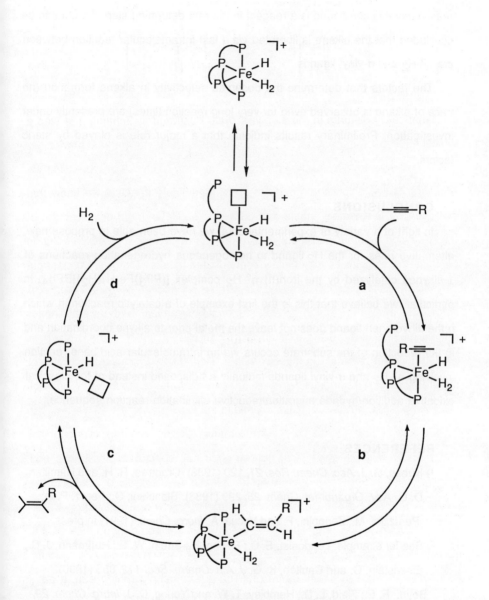

Scheme 4

reasonably this compound is a reagent in the rate determing step. If so, it can be concluded that the alkene is liberated *via* a fast intramolecular reaction between *cis* η^2-H_2 and σ-vinyl ligands.

The factors that determine the observed selectivity in alkene formation (no trace of alkane is observed even for very long reaction times) are presently under investigation. Preliminary results indicate that a major role is played by steric factors.

CONCLUSIONS

In light of a variety of experimental data, we have been able to propose new, alternative roles for the H_2 ligand in homogeneous hydrogenation reactions of 1-alkynes catalyzed by the iron(II) η^2-H_2 complex $[(PP_3)Fe(H)(H_2)]BPh_4$. In particular, we believe that this is the first example of a catalytic reaction in which i) the dihydrogen ligand does not leave the metal prior to alkyne coordination and ii) the reduction of the substrate occurs *via* an intramolecular acid/base reaction involving η^2-H_2 and σ-vinyl ligands mutually *cis* disposed instead of the classical oxidative addition/hydride migration/reductive elimination reaction sequence.

REFERENCES

[1] Kubas, G. J. *Acc. Chem. Res. 21*, 120 (1988). Crabtree, R. H. and Hamilton, D. G. *Adv. Organomet. Chem. 28,* 299 (1988). Bianchini, C.; Perez, P. J.; Peruzzini, M.; Zanobini, F. and Vacca, A. *Inorg. Chem.* (1991) in press.

[2] See for example: Lundquist, E. C.; Folting, K.; Streib, W. E.; Huffmann, J. C.; Eisenstein, O. and Caulton, K. G. *J. Am. Cherm. Soc. 112*, 855 (1990). Boyd, E. E.; Field, L. D.; Hambley, T. W. and Young, D. J. *Inorg. Chem. 29*, 1496 (1990) and references therein.

[3] Jia, G. and Morris, R. H. *J. Am. Chem. Soc. 29*, 581 (1990).

[4] Morton, D.; Cole-Hamilton, D. J. *J. Chem. Soc., Chem. Comm.* 1154 (1988).

Marinelli, G.; Rachidi, I. E.- I.; Streib, W. E.; Eisenstein, O. and Caulton K. G. *J. Am. Chem. Soc. 111*, 2346 (1989). Lin, Y. and Zhou, Y. *J. Organomet. Chem. 381*, 135 (1990). Andriollo, A.; Esteruelas, M. A.; Meyer, U.; Oro, L. A.; Sanchez-Delgado, R. A.; Sola, E.; Valero, C. and Werner, H. *J. Am. Chem. Soc. 110*, 7431 (1989). Bianchini, C.; Meli, A.; Peruzzini, M.; Zanobini, F.; Bruneau, C. and Dixneuf, P. H. *Organometallics 9*, 1155 (1990).

5) Bianchini, C.; Peruzzini, M. and Zanobini, F. *J. Organomet. Chem. 354*, C19 (1988).

6) Bianchini, C.; Masi, D.; Meli, A.; Peruzzini, M. and Zanobini, F. *J. Am. Chem. Soc. 110*, 6411 (1988).

7) Bianchini, C.; Meli, A.; Peruzzini, M.; Vizza, F. and Frediani, P. *Organometallics 9*, 2080 (1989).

8) Bianchini, C.; Laschi, F.; Peruzzini, M.; Ottaviani, M. F.; Vacca, A. and Zanello, P. *Inorg. Chem. 29*, 3394 (1990).

9) Bianchini, C.; Meli, A.; Peruzzini, M.; Vizza, F. and Frediani, P. *Organometallics 9*, 1146 (1990). Bianchini, C.; Innocenti, P.; Meli, A.; Peruzzini, M.; Zanobini, F. and Zanello, P. *Organometallics 9*, 2514 (1990).

CHEMOSELECTIVE HYDROGENATION CONTROLLED BY STERIC EFFECTS OF COORDINATED PHOSPHINES IN IRIDIUM CATALYSTS

Erica Farnetti and Mauro Graziani

Dipartimento Scienze Chimiche, Università di Trieste

Via Valerio 22, 34127 Trieste (Italy)

ABSTRACT. Iridium hydride complexes with phosphine ligands are efficient catalysts for the hydrogenation of α, β unsaturated ketones. It is possible to control the chemoselectivity of the reaction by tuning the steric situation around the iridium atom. In order to obtain selective keto group hydrogenation, the key point is to prevent C=C bond coordination, so that the substrate can approach the metal through the carbonyl group. This situation is operative in iridium complexes with three coordinated phosphines, whereas bisphosphino species catalyze C=C reduction, and tetraphosphino complexes are catalytically inactive.
A consistent behaviour is observed with potentially bidentate P-N ligands, which exhibit an interesting chemistry in solution, including intramolecular C-H and N-H oxidative addition.

INTRODUCTION

The catalyst design is one of the most fascinating aspects of homogeneous catalysis, and at the same time it represents one of the most challenging tasks for an organometallic chemist. Given an organic reaction and a target product, the problem consists in tuning the steric and electronic properties of the catalyst in order to optimize yield and selectivity. It is noticeable that examples of successful catalyst design cannot be found in profusion in the literature, and

this is an indirect proof of the difficulties that such
a project implies to the scientist.

We have been interested for some years in the
selective reduction of polyunsaturated organic
molecules, using either molecular hydrogen or a
hydrogen donor as reducing agent. A particularly
interesting problem in this field is the chemoselective
reduction of α,β unsaturated ketones, as all the
known catalytic systems invariably promote C=C bond
reduction.[1] In approaching this problem we could think
of two most obvious strategies to design a catalytic
system suitable for the selective keto group reduction
in such substrates. The first one is based on the
consideration that nucleophilic hydride attack on the
carbonyl group is favoured when the hydride possesses a
high negative charge. This approach implies that we
must modify the electronic properties of the catalyst,
for example by using more electron-donating ancillary
ligands. The second strategy is even more obvious: if
C=C bond reduction occurs owing to easy coordination of
this function, one must prevent such a coordination to
take place, and in principle this can be done by tuning
the steric properties of the catalyst.

We were able to prove that both approaches are
feasible. The electronic factors play a major role in
determining selectivity in hydrogen transfer reduction
catalyzed by iridium complexes with hybrid P-X ligands
(X=O,N).[2-4] At variance, steric effects are crucial in
determining the chemoselectivity of hydrogenation
reactions, where one can actually design a catalyst
whose steric situation is such as to prevent C=C
coordination, still allowing the approach of the
substrate via the carbonyl group.

We will presently relate our work concerning
iridium-based catalysts for the hydrogenation of

α,β unsaturated ketones: the chemoselectivity of the catalytic systems employed can be controlled by tuning their steric properties, so that either C=C bond or C=O group reduction can be performed in high yield.

IRIDIUM COMPLEXES WITH MONODENTATE PHOSPHINES

Iridium hydride complexes with phosphine ligands have proved extremely interesting catalysts in hydrogenation [5-16] and hydrogen transfer reactions [17-20]. Moreover, they offer the advantage of a wide choiche of ligands, as tertiary phosphines are available in a considerable range of steric and electronic properties. For these reasons we chose to study iridium phosphine complexes as catalysts for the hydrogenation of α,β unsaturated ketones.

By reacting [Ir(cod)(OMe)]$_2$ (cod=1,5 cyclooctadiene) with a monodentate phosphine under hydrogen flow different products are obtained, depending on the steric properties of the phosphine employed and on the [P]/[Ir] ratio. Let us consider first the ligand PEt$_2$Ph. In the presence of a twofold excess of this phosphine the iridium dimer undergoes methoxy bridge splitting, followed by β-hydrogen elimination to give the hydridic species HIr(cod)(PEt$_2$Ph)$_2$ (I), as shown in scheme 1. When the reaction mixture is treated with molecular hydrogen, via loss of hydrogenated cyclooctadiene the iridium bisphosphino species H$_5$Ir(PEt$_2$Ph)$_2$ (II) is formed. Such a complex possesses five coordinated hydrides, the two phosphines being in a mutually trans position. Complexes of the type H$_5$IrP$_2$

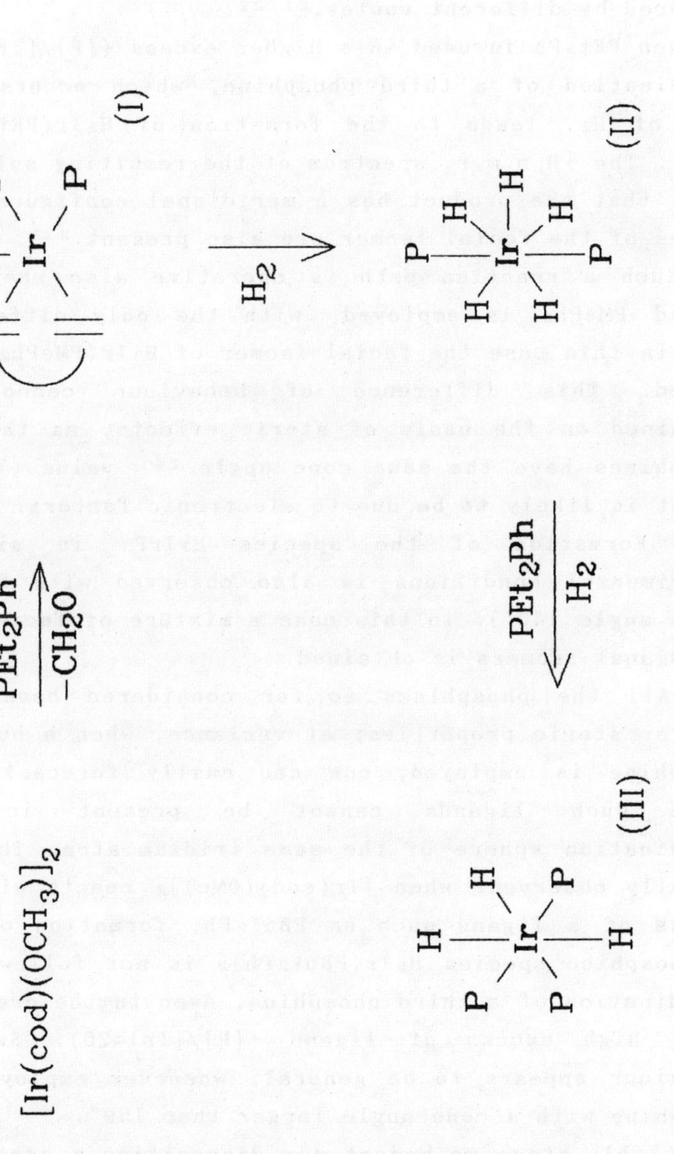

Scheme 1

are known in the literature, and have been previously prepared by different routes.[21,22)

When PEt₂Ph is used in a higher excess ([P]/[Ir]>4), coordination of a third phosphine, which occurs with loss of H₂, leads to the formation of $H_3Ir(PEt_2Ph)_3$ (III). The [1]H n.m.r. spectrum of the resulting solution shows that the product has a meridianal configuration; traces of the facial isomer are also present.[23).

Such a reaction path is operative also when the ligand PMePh₂ is employed, with the only difference that in this case the facial isomer of $H_3Ir(PMePh_2)_3$ is formed. This difference of behaviour cannot be explained on the basis of steric effects, as the two phosphines have the same cone angle [24) value (136°), but it is likely to be due to electronic factors.

Formation of the species H_3IrP_3 in similar experimental conditions is also observed with PEtPh₂ (cone angle 140°): in this case a mixture of facial and meridianal isomers is obtained.

All the phosphines so far considered have very similar steric properties; at variance, when a bulkier phosphine is employed, one can easily forecast that three such ligands cannot be present in the coordination sphere of the same iridium atom. This is actually observed: when [Ir(cod)(OMe)]₂ reacts with an excess of a ligand such as PBuᵗ₂Ph, formation of the bisphosphino species $H_5Ir(PBu^t_2Ph)_2$ is not followed by coordination of a third phosphine, even in the presence of a high excess of ligand ([P]/[Ir]=20). Such a behaviour appears to be general, whenever employing a phosphine with a cone angle larger than 150°.

At this stage we had at our disposition a series of complexes having in the coordination sphere of iridium two or three phosphines together with a certain number of hydrides; the trisphosphino complexes could be chosen with different configurations; in the bisphosphino species one could select the bulkiness of the phosphine within a large range.

With the idea of testing such complexes as catalyst precursors for the hydrogenation of α,β unsaturated ketones, we wondered whether all these factors (number of coordinated phosphines, size of the phosphine, configuration of the complex) would affect the selectivity of the reaction, and to what extent.

Hydrogenation of our model substrate benzylideneacetone PhCH=CHCOMe is promoted by H_5IrP_2 or H_3IrP_3, which are prepared in situ from $[Ir(cod)(OMe)]_2$ and the appropriate excess of the phosphine. By examining a large number of phosphines in a wide range of cone angle values (up to 195°) it turned out that the species H_5IrP_2 are efficient catalyst precursors for the hydrogenation of the C=C bond of the substrate; the saturated ketone so formed is subsequently reduced to give the saturated alcohol. Apparently, the different bulkiness of the phosphine has no effect on the chemoselectivity of the reaction, as long as the bisphosphino complex is the only species present in the reaction mixture: the same reaction rate and selectivity are observed with $H_5Ir(PEt_2Ph)_2$ and $H_5Ir(PBu^t_2Ph)_2$.

At variance, a dramatic difference in both catalytic activity and selectivity is observed when changing from bisphosphino to trisphosphino complexes as catalyst precursors. Let us compare the results obtained with $H_5Ir(PEt_2Ph)_2$ and $H_3Ir(PEt_2Ph)_3$: with the latter the olefin group hydrogenation is depressed, and only the slower carbonyl group reduction is observed; the substituted allylic alcohol so formed is not subsequently hydrogenated.

In table 1 are reported the results obtained with catalytic systems prepared with the ligands PMePh$_2$, PEt$_2$Ph, PEtPh$_2$ and PPh$_2$Pr^i which are all small enough to form a trisphosphino complex. At low P/Ir ratio H$_5$IrP$_2$ is formed, which catalyzes the C=C bond reduction; on increasing the excess of phosphine the amount of unsaturated alcohol, previously negligible, is increased; the latter is the only product formed at [P]/[Ir]>4, when no more H$_5$IrP$_2$ is present in the reaction mixture. The presence of an excess of ligand appears to be crucial in order to depress dissociation of a phosphine from H$_3$IrP$_3$: the larger the phosphine employed, the higher the excess of phosphine required to prevent formation of H$_5$IrP$_2$ (compare runs 8 and 11).

A most reasonable hypothesis which accounts for these results is the following. The α, β unsaturated ketone can coordinate to iridium either through the C=C bond or through the carbonyl group; the latter function coordinates in an end-on rather than in a side-on mode. Whenever this is possible, coordination occurs through the olefin group, which is the thermodynamically favoured mode, and this is the case with the species H$_5$IrP$_2$. At variance, the complex H$_3$IrP$_3$ has a rather crowded situation in the coordination sphere, so as to make difficult the approach of the substrate via C=C bond; however, even in this situation the coordination of the less sterically demanding carbonyl group is still possible. In the latter case we therefore observe a steric control on the coordination mode of the substrate and, as a consequence, on the chemoselectivity of the reaction, as it is the coordinated function which is selectively hydrogenated.

In this view, it looked interesting to test iridium complexes with four coordinated phosphines, in order to see if also in this very crowded situation the

Table 1. Hydrogenation of PhCH=CHCOMe catalyzed by [Ir(cod)(OMe)]₂ + Phosphine.

Run	Phosphine (cone angle°)	P/Ir	% conversion (hours)	% saturated ketone	% saturated alcohol	% unsaturated alcohol	% select.[a]
1	PMePh$_2$ (136)	2	98 (4)	92	5	1	1
2	"	3	98 (7)	26	26	46	47
3	"	5	94 (22)	11	1	82	87
4	"	10	51 (46)	0	0	51	100
5	PEt$_2$Ph (136)	4	70 (5)	10	6	54	77
6	"	10	96 (28)	5	1	90	94
7	PEtPh$_2$ (140)	2	97 (5)	86	10	1	1
8	"	5	92 (7)	7	1	84	90
9	"	10	99 (10)	2	1	96	97
10	PPh$_2$Pr^i (150)	2	99 (4)	92	7	0	0
11	"	5	88 (22)	36	17	35	39
12	"	10	93 (24)	6	2	85	92

Reaction conditions: [Ir]=4x10⁻⁴ M; [sub]/[Ir]=500; P(H₂)=20 atm; T=100°C; solvent toluene.
(a) % Selectivity=(% unsaturated alcohol/% conversion)x100.

coordination of the carbonyl group was still possible. Complexes of the type $H_2IrP_4^+$ (P=$PMePh_2$,PEt_2Ph) [25] were therefore tested as catalyst precursors for the hydrogenation of benzylideneacetone. Such precursors were found to promote the carbonyl group reduction [26] with a selectivity which is very close to the one of the species H_3IrP_3. However, the catalytic activity of the tetraphosphino complexes is lower in comparison to the trisphosphino complexes: an induction period of 12-24 hours is observed with the former systems, before appreciable hydrogenation rates are measured. N.m.r. investigations on the fate of the species $H_2IrP_4^+$ allowed us to understand that during the induction period H_3IrP_3 is slowly formed in hydrogenation conditions (20 atm H_2, 100°C), and the latter species is responsible for the catalytic activity: the complexes $H_2IrP_4^+$ as such are catalytically inactive. Apparently, such species have a too crowded coordination sphere to allow substrate approach even via carbonyl group: however, the effect of the positive charge in $H_2IrP_4^+$ cannot in principle be neglected.

IRIDIUM COMPLEXES WITH P-N LIGANDS

The two potentially bidentate phosphines P(o-$C_6H_4NH_2$)Ph_2 (= P-NH_2) and P(o-$C_6H_4NMe_2$)Ph_2 (= P-NMe_2) possess several features as to make them ligands of interest in homogeneous catalysis. The presence of both P and N donor atoms guarantees a good coordinating ability to metals in different oxidation states. The ligands can act as bidentate ones with formation of a five membered chelate ring; dissociation of the amino function is known to occur in the presence of Π-acceptor molecules. [27]

We expected that iridium complexes with such P-N ligands would exhibit interesting properties as catalysts for the hydrogenation of α,β unsaturated ketones. Catalytic systems prepared in situ starting from [Ir(cod)(OMe)]$_2$ + P-N were therefore tested in the hydrogenation of benzylideneacetone. As one can notice from the data reported in table 2, a different behaviour is exhibited by the catalytic system when changing from P-NH$_2$ to P-NMe$_2$. When the ligand P-NH$_2$ is employed, the chemoselectivity of the system is markedly dependent on the [P]/[Ir] ratio, with an increase of the yield in unsaturated alcohol when using a higher excess of ligand. At variance, the catalytic system with P-NMe$_2$ does not exhibit such a great change in chemoselectivity when increasing the [P]/[Ir] ratio, and a mixture of reduction products is formed.

On considering these results, and comparing them with those obtained with the systems employing monodentate phosphines, we expected that different iridium species were formed with the two P-N ligands. By following by n.m.r. the reaction between [Ir(cod)(OMe)]$_2$ and P-NH$_2$ or P-NMe$_2$, one can observe a different behaviour from the very first reaction steps (see scheme 2). Initial methoxy bridge splitting by the phosphine leads to formation of Ir(cod)(OMe)(P-N) (**IV** and **V**), whose fate depends on the nature of the coordinated phosphine. From species **IV** methanol is released to give the amido complex Ir(cod)(P-NH) (**VI**). In the case of **V** β-hydrogen elimination takes place, with loss of formaldehyde and formation of the hydride species HIr(cod)(P-NMe$_2$) (**VII**). From now on let us follow separately the two reaction paths.

In the presence of molecular hydrogen and of excess of P-NMe$_2$ species **VII** loses hydrogenated cyclooctadiene; coordination of a second phosphine is

Table 2. Hydrogenation of PhCH=CHCOMe catalyzed by [Ir(cod)(OMe)]$_2$ + P-N.

P-N	[P]/[Ir]	% conversion (hours)	% saturated ketone	% saturated alcohol	% unsaturated alcohol	% select.[a]
P-NH$_2$	1	82 (7)	69	8	5	6
	2	95 (7)	67	21	7	7
	3	70 (7)	30	5	35	50
	5	95 (7)	8	11	76	80
P-NMe$_2$	5	93 (46)	21	23	49	53

Reaction conditions: see table 1.

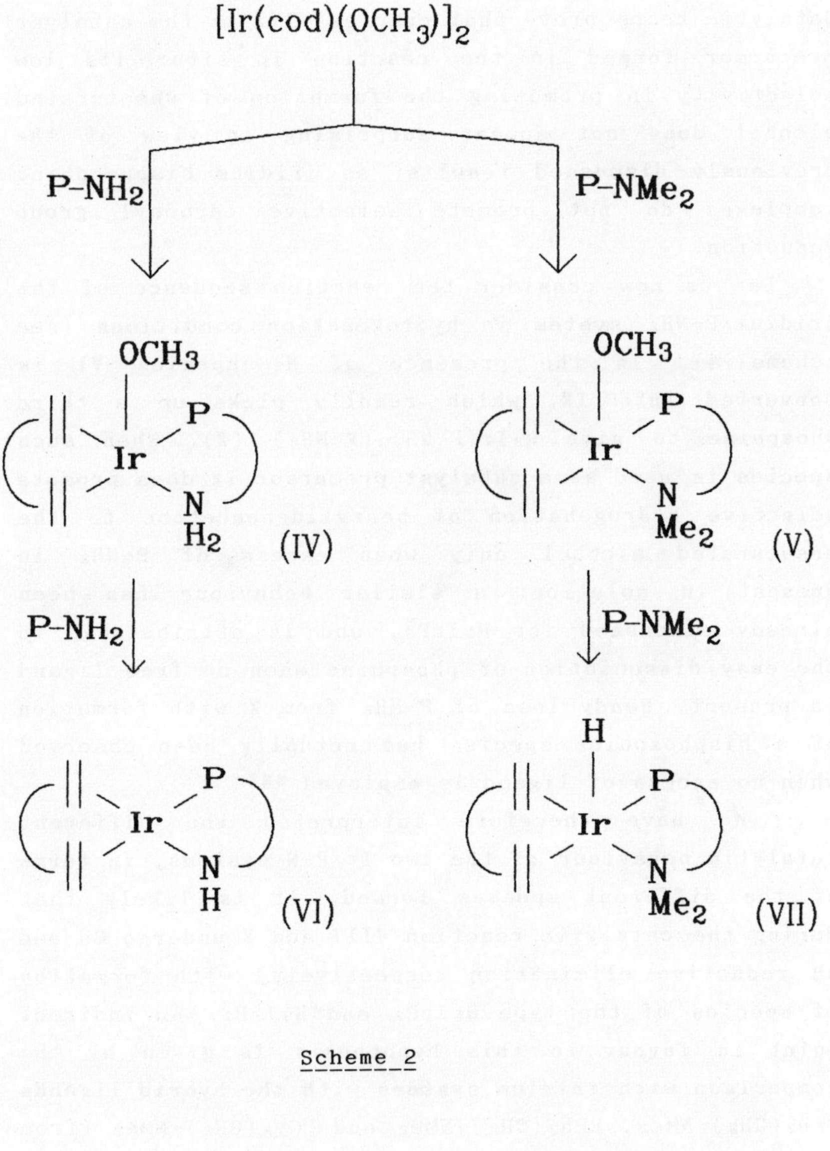

$$[Ir(cod)(OCH_3)]_2$$

P–NH$_2$ (left branch)   P–NMe$_2$ (right branch)

OCH$_3$

$$\begin{array}{c} P \\ Ir \\ N \\ H_2 \end{array} \quad (IV)$$

OCH$_3$

$$\begin{array}{c} P \\ Ir \\ N \\ Me_2 \end{array} \quad (V)$$

P–NH$_2$ P–NMe$_2$

$$\begin{array}{c} P \\ Ir \\ N \\ H \end{array} \quad (VI)$$

H

$$\begin{array}{c} P \\ Ir \\ N \\ Me_2 \end{array} \quad (VII)$$

<u>Scheme 2</u>

followed by C-H oxidative addition, with formation [4]
of $H_2Ir(\overline{P-NMeCH_2})(P-NMe_2)$ (VIII), probably via a
transition state such as that shown in scheme 3.
Catalytic tests prove that complex VIII is the catalyst
precursor formed in the reaction in situ: its low
selectivity in promoting the formation of unsaturated
alcohol does not appear surprising in view of the
previously discussed results, as iridium bisphosphino
complexes do not promote selective carbonyl group
reduction.

Let us now consider the reaction sequence of the
iridium/P-NH$_2$ system in hydrogenation conditions (see
scheme 4). In the presence of H$_2$ species VI is
converted into IX, which readily picks up a third
phosphine to give $H_2Ir(P-NH)_2(P-NH_2)$ (X). When such
species is used as a catalyst precursor it does promote
selective hydrogenation of benzylideneacetone to the
unsaturated alcohol only when excess of P-NH$_2$ is
present in solution: a similar behaviour has been
already discussed for H_3IrP_3, and is attributable to
the easy dissociation of phosphine when no free ligand
is present. Ready loss of P-NH$_2$ from X with formation
of a bisphosphino species has actually been observed
when no excess of ligand is employed [28].

We have therefore interpreted the different
catalytic behaviour of the two Ir/P-N systems, in terms
of the different species formed. It is likely that
during the catalytic reaction VIII and X undergo CH and
NH reductive elimination respectively, with formation
of species of the type H_5IrP_2 and H_3IrP_3. An indirect
point in favour to this hypothesis is given by the
comparison with iridium systems with the hybrid ligands
$PPh_2(CH_2)_2NMe_2$, $PPh_2(CH_2)_3NMe_2$ and $PCy_2(CH_2)_2NMe_2$ (from
now on indicated as $P(CH_2)_nN$). Depending on the
[P]/[Ir] ratio employed, the complexes $H_5Ir(P(CH_2)_nN)_2$

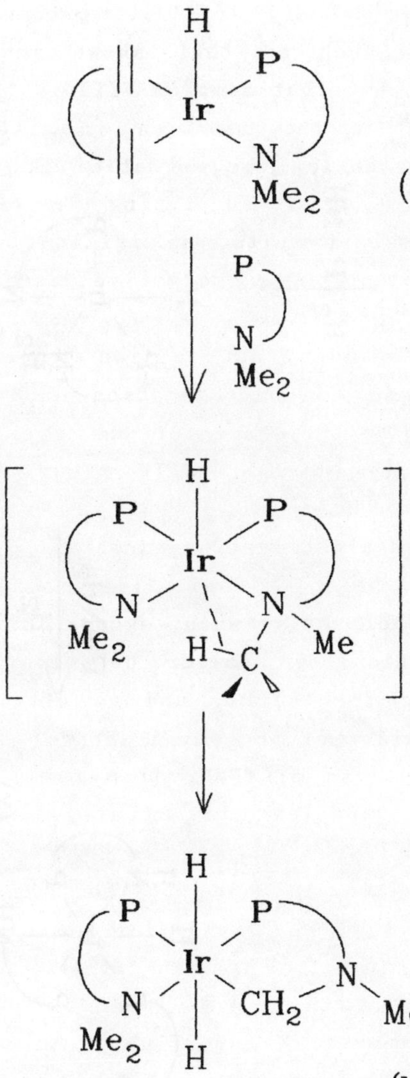

Scheme 3

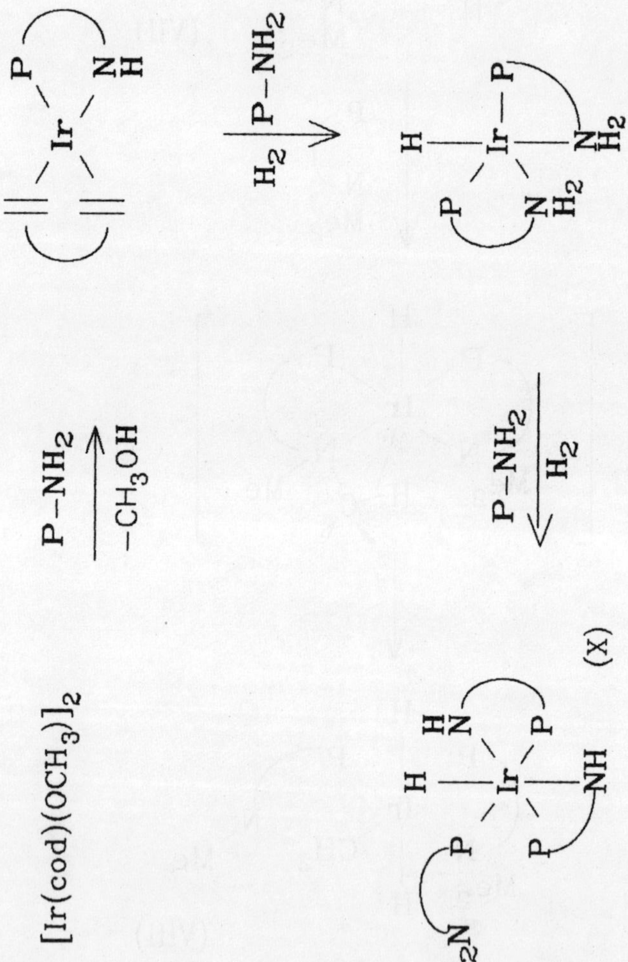

$[Ir(cod)(OCH_3)]_2$

(VI)

(IX)

(X)

$P-NH_2$
$-CH_3OH$

$H_2 \big| P-NH_2$

$P-NH_2 \big| H_2$

Scheme 4

and $H_3Ir(P(CH_2)_nN)_3$ are formed, which promote $C=C$ and $C=O$ bond hydrogenation respectively. No complexes with chelating $P(CH_2)_nN$ phosphines are detected in solution, and this can be ascribed to the less rigid conformation of the P-N rings formed. At variance, with P-NH2 and P-NMe2 stable chelate rings are formed, so that drastic experimental conditions are required to form $H_5Ir(P-NMe_2)_2$ and $H_3Ir(P-NH_2)_3$ from VIII and X respectively.

CONCLUDING REMARKS

In the above discussion we have been able to prove that if one can control the coordination mode of the substrate, it is possible to direct in the desired way the selectivity of the reaction under investigation. By tuning the steric properties of the catalyst the coordination of an α,β unsaturated ketone through the $C=C$ bond can be prevented, still allowing approach of the substrate via the less sterically demanding carbonyl group (see figure 1). Such control on the coordination mode is operative in complexes of the type H_3IrP_3, which promote the carbonyl group hydrogenation with a selectivity close to 100%. Although the data above discussed are all related to chemoselective hydrogenation, we feel that such an approach might be adopted also in other situations, and be successfully employed for designing a selective homogeneous catalyst.

AKNOWLEDGEMENTS

The authors thank C. N. R. (Roma) "Progetto Finalizzato Chimica Fine II" for finantial support.

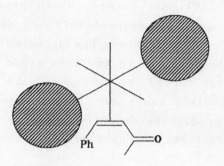

without steric control

H_5IrP_2

$H_2Ir(P-NMeCH_2)(P-NMe_2)$

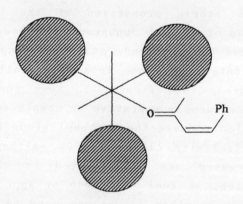

with steric control

H_3IrP_3

$HIr(P-NH_2)(P-NH)_2$

Figure 1

REFERENCES

1. Chaloner, P. A., "Handbook of Coordination Catalysis in Organic Chemistry", ed. Butterworth (1986).

2. Visintin, M.; Spogliarich, R.; Kaspar, J.; Graziani, M., J. Mol. Catal. 32, 349 (1985).

3. Farnetti, E.; Nardin, G.; Graziani, M., J. Chem. Soc. Chem. Commun. 1264 (1989).

4. Farnetti, E.; Kaspar, J.; Graziani, M., J. Mol. Catal., 63, 5 (1990).

5. Crabtree, R. H.; Demou, P. C.; Eden, D.; Mihelcic, J. M.; Parnell, C. A.; Quirk, J. M.; Morris, G. E., J. Amer. Chem. Soc. 104, 6994 (1982).

6. Crabtree, R. H.; Mellea, M. F.; Mihelcic, J. M.; Quirk, J. M., J. Amer. Chem. Soc. 104, 107 (1982).

7. Crabtree, R. H. and Davis, M. W., J. Org. Chem. 51, 2655 (1986).

8. Suggs, J. W.; Cox, S. D.; Crabtree, R. H.; Quirk, J. M., Tetrahedron Lett. 22, 303 (1981).

9. Lundquist, E. G.; Folting, K.; Streib, W. E.; Huffman, J. C.; Eisenstein, O.; Caulton, K. G., J. Amer. Chem. Soc. 112, 855 (1990).

10. Gomes Carneiro, T. M.; Matt, D.; Braunstein, P., Coord. Chem. Rev. 96, 49 (1989).

11. Goldman, A. S. and Halpern, J., J. Amer. Chem. Soc. 109, 7537 (1987).

12. Goldman, A. S. and Halpern, J., J. Organomet. Chem. 382, 237 (1990).

13. Coffey, R. S., Chem. Commun. 923 (1967).

14. Strohmeier, W. and Steigerwald, H., J. Organomet. Chem. 129, C43 (1977).

15. Yang, K. J. and Chin, C. S., Inorg. Chem. 26, 2732 (1987).

16. Chin, C. S.; Shin, J. H.; Kim, J. B., J. Organomet. Chem. 356, 381 (1988).

17. Trocha-Grimshaw, J. and Henbest, H. B., Chem. Commun. 544 (1967).

18. James, B. R. and Morris, R. H., J. Chem. Soc. Chem. Commun. 929 (1978).

19. Spogliarich, R.; Mestroni, G.; Graziani, M., J. Mol. Catal. 22, 309 (1984)s.

20. Farnetti, E.; Vinzi, F.; Mestroni, G., J. Mol. Catal. 24, 147 (1984).

21. Mann, B. E.; Masters, C.; Shaw, B. L., J. Inorg. Nucl. Chem. 33, 2195 (1971).

22. Crabtree, R. H.; Felkin, H.; Morris, G. E., J. Organomet. Chem. 141, 205 (1977).

23. Farnetti, E.; Kaspar, J.; Spogliarich, R.; Graziani, M., J. Chem. Soc. Dalton Trans. 947 (1988).

24. Tolman, C. A., Chem. Rev. 77, 313 (1977).

25. Haines, L. M. and Singleton, E., J. Chem. Soc. Dalton Trans. 1891 (1972).

26. Farnetti, E.; Pesce, M.; Kaspar, J.; Spogliarich, R.; Graziani, M., J. Chem. Soc. Chem. Commun. 746 (1986).

27. Rauchfuss, T. B. and Roundhill, D. M., J. Amer. Chem. Soc. 96, 3098 (1974).

28. Farnetti, E.; Nardin, G.; Graziani, M., J. Organomet. Chem. 000 (1991).

CONTROL FACTORS FOR SELECTIVE HOMOGENEOUS CATALYSIS

John M. Brown, Joseph V. Carey, Alistair D.Conn, Guy C. Lloyd-Jones and Simon C.Woodward.

(Dyson Perrins Laboratory, South Parks Rd. OXFORD OX1 3QY)

Homogeneous catalysis by transition-metal complexes is a mature branch of chemistry Since the first effective examples are well over thirty years old, it may be useful to examine one of the most successful examples from early work so that the basic principles can be better understood. Since this lecture will mainly be concerned with the application of homogeneous catalysis to olefins by reductive addition of hydrogen, or related procedures, it may be useful to consider the reaction pathway taken in hydrogenation with Wilkinson's catalyst.

Reaction proceeds through dissociation of one phosphine ligand and association of first dihydrogen and then the olefin. There is a critical step which involves the migration of one hydride to the double bond and formation of a rhodium alkylhydride. This then undergoes fast elimination to produce the product and regenerate the 14ε catalyst species. The set of reactions illustrated here forms the basis for much of homogeneous catalysis.

Consider now how catalysis along these lines might be controlled to give selective chemistry. What do we mean by selectivity in this context? In terms of the product formed, this can be manifested as **chemoselectivity** whereby one functional group reacts in preference to another (e.g. in the reduction of one double bond in a polyunsaturated molecule or of the C-C double bond in an unsaturated carbonyl compound). Alternatively it may be seen as **regioselectivity** which leads for example to the controlled addition of H-X to an unsymmetrical double bond or to reaction at one terminus of an allylic system. For organic synthesis the most important aspect is **stereoselectivity**, and this may be further divided as shown below. With a prochiral reactant the product is chiral, and if one hand of product is formed selectively then the reaction shows **enantioselectivity**. If the reactant is itself chiral and the existing asymmetry is in proximity to the reaction centre, then the new asymmetric centre may be formed as a result of **diastereoselectivity**.

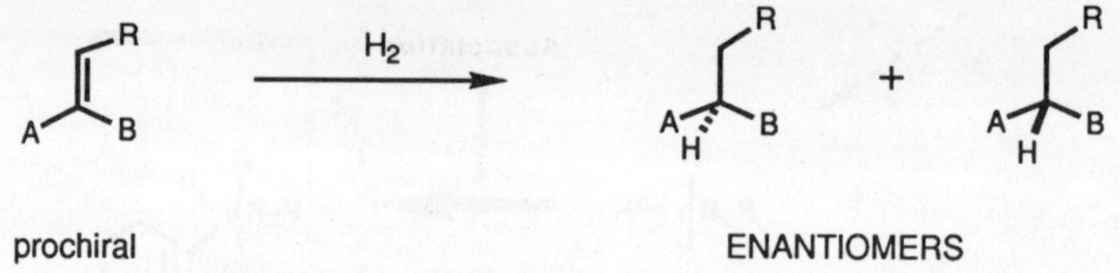

prochiral   ENANTIOMERS

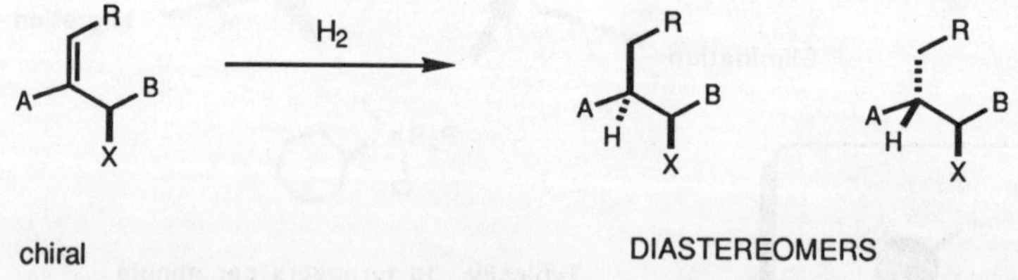

chiral   DIASTEREOMERS

At this point it is convenient to introduce the concept of **control elements** - the selectivity of the reaction procedure is dependent on a flow of information from the catalyst to the substrate and reagent so that there can be discrimination between possible reaction pathways. It will be apparent that the structure and stereochemistry of ligands attached to the catalytic metal is a critical factor. We can imagine several ways in which this selectivity can be brought about.

The simplest control element is *ligand-metal binding;* the combined bulk of the ligand-metal assembly and substrate operates to exclude alternatives so that one reaction path is specifically favoured. It is uncommon for this to be effective when operating in the absence of other control elements. This readily explains why stereoselective hydroformylation of simple prochiral olefins is rarely enantioselective when the hydrogenation of function-bearing olefins can be highly enantioselective. A second, and more generally effective control element is therefore *reactant-metal binding* secondary to the main coordination site. The prime illustration of this, for which the reaction mechanism is well understood, is asymmetric hydrogenation of dehydroaminoacids by rhodium complexes. In this reaction the amide group of the reactant is bound to rhodium throughout the catalytic cycle and plays a central role in the overall recognition process.

Under turnover conditions ca. 90% of Rh⁺ is present as major enamide.

The hydrogenation of the less-favoured species is ca. 500 x faster leading to 95 E.e.

In the catalytic cycle the less stable enamide complex reacts more rapidly with hydrogen, probably because of steric effects which operate between the ligand and bound reactant as the coordination geometry changes to accommodate the developing Rh-H bonds. The

302

dihydride formed is not observable even at low temperatures and the first intermediate to be characterised is an alkylhydride complex which itself decomposes to product at -40⁰C. Coordination of the amide carbonyl group is critical for high reactivity and selectivity since it limits the degrees of freedom of the system as reaction proceeds[1].

A third control element which can be envisaged is *reactant-ligand binding*; the potential of this has not been realised and only scattered examples exist at present. The most systematic attempts to exploit such interactions stem from the work of Hayashi and colleagues and their gold catalysed isonitrile aldol condensations provide the most striking example to date [2]. Whilst the detailed mechanism (and therefore the precise mode of involvement of the function-bearing ferrocene ligand) are not settled the main features seem clear. The biphosphine-gold unit acts as a template for binding the isonitrile and the protonated tertiary amine side chain acts as a electrophile towards the aldehyde which will develop negative charge on carbonyl oxygen as the reaction proceeds. A tentative description of the transition-state region is shown below.

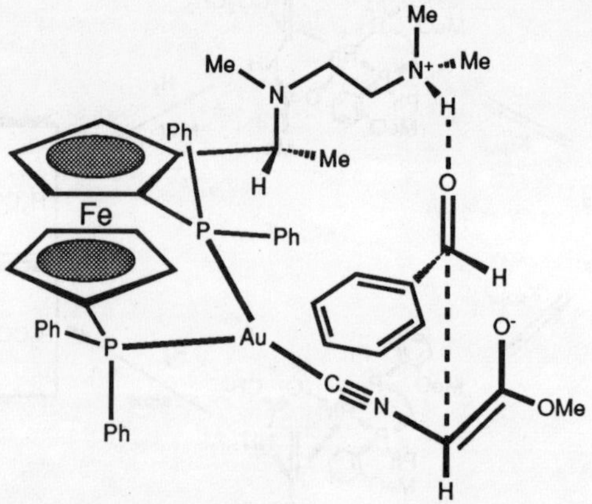

DIRECTED HYDROGENATION

Having demonstrated these basic principles of selecive homogeneous catalysis, the remainder of the lecture will be devoted to applications from our own current work. Firstly, the notion of *reactant-metal binding* as a control element control can lead to diastereoselectivity in hydrogenation and further to kinetic resolution when a homochiral catalyst and racemic reactant are used [3]. These ideas may be illustrated with reference to alkylitaconate reduction as indicated.

DIASTEREOSELECTIVITY

KINETIC RESOLUTION

Catalyst A   Catalyst B

In the first reaction the anti-isomer of catalyst is formed with a preference of 100:1 or greater for simple alkyl groups as substituent X and 50:1 when X=OMe. With an optically active catalyst as in **B** the R-enantiomer of racemic reactant is reduced 10-15 times faster than the S-enantiomer so that the overall process leads to accumulation of the less reactive hand in a kinetic resolution; at 65% reaction the starting material is essentially optically pure. A combination of these two procedures leads to optically pure 2,3-dialkyl succinates. It seems clear by analogy with the asymmetric hydrogenation of enamides that binding of the carbonyl of the ester at the chiral centre is essential for the success of these processes, and indeed it can be replaced by an amide or alcohol without compromising the effectiveness of the procedure.

What about the detailed mechanism by which these processes take place? The diastereoselective hydrogenation leading to the anti-isomer implies that one chiral face of the olefin is bound selectively and that cis-addition of hydrogen from the metal controls the outcome. It is likely that this discrimination is steric in origin and results from a clash between the alkyl group at the chiral centre and the in-plane ester group bound to the olefin. If we carry out molecular mechanics calculations at MM2 level on the alternative conformations of the reactant which can coordinate through the ester and olefin then the favoured form (left-hand side of figure) is about 2.5 Kcalsmole-1 more stable than the disfavoured form (right-hand side of figure). Furthermore the X-ray crystal structure of an iridium complex of a chiral olefin, closely related to the methylitaconate reactant is in this diastereomeric form. Since in many cases the discrimination between syn- and anti-products is better than 99% the energy difference is quite substantial. Even with homoallylic reactants, selectivity of 10:1 or better can be obtained[4].

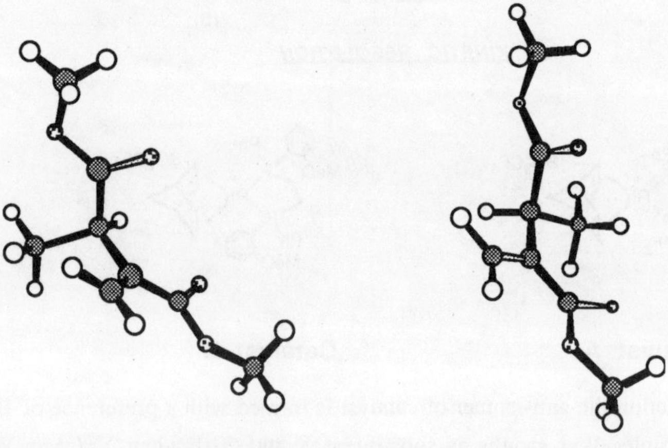

Further mechanistic information is revealed by a detailed study of the reaction kinetics, using the catalyst Rh+DIPAMP and the itaconate described above. Reaction is conveniently carried out in methanol solution at 0^0C. Catalytic kinetic resolution was used to prepare both hands of the reactant in optically pure form and as expected they were hydrogenated at vastly different rates, with the R-enantiomer the more reactive. Some care was needed to correct for the diffusion of hydrogen from the gas-phase into solution and at high catalyst concentration this could be the limiting step. The shape of a plot of hydrogen uptake against time was very revealing, since it provided information both on the rate of addition to the reactive rhodium complex and the binding constant for coordination of the substrate to rhodium. Plots for the two enantiomers are shown below, together with the simulated curve provided by analysis using the GEAR routine. It is clear that the slow-reacting enantiomer binds much more strongly to rhodium, and that the true difference in reaction rate is quite striking, around 100:1. This is much greater than the discrimination shown in the kinetic resolution experiment which was around 10:1.

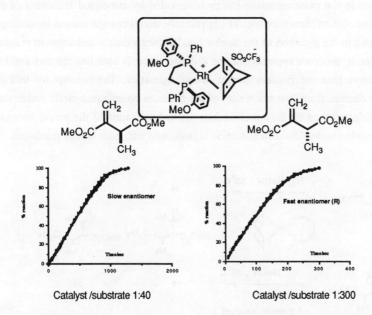

Catalyst /substrate 1:40   Catalyst /substrate 1:300

The real test of this analysis is whether the course of racemate hydrogenation with chiral catalyst can be predicted. In fact the experiment shows that reaction occurs with a highly biphasic uptake of H₂, corresponding to reduction first of one enantiomer, then the other.

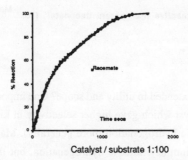

Catalyst / substrate 1:100

This set of results demonstrates that the two-step mechanism involving first binding of the reactant to a solvate complex and then addition of hydrogen proceeds in the case of

306

directed hydrogenation / kinetic resolution. Further, the kinetic resolution is a simple competition between the two hands of racemic reactant for the chiral catalyst.

A limitation in the existing methodology is revealed by attempted reduction of the trisubstituted olefins shown below. The apparently trivial change caused by adding a methyl-group to the β-carbon of the double bond causes a drastic reduction in reaction rate. Further, it becomes apparent that the Z-diastereomer is both less reactive and less stereoselective than the E-diastereomer in hydrogenation. The reasons for this are apparently derived from low reactivity of the rhodium-coordinated olefin rather than weak binding, because the E-isomer inhibits the hydrogenation of the parent itaconate when present in excess. The slow reduction is associated with poor kinetic resolution.

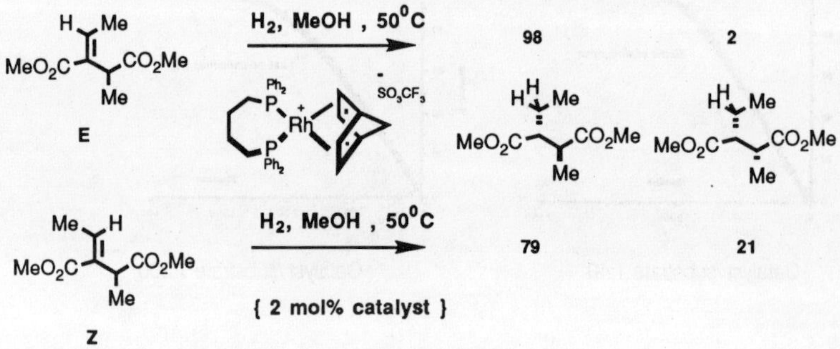

Z Isomer is ca 3 times less reactive than E Isomer - but Inhibits its reduction.

E Isomer is 10^2-10^3 less reactive than parent Itaconate!

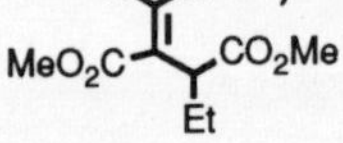

LIGAND SYNTHESIS

How can the reaction be extended in utility and scope? One important development would be a hydrogenation catalyst which gave higher selectivity in kinetic resolution (and by implication in asymmetric hydrogenation more generally). Many types of ligand have been employed for rhodium asymmetric hydrogenation, but the P-chiral biphosphine DIPAMP is unique in that the chiral centres are at phosphorus rather than in the ligand backbone. To develop this general area, new methodology is required.

We chose first to exploit the chemistry of ephedrine derivatives of phosphorus (V) which were first studied in detail by Inch and then further by Jugé [5]. Previous attempts to carry out a nucleophilic ring opening on cyclic oxazaphospholidines were unpromising but in the present case the reaction proceeded smoothly with o-methoxyphenyl and other arylmagnesium halides, occurring with retention of configuration, as shown. The sequence then followed literature precedent in cleavage of the remaining P-N bond to give the required triarylphosphine oxide. Firstly, the acid-catalysed replacement of the ephedrinium group by methoxyl, known to occur with inversion of configuration gives a species with a better leaving group. This enables the final displacement to be carried out using an arylmagnesium halide or aryllithium-TMEDA complex under mild conditions and again this occurs with inversion of configuration. Note that this represents a synthesis of a stereochemically pure (94% e.e.) triarylphosphine from $PhPCl_2$, since the stereospecific reduction of P=O (with inversion of configuration) has already been demonstrated [6].

Two further refinements have been achieved. In the first, biphosphines carrying a single chiral centre are made available through a parallel sequence involving vinylmagnesium bromide addition to the oxazaphospholidine. The corresponding methoxy vinylphosphonite was prepared as before in acidic methanol. The required step which converts this intermediate into a biphosphine precursor is $AlMe_3$-promoted Michael addition of $Ph_2P=O$ to the double bond. This procedure occurs smoothly and at room temperature to give the desired adduct free from side-products. All that is then required to give a <u>bis</u>-(diarylphosphino)-ethane with one chiral and one achiral phosphorus is that a single nucleophilic displacement (e.g. with aryllithium-TMEDA) is effected followed by the conventional phosphine oxide reduction.

92 % this diastereomer needs recrystallising

MeOH
HCl, 0°C

95% e.e

98 %e.e.

A second development involves the use of stereochemically pure chloro - oxazaphospholidine and permits the synthesis of chiral triarylphosphines from PCl₃ by three sequential stereoselective nucleophilic displacements. As expected the first stage occurs with retention of configuration and specific replacement of chloride, without ring-opening. The initial product is subject to oxidation by t-BuOOH and from then on the methodology is as described earlier. This widens the range of aryl (or other) substitutents which can be utilised, as all three steps introduce a separate entity. This basic methodology is now being applied to the synthesis of more ambitious targets, and to the development of ligands which fulfil the conditions for *ligand-reactant binding*, the third control factor described earlier. The approach through displacements at P=O complements that of Genet and Jugé, who have utilised phosphineborane displacement chemistry in a new synthesis of the ligand DIPAMP [7], following Imamoto's application of the enhanced C-H acidity of a P-methyl group adjacent to boron in synthesis of symmetrical chiral biphosphines [8].

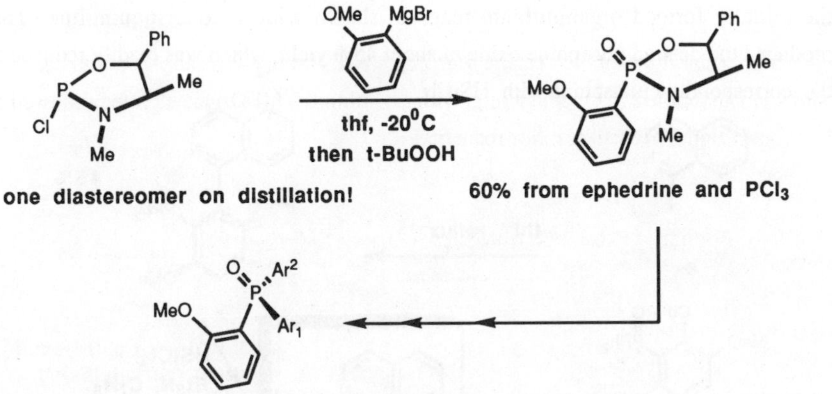

OMe MgBr

Ph

Me

Cl

P

O

N

Me

thf, -20°C
then t-BuOOH

one diastereomer on distillation!

Ph

Me

Me

O

P

O

N

MeO

60% from ephedrine and PCl₃

O

P

Ar²

Ar₁

MeO

A further requirement in the development of homochiral ligand synthesis has been the need to develop good functionalisation reactions of arylphosphine oxides. Our specific target here has been the preparation of a chiral (phosphinoaryl)isoquinoline for asymmetric cross-coupling studies, since the best ligands for this procedure are chelating aminophosphines. The desired parent compound has been synthesised by the route shown below. The critical part of this synthesis is the metallation of a ring C-H adjacent to phosphorus in the form of a arylphosphine oxide, The ortho-methoxy group must play a crucial role in this, since the parent lithio-comopund is rather unstable. In fact, examples of ortho-metallation of arylphosphine oxides are rather rare because the electron-withdrawing P=O group activates the ring towards undesired competing nucleophilic attack by the metallating agent.

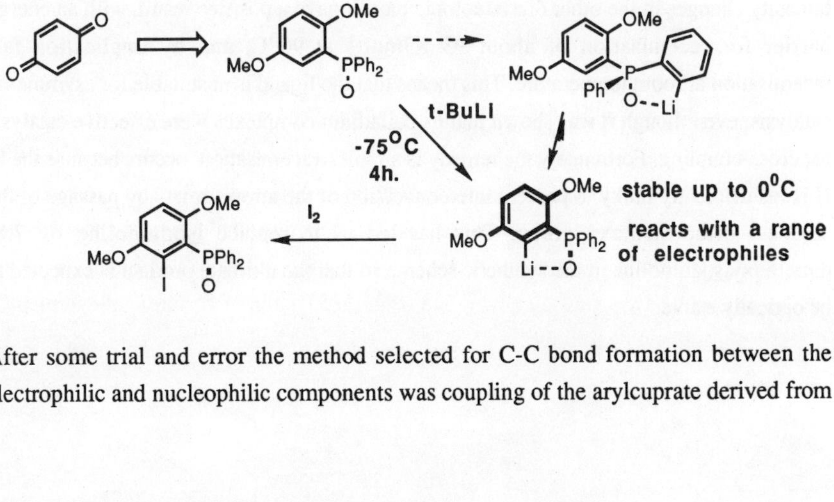

O

O

OMe

MeO

PPh₂

O

t-BuLI
-75°C
4h.

OMe

MeO

Ph

P

O--Li

stable up to 0°C

reacts with a range
of electrophiles

OMe

MeO

PPh₂

Li--O

I₂

OMe

MeO

PPh₂

I

O

After some trial and error the method selected for C-C bond formation between the electrophilic and nucleophilic components was coupling of the arylcuprate derived from the initially formed organolithium reagent shown with 1-iodoisoquinoline. This produced the desired phosphine oxide in about 45% yield, which was readily reduced to the corresponding phosphine with HSiCl₃.

Resolution was attempted according to a standard method utilising the PdCl₂ complex of R-phenylethylamine. It was discovered that the two diastereomers readily interconverted in solution with a half-life of around a day - rendering the approach unsuitable for asymmetric catalysis, which obviously requires optically stable ligands. Further investigation of the parent phosphinoisoquinoline using NMR spin-saturation transfer techniques showed that the two enantiomers interconverted rapidly at 90°C. The experiment involves irradiation of one diastereotopic pair of m-aryl protons and seeing intensity changes in the other diastereotopic pair. It gave a positive result, with an energy barrier for recemisation of about 93 KJmol⁻¹ at 90°C, and by implication fast racemisation at room temperature. This means that the ligand is unsuitable for asymmetric catalysis, even though it was shown that its palladium complexes were effective catalysts for cross-coupling. Fortunately the remedy is simple; racemisation occurs because the 8-H is insufficiently bulky to prevent interconversion of the atropisomers by passage of the adjacent ortho-methoxy group. This has led us to replace isoquinoline by 7,8-dimethoxyisoquinoline in the synthetic scheme,so that the ultimate product is expected to be optically stable.

Palladium complex crystallises as 1:1 mixture

Acetone solution slowly epimerises

Fast $\langle\!\!\!\!\begin{array}{c}\\ N\end{array}\!\!\!\!-Pd$ **dissociation ?**

CATALYTIC HYDROBORATION

The hydroboration of olefins is one of the best established reactions in organic synthesis, and its regiochemistry can be controlled by the use of bulky secondary boranes such as the bicyclic 9-BBN. In addition, chiral boranes such as the α-pinene derived di-(isopino)-camphenylborane can provide substantial enantioselectivity. Heteroatom-substituted boranes such as catecholborane are much less reactive towards olefins. The discovery was made by Mannig and Noth in 1985 that addition of catecholborane to terminal olefins is efficiently catalysed by rhodium complexes such as ClRh(PPh$_3$)$_3$ and the chemoselectivity is altered; non-conjugated unsaturated ketones, where the carbonyl group is preferentially reduced by catecholborane alone, experience a switch to double bond addition when the rhodium catalyst is present [9]. Subsequent workers have demonstrated that the reaction can be diastereoselective, e.g. with chiral allylic alcohols, and in addition a repertoire of asymmetric syntheses has been established through the work of Burgess, Suzuki and Hayashi [10]. In all of these reactions the borane is delivered in the form of catecholborane, and pessimistic comments have been made about the potential of other hydroborating agents. The catalysed reaction offers the opportunity for another type of control element, namely *reagent-metal control,* which would be particularly useful if it were possible systematically to alter the reagent structure. This may be illustrated in terms of a putative mechanism for the catalytic reaction with the substituent groups on boron able to influence the selectivity of the addition step.

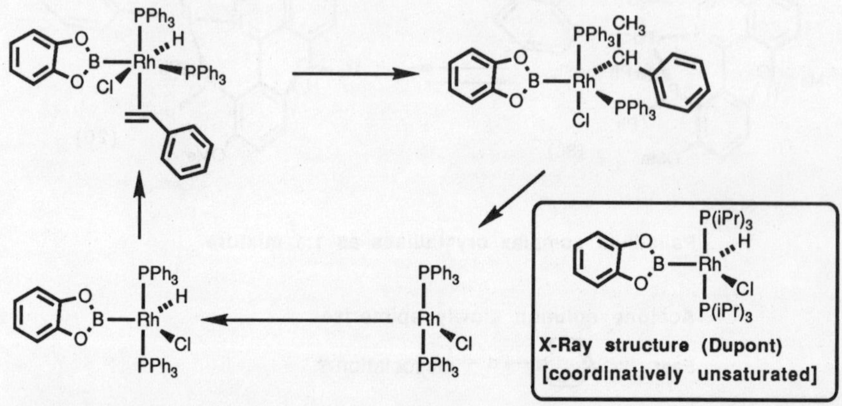

We were attracted to the idea that cyclic boranes derived from aminoalcohols had a structure sufficiently similar to catecholborane that they might react with olefins under rhodium catalysis, and first prepared the known [11] derivatives from ephedrine and pseudoephedrine. For pseudoephedrine the reaction proceeds in two stages, first formation of a B-O bond at ambient temperature and then the elimination of a second molecule of hydrogen at 100⁰C. On standing the reagent initially formed gives rise to a dimer or oligomer for which the structure shown is at least consistent with the B[11] NMR.

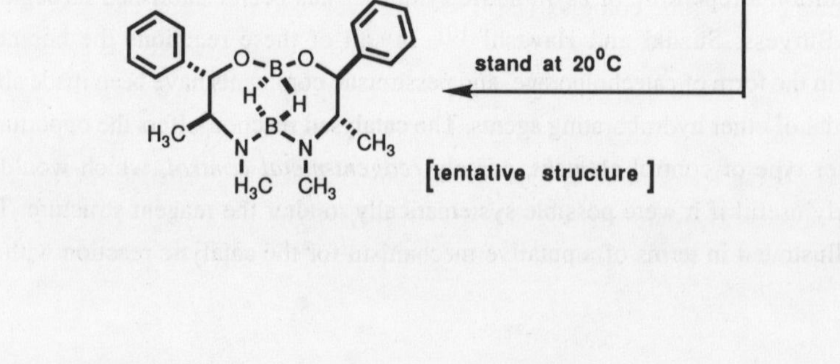

The first-formed reagent undergoes a catalytic reaction with olefins in the presence of $ClRh(PPh_3)_3$ but the only product is that of hydrogenation; isomerisation can be a competing side-reaction. It is not known at present whether this is a true transfer hydrogenation or whether the borane decomposes in the reaction medium, and further work is required to address this point.

In contrast to this, the secondary oxazaborolidine reacts as a catalytic hydroborating agent, turning over p-methoxystyrene over a few hours at room temperature in the presence of 1 mol % of various rhodium catalysts. It was naturally of interest to determine whether the chiral reagent influenced the stereochemical course of reaction. With Wilkinson's catalyst or $HRh(PPh_3)_4$, the ephedrine-based reagent gave 17% e.e. and the pseudoephedrine-based reagent 56% e.e., with some regioselectivity towards the chiral secondary alcohol after oxidation, which provided a very encouraging beginning. Clearly the chirality of the ephedrine backbone is influencing the reaction at the point when the stereochemistry is set through H-transfer to the prochiral olefin. The utilisation of a chelating biphosphine complex (BUTAPHOS) caused interesting changes in the reaction course. Now the regioselectivity towards is very high towards the secondary product, but the enantioselectivity is low irrespective of whether the ephedrine or pseudoephedrine borane reagent is used. This implies that the chelate is undesirably flexible, and a better result could be obtained with a more rigid biphosphine chelate. The best result obtained to date realises this idea by using the Rh complex of 1,1'-bis-

(diphenylphosphino)ferrocene and pseudoephedrine when regioselectivity in excess of 80% and enantioselectivity of 78% is observed in a fast catalytic reaction [12].

58% A; 56R   96% A; 6S   82% A; 78R

The final experiment to be described involves double asymmetric induction using the two enantiomeric rhodium complexes of BINAP. Only one hand was effective with 1S,2S - pseudoephedrine-derived borane, and that same hand was the only one effective with 1S,2R-ephedrine. Optical yields of up to 90% of the derived secondary alcohol were obtained but there was an absence of regiochemical control, limiting the synthetic utility of the reaction. Notably, the stereochemical course taken is opposite to that observed with catecholborane and the same catalyst. These results throw up many challenges for ultimate synthetic improvement, but for the moment it is worth noting that catalytic hydroboration provides an example of the combined effects of control by *ligand-metal binding* and *reagent-metal binding* to give promising results with a non-functional prochiral olefin.

The three enantioselective catalytic hydroborations (corrected to S-BINAP stereochemistry for consistency)

	94	6 [-78°C]
	7	93
	8	92

REFERENCES

1] Brown, J.M., Chaloner, P.A., and Morris, G.A., J.Chem. Soc. Perkin 2, 1583, (1987); Halpern, J. and Landis, C.R., J.Am. Chem. Soc. 109, 1746, (1987).

2] Ito, Y., Sawamura, M., and Hayashi, T. J.Am. Chem. Soc., 108, 6405, (1986) ; Togni, A. and Pastor, S.D., J. Org. Chem., 55, 1649, (1990).

3] Brown, J.M., Angew.Chem.Int.Ed.Engl., 26, 190,(1987);Brown, J.M., Cutting, I. and James, A.P. Bull.Soc.Chim.France 211, (1988); Brown, J.M., Evans, P.L. and James, A.P., Organic Syntheses, 68, 64, (1989)

4] Birtwistle, D.H., Brown, J.M., Herbert, R.H., James, A.P.,Lee, K.F., and Taylor, R.J. J.Chem.Soc.Chem.Commun., 1989, 194..

5] Cooper, D.B., Inch, T.D., and Lewis, G.J. J.Chem.Soc.Perkin 1 , 1043 , (1974); Hall, C.R. and Inch, T.D. J.Chem.Soc.Perkin 1, ,2368, (1981); idem, ibid, 1104, (1979); idem, ibid, 1646, (1979); Cooper,D.B., Hall, C.R. Harrison, J.M.and Inch, T.D. ibid, 1969 (1977). Hall,C.R., Inch, T.D. and Lawston, I.W. Tetrahedron Lett. 20, 2729 (1979); Juge, S. and Genet, J.P. Tetrahedron Lett.,30, 2783, (1989) and patents referred to therein.

6] Korpiun, O., Lewis, R.A., Chickos, J. and Mislow, K. J.Am.Chem.Soc. ,90, 4842,(1968) ;.Lewis, R.A. and Mislow, K.ibid, 91,7009, (1969);Naumann,K., Zon, G. and Mislow, K. ibid, 91,7012, (1969),

7] Brown, J.M., Carey, J.V. and Russell, M.J.H., Tetrahedron 46, 4877, (1990); Juge, S., Stephan,M., Laffitte, J.A. and Genet, J.P., Tetrahedron Lett. 31, 6357, (1990).

8] Imamoto, T.,.Kosumoto, T., Suzuki, N. and Sato, K. J.Am.Chem.Soc. ,107, 5301, (1985); Imamoto,T., Oshiki, T., Onozawa, T., Kusumoto,T. and Sato, K. J. Am. Chem. Soc. 112, 5244, (1990).

9] Mannig, D. and Noth,H. Angew. Chem. Int. Ed. Engl. 24, 878 , (1985); Evans, D.A., Fu, G.C. and Hoveyda, A.H. J. Am. Chem. Soc. 110, 6917, (1988) ; Evans, D.A. and Fu, G.C., J. Org. Chem. 55, 2280, (1990).

10] Burgess, K. and Ohlmeyer, M.J. J. Org. Chem. 53 , 5178, (1988); Hayashi, T, Matsumoto, Y. and Ito, Y. J. Am. Chem. Soc. 111, 3426, (1989). Satoh, M., Nomoto, Y. Miyaura, N. and Suzuki, A. Tetrahedron Lett. 30, 3789, (1989)

11] Joshi,N.N., Srebnik, M. and Brown,H.C.,Tetrahedron Lett. , 30, 5551, (1989).

12] Brown, J.M. and Lloyd-Jones, G.C., Tetrahedron Asymmetry, 1, in press (1990)

ENANTIOSELECTIVE CATALYSIS BY CHIRAL SOLIDS

HANS-ULRICH BLASER

Central Research Services, CIBA-GEIGY AG, R 1055.607, CH-4002 BASEL

ABSTRACT

The influence of system parameters and mechanistic investigations are reviewed for several heterogeneous enantioselective catalyst systems. Conclusions concerning the possibilities of catalyst design are presented.

INTRODUCTION / SCOPE

Enantioselective synthesis is a topic of undisputable importance in current chemical research and there is a steady flow of articles, reviews and books on almost every aspect involved. This overview will concentrate on structure-activity relationships found for solid chiral catalysts and will discuss the possibilities for catalyst design. Excluded are studies on modified electrochemical systems and on immobilized versions of active homogeneous complexes or of bio-catalysts. A more general review that covers historical and synthetic aspects of heterogeneous enantioselective catalysis has been published recently[1].

First, a few fundamental concepts and definitions should be explained. A molecule is chiral if its image and mirror-image are not superimposable and therefore enantiomeric. A reaction or a catalyst is called enantioselective (or asymmetric or enantio-face-differentiating[2]) if one of the enantiomers is produced preferentially starting from non-chiral substrates. If a reaction occurs faster with one enantiomer of a racemic substrate we speak of kinetic resolution (or enantiomer-differentiation[2]). Enantioselectivity (or enantiomeric excess (ee) or optical yield) is only possible if a chiral agent is present during the reaction and interacts with the substrates in the product-determining step. It is a kinetic phenomenon, due to the difference in activation energy between the diastereomeric transition states leading to the two enantiomers (distinguished by the prefix R and S or d and l). The enantioselectivity is defined as ee (%) = 100 x ([R]-[S]] / ([R]+[S]). At 25 °C, an energy difference of 1.5 kcal/mol and 3 kcal/mol leads to about 80% (90 : 10) and 98% (99 : 1) enantiomeric excess, respectively. The observed ee will be below the <u>inherent</u> catalyst selectivity if the racemic reaction occurs uncatalyzed or on non-chiral sites as well.

From this follows that an enantioselective catalyst has two functions: First, it has to perform what one could call the chemical catalysis, here named <u>activating function</u>. In addition, it has to control the stereochemical outcome of the reaction and we term this the <u>controlling function</u>. The two functions can be performed by the same or by two different agents. At least two extreme cases can be distinguished for inherently chiral or chirally modified <u>solid</u> catalysts: in the first case reactions are being catalyzed only at the <u>surface</u> of a "hard" solid (e.g. a metal), in the second case the reaction occurs <u>inside</u> a "soft" material (e.g. an organic polymer).

CATALYST DESIGN

Designing a catalyst for a given problem as opposed to finding or improving a catalyst empirically requires an exact knowledge of the relevant catalyst parameters, the ability to control these parameters and also some understanding of the mechanism of the reaction. This is a difficult task for any selective catalytic reaction but even more so for an enantioselective catalyst where the control of selectivity is very difficult to achieve. It is important to realize that we have to design not just a catalyst in the classical sense but rather a <u>catalytic system</u> where the activating and the controlling function are in perfect balance. In addition, the ratio between the modified (enantio-selective) catalytic sites and the unmodified (unselective) sites will be a crucial point.

This review will describe investigations where structure - selectivity (and activity) relationships have been elucidated systematically and where the reaction mechanism has been studied to some degree. Unfortunately, there is only a small number of cata-lytic systems where this has been done and in most cases the degree of understanding is still quite low. This means that the conclusions that we can draw from these studies will be rather limited.

The approach most often used in order to learn about the influence of system para-meters is the time honored method of "change one thing at a time and keep everything else constant". Accordingly, in most cases we will describe the influence of isolated parameters (e.g. catalyst morphology, modifier structure, reaction conditions, ad-sorption studies, kinetic experiments etc.) for a specific class of substrates. Sometimes, this can lead to wrong generalizations because the conclusions are quite often depen-dent on the choice of other parameters. Factorial design experiments with qualitative and/or quantitative parameters are often helpful.

There will be three sections organized according to catalyst systems:

a)   Hydrogenation reactions catalyzed by tartrate modified catalysts.

b)   Hydrogenation reactions catalyzed by cinchona modified catalysts.

c)   Epoxidation reactions catalyzed by polypeptides.

With the exception of some enantioselective electrochemical reactions[3], we are aware of no other enantioselective heterogeneous catalyst types where systematic investigations have been reported.

A) TARTRATE MODIFIED CATALYSTS.

This is by far the best studied family of catalysts and reactions. Since very good reviews[2,4-7] cover almost every aspect of these catalytic systems we will only give illustrative examples and will try to summarize the important conclusions.

Substrates

β-ketoesters, acetylacetone and methylketones are preferred substrates and optical yields >80% can be obtained in many cases[1,2,4]. Because most investigations described below have been carried out with methyl acetoacetate as substrate, the resulting conclusions can only be generalized with caution.

Reaction Conditions, Solvent and Additive Effects.

When comparing structure activity effects one has to be very careful that these are not due to external factors. The following ones have been described in the literature to influence activity and selectivity.

The solvent has a strong influence on the performance of the Ni catalysts. While little systematic information is available, it is clear that aprotic semipolar solvents, especially methyl propionate, give the highest ee's[2,4]. Additives can affect the reaction. The presence of weak acids often increases the ee's, especially pivalic acid for the hydrogenation of methyl ketones, while water is detrimental[2,4]. Temperatures between 60-100 °C and H_2 pressures between 80-120 bar give good results. No simple correlation has been found between ee and p or T[2,4]. The reaction can also be carried out in the gas phase but optical yields are lower[7].

Catalysts

Catalyst type. Raney nickel is the preferred catalyst for preparative purposes,

320

Ni-powder and supported Ni catalysts are also suitable[2,4]. Bimetallic and noble metal catalysts have been studied but with the exception of some NiPd/SiO$_2$ catalysts these give very low ee's[5,6].

Catalyst preparation. Freshly prepared Raney nickel gives the best results. For other Ni catalysts the preparation method has been shown to be very important[2,4].

Modifying conditions. Modifier concentration, pH, temperature, time and sometimes procedures are crucial for a good catalyst performance[2,4]. Co-modifiers are necessary for ee's >80%. NaBr is the most important co-modifier as it enhances the optical yields by 10-30%. Others have been studied[2,4].

Catalyst stability. Corrosion by acidic substrates is a serious problem, embedding the modified catalyst in a silicone polymer[2,9] or pre-treatment with an amine enhances the catalyst stability and repeated use is possible[10].

Catalyst structure. It is difficult to characterize and control structural features of Raney type catalysts, but other Ni catalysts have been investigated thoroughly. An additional problem is the corrosive nature of the modification step which probably changes the nature of the Ni surface very strongly. Nitta et al.[11-14] have demonstrated that the Ni dispersion has a decisive influence on the enantioselectivity but other factors (support, impurities, preparation procedure, modification procedure, reaction conditions etc.) can mask this correlation (see for example Fig. 1, 2a). The optimal Ni particle size was estimated to be 10-20 nm. Sachtler[15] on the other hand has shown that the ee's are not affected by the crystallite size if the Ni dispersion was changed by

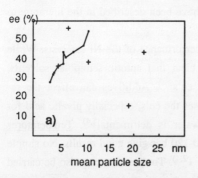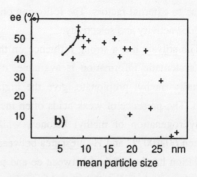

Fig. 1. Effect of the Ni particle size on the optical yield for the liquid phase hydrogenation of methyl acetoacetate. a) 50% Ni/SiO$_2$ catalysts, same method of preparation. (——) Wakogel supports, (+) supports of different suppliers. b) (——) Ni/SiO$_2$ catalysts with different Ni content, (+) Ni catalysts on different supports[11].

Ostwald ripening (see Fig. 2b). As a conclusion, there does not seem to exist a generally valid correlation between the enantioselectivity of a tartrate modified Ni catalyst and any single catalyst parameter[2,4,5].

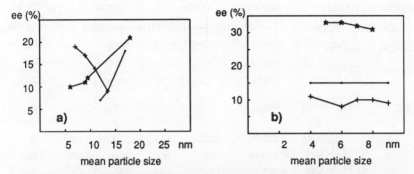

Fig. 2. Effect of the Ni particle size on the optical yield for the hydrogenation of methyl acetoacetate. a) Ni/SiO$_2$, liquid phase hydrogenation. (—+—) 7.5% Ni/SiO$_2$ with variable S$_{BET}$, reaction control, (—*—) 7.5% Ni/SiO$_2$ with variable S$_{BET}$, diffusion control,(—.—) 4-11% Ni, wide pore support, reaction control[13]. b) Ni/SiO$_2$, particle size changed by sintering. (—.—) 6% Ni, gas phase hydrogenation, (—+—) 9% Ni, gas phase hydrogenation,(—*—) 10% Ni, liquid phase hydrogenation[15].

Modifier

Modifier structure. Tartaric acid is clearly superior to α-amino acids or other α-hydroxy acids[2,4] as a modifier for Ni catalysts. Fig. 3 shows that the influence of

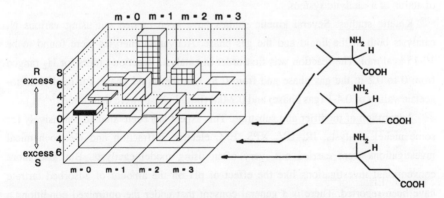

Fig. 3. Effect of the modifier structure on the optical yield for the hydrogenation of various ketoesters CH$_3$-CO-(CH$_2$)$_m$-COOMe (m = 0, 1, 2 and 3) on Raney Ni modified with three different (S)-amino acids[17].

modifier structure can be quite different for even slightly different substrates. Fig. 4 shows representative examples which indicate that even small structural changes can affect the enantioselectivity for the hydrogenation of methyl acetoacetate very strongly.

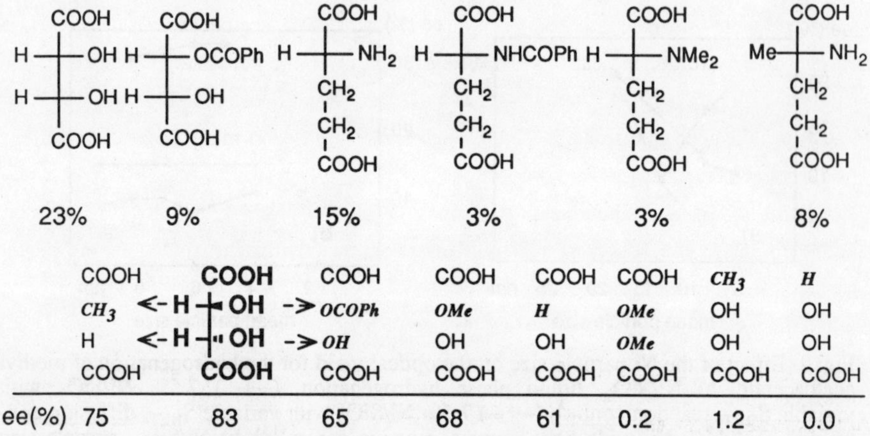

$$
\begin{array}{cccccc}
\text{COOH} & \text{COOH} & \text{COOH} & \text{COOH} & \text{COOH} & \text{COOH} \\
\text{H}\!-\!\text{OH} & \text{H}\!-\!\text{OCOPh} & \text{H}\!-\!\text{NH}_2 & \text{H}\!-\!\text{NHCOPh} & \text{H}\!-\!\text{NMe}_2 & \text{Me}\!-\!\text{NH}_2 \\
\text{H}\!-\!\text{OH} & \text{H}\!-\!\text{OH} & \text{CH}_2 & \text{CH}_2 & \text{CH}_2 & \text{CH}_2 \\
\text{COOH} & \text{COOH} & \text{CH}_2 & \text{CH}_2 & \text{CH}_2 & \text{CH}_2 \\
 & & \text{COOH} & \text{COOH} & \text{COOH} & \text{COOH} \\
\end{array}
$$

23%	9%	15%	3%	3%	8%

	COOH	**COOH**	COOH	COOH	COOH	COOH	CH_3	H
	CH_3 ←-H$-$OH ->$OCOPh$	OMe	H	OMe	OH	OH		
	H ←-H$-$"OH ->OH	OH	OH	OMe	OH	OH		
	COOH	**COOH**	COOH	COOH	COOH	COOH	COOH	COOH
ee(%)	75	83	65	68	61	0.2	1.2	0.0

Fig. 4. Effect of the modifier structure on the optical yield for the hydrogenation of methyl acetoacetate. a) Raney Ni (early results)[2]. b) Raney Ni/NaBr[16].

Mode of Action

In addition to knowledge on structural relationships, information on kinetic and adsorption aspects is needed in order to formulate a meaningful hypothesis on the mode of action of a catalytic system.

Kinetic studies. Several kinetic studies have been carried out using various Ni catalysts both in the liquid and the gas phase. Activation energies were found to be 10-15 kcal/mol. The reaction was first order in catalyst. Reaction orders for H_2 ranged from 0 to 0.2 in the gas phase and from 0 to 1 in the liquid phase, for methyl aceto-acetate values of 0.4-1 (gas phase) and 0.2-0.8 (liquid phase) were determined[2,4,7].

Adsorption of modifier and substrate. This aspect has been studied extensively for some nickel catalysts: IR, UV, XPS, EM, electron diffraction and electrochemical investigations were carried out, very often using model catalysts. But also more conventional investigations like the effect of pH on the amount of adsorbed tartrate have been reported. There is a general consent that under the optimized conditions a corrosive modification of the nickel surface occurs and that the tartrate molecule is chemically bound to Ni via the carboxyl groups. There is also agreement that during the hydrogenation (which is carried out in an organic solvent) the adsorbed tartrate does not leave the surface. But there are two different suggestions concerning the nature of the modified catalyst: Sachtler[7] proposes an adsorbed $[Ni_2 tartrate_2]_n$ complex; japanese[2,4] and russian[6] groups prefer a direct adsorption of the tartrate on the Ni surface. In the gas phase, it has been shown that methyl acetoacetate is adsorbed as enolate and there are indications that the adsorption of the substrate is stronger if the catalyst is modified[7].

Mechanistic conclusions. Based on these findings and on many other observations two mechanistic schemes were proposed:

Izumi's[2,4] and Klabunovskii's[6] groups favor a classical Langmuir-Hinshelwood approach where the adsorbed substrate reacts with activated hydrogen on the nickel surface in a stepwise fashion. The orientation of the β-ketoester adsorption is controlled via hydrogen bonding to the adsorbed tartrate (compare Fig. 5). There are results which suggest that the enantio-differentiation is determined in the adsorption step of the ketoester and not during the addition of hydrogen, but without structural evidence this is just a hypothesis. The important NaBr effect is explained as blocking of non-modifiable sites since the ratio of modified to non-modified sites determines the resulting optical yield[2,4,6].

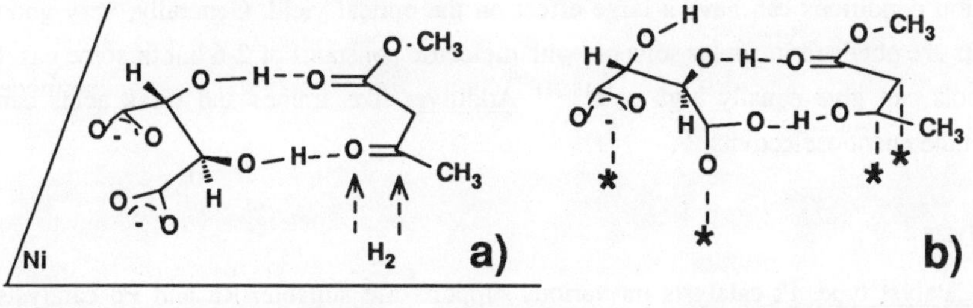

Fig. 5. Mode of interaction proposed for methyl acetate on tartrate modified Ni surfaces. a) Izumi's model, interaction of the keto form with the two hydroxy groups. b) Yasumori's model, interaction of the enol with one carboxy and one hydroxy group.

Sachtler[7] proposes a "dual site" mechanism where the hydrogen is dissociated on the Ni surface and then migrates to the substrate which is coordinated to the adsorbed nickel-tartrate complex. In this context it is of interest that the well known Sharpless epoxidation probably takes place on a dimeric tartrate complex of Ti. Sachtler suggests that both the anion and the cation have a function which varies according to the conditions used. It is not clear whether the spillover mechanism is also proposed for the reaction in solution.

B) CINCHONA MODIFIED CATALYSTS.

Substrates.

Preferred substrates are α-ketoesters which are hydrogenated with very good optical yields[1,18,19]. Most investigations have been carried out with the methyl or ethyl ester of pyruvic acid as substrate and the resulting conclusions should not be generalized.

Reaction Conditions, Solvent and Additive Effects.

As observed for tartrate modified Ni catalysts, optical yields of cinchona modified Pt catalysts too are strongly affected by external factors which can mask certain structure - selectivity relationships.

Reaction conditions. Temperatures between 20-50 °C and pressures >10 bar give good results. Usually higher pressures lead to slightly higher ee's and an increase in rate, while an increase of the temperature also leads to higher rates but to a decrease in selectivity. But exceptions have been reported as well[18,20]. Several systems have been studied concerning solvent effects. Quite small changes in substrate, modifier or reaction conditions can have a large effect on the optical yield. Generally, very good results are obtained in apolar solvents with dielectric constants of 2-6 but in some cases alcohols can give equally high ee's[18,21]. Additives like amines and weak acids can affect the enantioselectivity[19].

Catalysts

Catalyst type. Pt catalysts on various supports are suitable. Rh and Pd catalysts give moderate ee, Ru and Ni are not effective[1,18].

Catalyst preparation. Activity and selectivity of the cinchonidine modified Pt catalysts have been shown to depend primarily on the platinum salt used for impregnation and the reduction method. Support material and platinum content also influence the catalyst performance[19,22]. Commercial catalysts can be used[18,19].

Catalyst pretreatment. Already in their first reports Orito et al.[19] described the beneficial effects of preheating the catalyst in hydrogen at 300-400 °C, followed by soaking in a solution of the modifier. These findings were later confirmed in principle and refined[18,20]. The effect of the thermal pretreatment of Pt/Al_2O_3 has been studied. It has been found that Pt dispersion and Al_2O_3 texture are not affected but the degree of reduction and maybe the crystallinity of the Pt is improved[23].

Catalyst structure. By varying the preparation method (support material, platinum precursor, platinum loading and reduction procedure) it was possible to obtain a large series of Pt catalysts with platinum dispersions between < 0.05 and 0.78[22]. The enantioselectivity for the ethyl pyruvate hydrogenation increased with decreasing platinum dispersions, reaching 80% at dispersions ≤ 0.2. The activities of the different catalysts showed a similar trend. As can be seen in Fig. 6, a strong scattering of the resulting values is observed, indicating that the platinum dispersion is by no means the only important catalyst parameter. Other factors such as preparation method and texture of the support may affect the catalyst performance as well (for an example see Fig. 7).

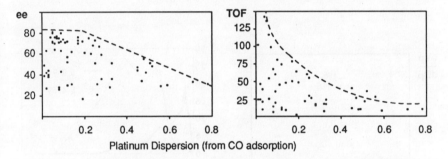

Fig. 6. Dependence of optical yield (ee, %) and turnover frequency (TOF, 1/s) on the platinum dispersion. Hydrogenation of ethyl pyruvate in ethanol in presence of cinchonidine using different Pt/Al_2O_3 catalysts[22].

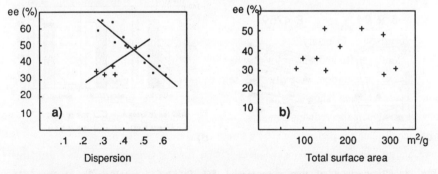

Fig. 7. Optical yields for the hydrogenation of ethyl pyruvate in ethanol in presence of cinchonidine using different Pt/Al_2O_3 catalysts. a) Dispersion changed by reduction temperature or redispersion (+) and by sintering (.)[21]. b) Pt catalysts on different aluminas[22].

326

Texture effects were investigated in more detail by comparing two well characterized commercial catalysts with platinum dispersions of 0.22 and 0.24[24]. Their textural properties and their catalytic performance for the hydrogenation of two different α-ketoesters are presented in Fig. 8. Catalyst E 4759 has rather small pores and a low pore volume while 5 R 94 is a wide-pore catalyst with a large pore volume (Fig. 8a). It was shown that the alumina particle size (Fig. 8b) does not affect the rate or optical yield[25]. In addition, HRTEM and XRD studies revealed that E 4759 consists of γ-alumina and has a well ordered, layered structure while 5 R 94 is a mixture of γ- and Θ-alumina where the alumina crystallites are of irregular shape with larger interstices (Fig 8c). The catalytic performance was tested under different conditions for two α-ketoesters. In every case catalyst 5 R 94 showed a consistently higher enantioselectivity and a 2-3 fold higher turnover frequency (Fig. 8d).

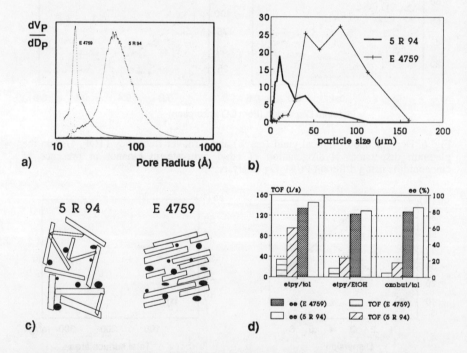

Fig. 8. Comparison of two commercial 5% Pt/Al₂O₃ catalysts[24]. a) Pore size distribution. b) Particle size distribution. c) Schematic representation of the alumina structure. d) ee and TOF for the hydrogenation of ethyl pyruvate and ethyl 4-phenyl-2-oxobutyrate.

Modifier

Modifier structure. In order to investigate the effect of modifier structure, two naturally occuring cinchona alkaloids were altered at various positions (see Figure 9) and then tested in the hydrogenation of ethyl pyruvate under standard conditions[24].

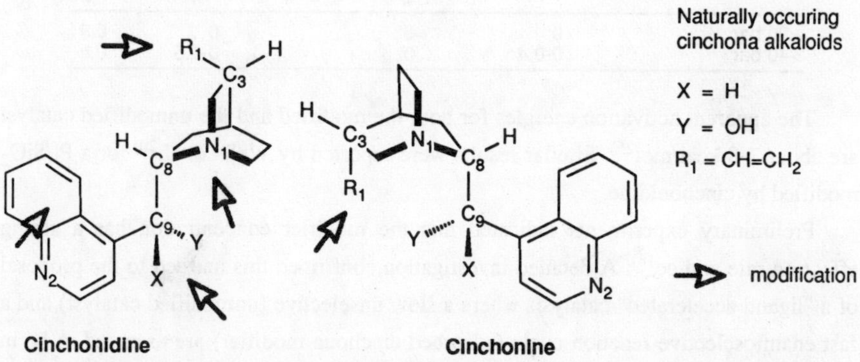

Naturally occuring
cinchona alkaloids

$X = H$
$Y = OH$
$R_1 = CH=CH_2$

Cinchonidine   Cinchonine

Fig. 9. Relative and absolute configuration of the diastereomeric cinchona alkaloid derivatives prepared[24].

The following points are noteworthy:
- Naturally occuring cinchona alkaloids give the best results.
- The absolute configuration at C_8 determines whether (S)- or (R)-methyl lactate is formed in excess.
- Changes at C_9 in most cases result in lower optical yields, but (R)-ethyl lactate is always formed in excess. In order to get very high optical yields the substituent Y at C_9 has to be either OH or OCH_3.
- If N_1 is alkylated, optical induction is lost completely.
- Hydrogenation of the quinoline nucleus leads to lower enantioselectivities.
- The nature of R_1 has little effect on the optical yield.

Modifier stability. Under the conditions used for preparative experiments, the optical yield remains constant up to complete conversion[26]. Later, it was found that some ring hydrogenation occurs under the reaction conditions and for experiments with low modifier concentrations the optical yield decreases with reaction time[20,27,28].

Mode of Action

Kinetic studies. In our laboratory a kinetic study is in progress with a Pt/Al_2O_3 catalyst, modified with 10,11-dihydrocinchonidine (HCd) using ethyl pyruvate (Etpy).

The reaction for the modified and the unmodified catalyst was found to be first order in the Pt/Al_2O_3 catalyst. Depending on H_2 pressure the following reaction orders were determined:

H_2 pressure	Unmodified Pt/Al_2O_3 Etpy	H_2	$Pt/Al_2O_3/HCd$ Etpy	H_2
<20 bar	0	>0	0	0.8
>40 bar	0-0.4	0	0-0.5	0.8

The apparent activation energies for both the modified and the unmodified catalyst are about 7-8 kcal/mol[25]. Similar results were reported by Wells et al.[20] for a Pt/SiO_2 modified by cinchonidine.

Preliminary experiments indicated that the modifier concentration has a strong effect on rate and ee[18]. A detailed investigation confirmed this and led to the proposal of a "ligand accelerated" catalysis where a slow unselective (unmodified catalyst) and a fast enantioselective reaction cycle (adsorbed cinchona modifier) are assumed to be in a dynamic equilibrium[28] (see Fig. 11).

Adsorption of modifier and substrate. For the Pt/cinchona catalysts preliminary adsorption studies have shown that the substrate and the modifier adsorb both on the metal and the carrier surface[18,20]. From the fact that in situ modification is possible and that under preparative conditions a constant optical yield is observed we conclude that in this case there is a dynamic equilibrium between cinchona molecules in solution and adsorbed modifier. This is supported by an interesting experiment by Margitfalvi[27]: When *cinchonine* is added to the reaction solution of ethyl pyruvate and a catalyst pre-modified with *cinchonidine*, the enantiomeric excess changes within a few minutes from (R)- to (S)-methyl lactate, suggesting that the cinchonidine has been replaced on the platinum surface by the excess cinchonine.

Mechanistic conclusions. The results concerning the influence of catalyst and modifier structure and of the kinetic and adsorption measurements summarized above make it possible to draw some conclusions concerning the mode of action of the modified catalyst.

We have postulated that an enantioselective active site is formed dynamically by adsorption of one cinchona molecule on well defined platinum ensembles[28]. The effect of particle size on rate and enantioselectivity indicates that not all surface platinum atoms are suited for this coordination. The observed influences of the structure of the modifier molecule on the performance of the modified catalyst make it possible to assign a specific function to the different parts of the cinchona modifier (see Fig. 12), but at the present time there is little information on the exact nature of the metal - substrate - modifier interaction.

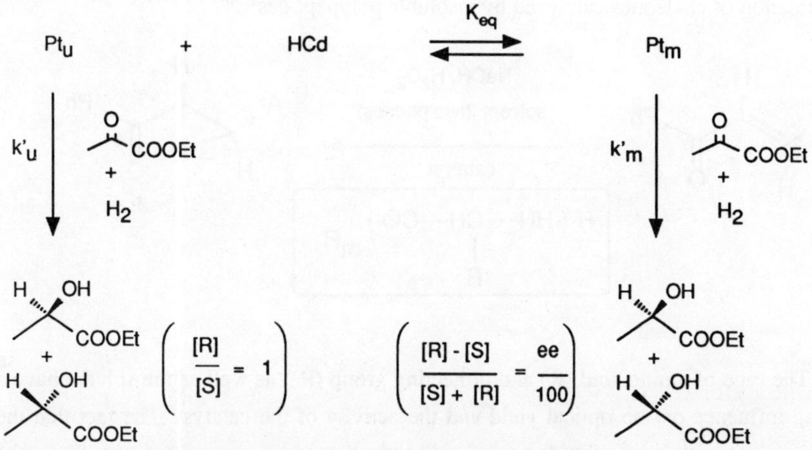

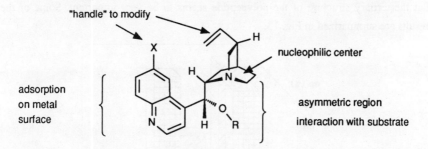

Fig. 11. Two cycle model for the enantioselective hydrogenation of α-ketoesters by cinchona modified Pt catalysts. If $k'_m > k'_u$ the reaction is called "ligand accelerated".

"handle" to modify

X

adsorption
on metal
surface

nucleophilic center

asymmetric region
interaction with substrate

Fig. 12. Possible functions of different parts of the cinchona molecule (see also Wynberg[31]).

Wells[20] and Thomas[29] have proposed that the cinchonidine molecules form an ordered array on the Pt surface which provides better access for hydrogen activation and controls the stereochemistry of the hydrogen addition. Margitfalvi[27] on the other hand explains the effect of the modifier by interactions in solution.

C) EPOXIDATION REACTIONS CATALYZED BY POLYPEPTIDES.

As mentioned in the introduction, chiral polymers can be used in order to control the stereochemical outcome of a reaction. While several attempts have been described to use this strategy only one system has been investigated in greater detail: the epoxidation of chalcones catalyzed by insoluble polypeptides[1,30].

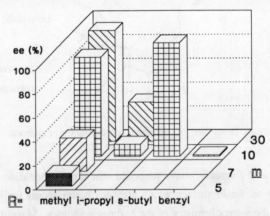

The type of amino acid (R) and protecting group (R') as well as the solvent have a strong influence on the optical yield and the activity of the catalyst. The fact that the ee's increase with increasing degree of polimerization (m) suggests that very likely the reaction occurs inside a chiral matrix and that it is controlled by supramolecular interactions. At this time the function and nature of the catalytic site is not clear at all but the tertiary structure of the polypeptide seems to be very important. Some of the results are summarized in Fig. 13.

Fig. 13. Effect of structure of the amino acid (R) and the degree of polymerization (m) on the optical yield of the epoxidation of the chalcone Ar = Ph (R' = HNBu)[30].

CONCLUSIONS

From the results summarized and commented above it is obvious that we are far from being able to really design a heterogeneous catalyst which can control the enantioselectivity of a given reaction. This is not surprising if one considers that asymmetric synthesis is very difficult to achieve and that there are relatively few systems known where enantioselective catalysis by chiral solids occurs with practically useful ee's.

For the case of the modified hydrogenation catalysts we can propose a few tentative rules which might help to judge the chance to find (or improve) a catalytic system for the enantioselective reduction of a carbonyl group (up to now, there are no chiral solid catalysts known that are able to hydrogenate other functional groups with ee's > 30-50%).

- The problem is enantioselectivity, not activity.
- There is a high specificity, that means that the nature and structure of metal, modifier and substrate must harmonize.
- Up to now Ni and Pt catalysts have the largest potential, the metal particles should not be too small (low dispersion) and should probably have rather large, flat plains.
- The modifier must have two functional parts, one for adsorption on the catalytic surface and one for binding interactions with the substrate.
- The prochiral substrate also should have a an additional group (besides the reacting function) in order to interact with the modifier and/or the metal surface.
- Modification procedure and reaction conditions must be carefully optimized for any combination of substrate, modifier and catalyst.

The polymeric heterogeneous catalysts described in this review can be regarded as enzyme models. The catalysis very likely occurs inside the chiral matrix and the reaction is probably controlled by supramolecular interactions. At the moment there does not exist any basis for predicting the effect of a structural change of the catalyst.

In order to allow a more general understanding of the important properties of enantioselective solid catalysts more types of natural and artificial chiral solids must be tested as asymmetric catalysts and the successful ones must be investigated systematically for structure - selectivity correlations. This will require a concerted effort by synthetic and physical chemists both from industry and from university.

REFERENCES

1   Blaser, H.U. and Müller, M., 2. Int. Symp. on Heterogeneous Catalysis and Fine Chemicals, Poitiers 1990. To be published in Studies in Surface Science and Catalysis. Elsevier, Amsterdam.

2   Izumi, Y., Adv. Cat. 32, 215 (1983).
3   Tallec, A., Bull. Soc. Chim. Fr. 743 (1985) .
4   Tai, A. and Harada, T., in Iwasawa, Y. (Ed.), Taylored Metal Catalysts, D. Reidel, Dordrecht, 1986, p. 265.
5   Bartok, M., in Stereochemistry of heterogeneous metal catalyts, chapt. XI, J. Wiley, New York, 1985, p. 511.
6   Klabunovskii, E.I., Izv. Akad. Nauk. SSSR, Ser. Khim. 505 (engl. 463) (1984).
7   Sachtler, W.M.H., in Augustine, L., (Ed.), Catalysis in Organic Reactions, Chem. Ind. 22 189 (1985) .
8   Fish, M.J. and Ollis, D.F., Cat. Rev.-Sci. Eng. 18 259 (1978).
9   Tai, A., Tsukioka, K., Imachi, Y., Inoue, Y., Ozaki, H., Harada, T. and Izumi, Y., Proc. 8th Int. Congr. Cat. 531 (1984).
10   Tai, A., Tsukioka, K., Ozaki, H., Harada, T. and Izumi, Y., Chem. Lett. 2083 (1984).
11   Nitta, Y., Yamanishi, O., Sekine, F., Imanaka, T. and Yerashi, S., J. Catal. 79 475 (1983).
12   Nitta, Y., Sekine, F., Imanaka, T. and Teranishi, S., J. Catal. 74 382 (1982).
13   Nitta, Y. and Imanaka, T., Bull. Chem. Soc. Jap. 61 295 (1988).
14   Nitta, Y., Sekine, F., Imanaka, T. and Teranishi, S., Bull. Chem. Soc. Jpn. 54 980 (1981) .
15   Fu, L., Kung, H.H. and Sachtler, W.M.H., J. Mol. Catal. 42 29 (1987).
16   Tai, A., Harada, T., Hiraki, Y. and Murakami, S., Bull. Chem. Soc. Jpn. 56 1414 (1983).
17   Okamoto, S., Harada, T. and Tai, A., Bull. Chem. Soc. Jpn. 52 2670 (1979).
18   Blaser, H.U., Jalett, H.P., Monti, D.M., Reber, J.F. and Wehrli, J.T., in Studies in Surface Science and Catalysis 41 (Heterogeneous Catalysis and Fine Chemicals), Guisnet, M. et al. (Eds.), Elsevier, Amsterdam, 1988, pp. 153-163.
19   Orito, Y., Imai, S., Niwa, S. and Nguyen G-H, J. Synth. Org. Chem. Jpn. 37 173 (1979). Orito, Y., Imai, S. and Niwa, S., J. Chem. Soc. Jpn. 1118 (1979), 670 (1980) and 137 (1982).
20   Sutherland, I.M., Ibbotson, A., Moyes, R.B. and Wells, P.B., J. Catal. 125 77 (1990)
21   Wehrli, J.T.. Baiker, A., Monti, D.M. and Blaser, H.U., J. Mol. Catal. 49 195 (1989).
22   Wehrli, J.T.. Baiker, A., Monti, D.M. and Blaser, H.U., J. Mol. Catal. 61 207 (1990) .
23   Blaser, H.U., Jalett, H.P., Monti, D.M. and Wehrli, J.T., Appl. Catal. 52 19 (1989).
24   Blaser, H.U., Jalett, H.P., Monti, D.M., Baiker, A. and Wehrli, J.T., ACS Symposium on Structure-Activity Relationships in Heterogeneous Catalysis, 1990, Boston. Manuscript in print.
25   Blaser, H.U.. Garland, M., Jalett, H.P., Müller, M. and Pittelkow, U., (Ciba-Geigy), unpublished work.
26   Wehrli, J.T., Baiker, A., Monti, D.M., Blaser, H.U. and Jalett, H.P., J. Mol. Catal. 57 245 (1989).
27   Margitfalvi, J.L., Marti, P., Baiker, A., Botz, L. and Sticher, O., Catal. Lett. 6 281 (1990) .
28   Garland, M. and Blaser, H.U., J. Amer. Chem. Soc. 112 7048 (1990).
29   Thomas, J.M., Angew. Chem. Adv. Mater. 101 1105 (1989).
30   Aglietto, M., Chinellini, E., D'Antone, S., Ruggeri, G. and Solaro, R., Pure & Appl. Chem. 60 415 (1988).
31   Wynberg, H., Topics in Stereochemistry, Vol.16, Wiley-Interscience, New York, 1986, p. 87-129.

Selective Oxidation of the Alcoholic Function by Peroxomolybdenum Complexes

S. Campestrini, V. Conte, F. Di Furia* and F. Novello

Centro Studio Meccanismi Reazioni Organiche del CNR, Dipartimento di Chimica Organica, Università di Padova, via Marzolo 1, I-35131 Padova, Italy.

1. ABSTRACT

Anionic peroxomolybdenum complexes containing bidentate ligands, namely the picolinate (PIC) and picolinate-N-oxido (PICO) anions and a lipophilic countercation such as nBu_4N^+, are able to oxidize both primary and secondary alcohols to the corresponding carbonyl compounds in non polar solvents. The synthetic applicability of the PICO complex, which is generally 20, 50-fold more reactive than the PIC one, has been investigated in the oxidation of the alcoholic function also by comparison with other oxidative procedure(activated DMSO and the perruthenate anion). The results point to a remarkable selectivity of the PICO complex in the oxidation of multifunctional molecules. The mechanism of the oxidation has been investigated, also for glycol oxidations, and evidence has been provided of an associative process where the PICO complex may act as an one-electron oxidant.

2. INTRODUCTION

In the course of the oxidation of organic substrates by hydrogen peroxide (see Scheme 1) in the presence of a transition metal catalyst, namely Ti(IV), V(V), Mo(VI) and W(VI) derivatives, peroxometal complexes are formed which are the real oxidants in solution[1].

Scheme 1

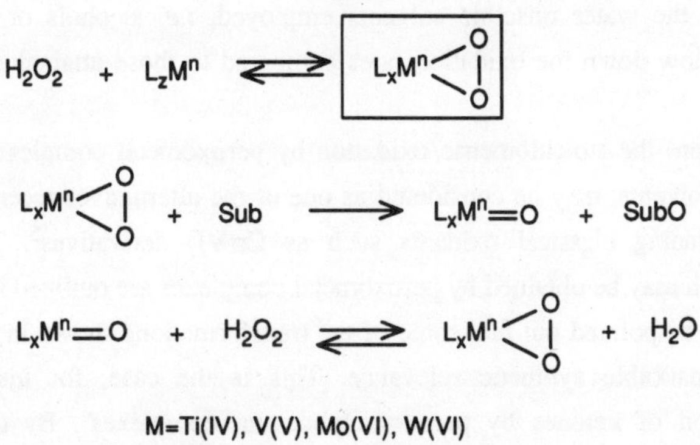

$$H_2O_2 + L_zM^n \rightleftharpoons L_xM^n\diagdown\diagup\begin{matrix}O\\|\\O\end{matrix}$$

$$L_xM^n\diagdown\diagup\begin{matrix}O\\|\\O\end{matrix} + Sub \longrightarrow L_xM^n{=}O + SubO$$

$$L_xM^n{=}O + H_2O_2 \rightleftharpoons L_xM^n\diagdown\diagup\begin{matrix}O\\|\\O\end{matrix} + H_2O$$

M=Ti(IV), V(V), Mo(VI), W(VI)

These are well defined compounds whose oxidative ability is often orders of magnitude larger than that of hydrogen peroxide, thus providing a rationale for the catalytic effect observed. Their oxidation chemistry has been carefully investigated in the past twenty years[1,2,3] by taking advantage of the fact that several peroxometal complexes are stable species which may be isolated and characterized[3].

From the application point of view, one of the most attractive oxidation procedures may be considered the two-phase one, outlined in Scheme 2, where dilute hydrogen peroxide is used to form in the aqueous phase a peroxocomplex[4]. The peroxocomplex is then extracted, either as a neutral or an anionic species, into an organic non polar solvent where the oxidation of the substrate takes place[4].

Scheme 2

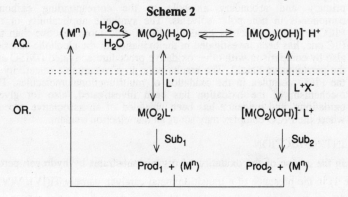

However, the two-phase procedure is not of general applicability for a series of reasons mainly related to the nature of the substrate itself or of the product. Problems may also arise when dilute hydrogen peroxide is used in an homogeneous catalytic system where the water miscible solvents employed, *i.e.* alcohols or cyclic ethers, significantly slow down the oxidation rates compared to those attainable in non polar solvents.

Therefore the stoichiometric oxidation by peroxometal complexes, carried out in non polar solvents, may be considered as one of the alternatives recently developed aimed at replacing classical oxidants such as Cr(VI) derivatives[5]. The oxidation reactions which may be obtained by peroxometal complexes are outlined in Figure 1.

It may be pointed out that some of the transformations shown in Figure 1 have already a remarkable synthetic relevance. This is the case, for instance, of the α-hydroxylation of ketones by peroxomolybdenum complexes[6]. By contrast, other reactions are not yet synthetically useful because of the low yields obtained or of the drastic conditions required. However, such drawbacks could be eventually overcome also by gaining a better understanding of their mechanisms.

Figure 1

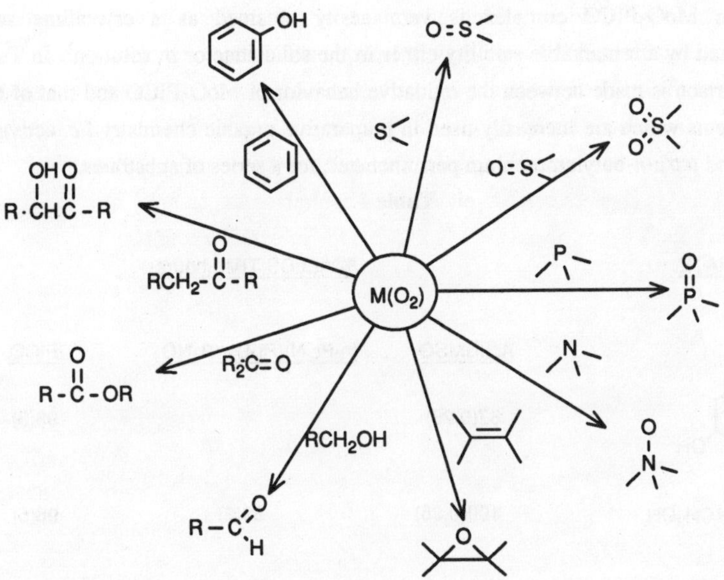

At any rate the oxidation of alcohols by anionic peroxomolybdenum species are among the reactions which may be considered of applicative interest. Such complexes are shown in Figure 2[7,8].

Figure 2

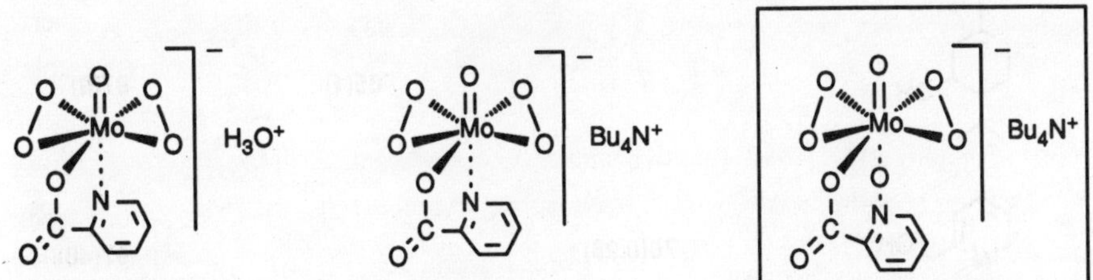

Mares et al (1979)   MoO₅PIC (1986)   MoO₅PICO (1986)

Herein, we concentrate on the MoO₅PICO complex which is by far the most reactive of the three complexes, by illustrating its oxidative ability and its selectivity toward the alcoholic function of different substrates. Some hints, related to the mechanism of oxidation, will also be presented.

3. OXIDATION OF THE ALCOHOLIC FUNCTION BY MoO$_5$PICO: SYNTHETIC ASPECTS

The MoO$_5$PICO complex is very easily obtained as a crystalline solid characterized by a remarkable stability either in the solid state or in solution[8]. In Table 1 a comparison is made between the oxidative behavior of MoO$_5$PICO and that of two other reagents which are increasingly used in preparative organic chemistry *i.e.* activated DMSO[5] and *tetra-n*-butylammonium perruthenate[9], for a series of substrates.

Table 1

SUBSTRATE	%YIELDS(TIME,hours)		
	Act.DMSO	(n-Pr$_4$N)(RuO$_4$)/R$_3$NO	PICO
2-cyclohexen-1-ol	87(0.25)	/	99(3)
phenyl–CH$_2$OH	100(0.25)	80(2)	96(5)
long-chain alkenol (...OH)	/	70(3)	99(9)
cyclobutanol	96(0.25)	95(11)	98(5)
menthol	/	85(1)	97(9)
2-pyridyl–CH$_2$OH	70(0.25)	/	97(48)

The results for these two systems are taken from literature data and refer to the various experimental conditions which allow to obtain the best yields depending on the substrate. The data for MoO$_5$PICO have been obtained in our laboratory[8,10] by using equivalent amounts of substrate and oxidant in dichloroethane at 50 or 60°C.

Although with both activated DMSO and perruthenate ion the reaction times are shorter that those with MoO$_5$PICO, it may be observed that this latter usually provides better yields. At any rate, an important feature which characterizes the three systems examined is the remarkable selectivity in the oxidation of primary alcohols to aldehydes without overoxidation to carboxylic acids.

The MoO_5PICO, like the other two systems, allow the oxidation of the alcoholic function in multifunctional molecules, as indicated by the data collected in Table 2.

Table 2

$[Substrate]_0 = [Active\ Oxygen]_0$

SUBSTRATE	TIME, h	PRODUCT	YIELD, %
	10		95
	20		70
	0.5		80
	48		97
	24		20
	7		94

338

[Substrate]$_0$ = [Active Oxygen]$_0$

SUBSTRATE	TIME, h	PRODUCT	YIELD, %
(structure)	15[a]	(structure)	81
(structure)	15[b]	(structure)	72
(structure)	10[b]	(structure)	86
		+ (structure)	14

a = at 60°C
b = [Substrate]$_0$/[Active Oxygen]$_0$ = 0.5

Particularly interesting from a synthetic standpoint is the oxidation of epoxyalcohols, which is usally the second step after the Sharpless[11] epoxidation of allylic alcohols in the route to complex molecules and the oxidation of amidoalcohols as an entry to the synthesis of aminoaldehydes and aminoketones which are obtained only in low yield by direct oxidation of the parent aminoalcohol(see Table 2) likely because the basic substrate is able to displace the PICO ligand from the complex. It may also be noted that the oxidation of diols and glycols takes place readily and that, for the latter, little cleavage of the carbon-carbon bond is observed even in a substrate particularly prone to such a reaction like *meso*-hydrobenzoin[12].

4.   OXIDATION OF THE ALCOHOLIC FUNCTION BY MoO$_5$PICO: MECHANISTIC ASPECTS

From a mechanistic point of view, the alcohol oxidation by MoO$_5$PICO may be envisaged to proceed either by an associative pathway, involving the the formation of an intermediate or by a simple bimolecular reaction[12].

In the former case, being MoO$_5$PICO a coordinatively saturated species, it must be envisaged that the substrate coordinates to the metal through the displacement of a previously bound ligand. A likely candidate to undergo such a displacement should be the neutral tooth of the bidentate picolinate-N-oxido ligand.

In both instances, *i.e.* either an associative or a bimolecular process, the possibility of a polar or of a radical pathway must be taken into account. A polar mechanism should involve either a positively charged transition state, as a result of a hydride abstraction or, less likely, a negatively charged transition state deriving from a β-hydrogen elimination. In the case of a radical mechanism, the intermediacy of a ketyl radical should be envisaged.

Such an intermediacy may be in some cases, easily proved by carrying out the reactions in the presence of dioxygen owing to the tendency of the ketyl radical to start an autoxidative chain revealed by a more-than-stoichiometric production of the carbonyl products[13].

In order to verify the various alternatives presented above we have carried out a kinetic investigation of the alcohol oxidation by MoO$_5$PICO. Unfortunately such an investigation does not yet allow to propose a detailed mechanism. At any rate, some useful evidence has been obtained. In Table 3, a comparison is made between the oxidation of cyclohexanol (Cy) to cyclohexanone and that of thioanisole (MPS) to methylphenylsulfoxide by MoO$_5$PICO and MoO$_5$PIC in DCE.

Table 3

SUBSTRATE	OXIDANT	T °C	YIELD,%	REL. RATE	$\Delta H^{\neq}$, kJmol^{-1}	$\Delta S^{\neq}$, JK^{-1}mol^{-1}
Cy	PIC	60	97	1		
	PICO	60	98	22	89	-15
MPS	PIC	40	98	1		
	PICO	40	98	0.8	56	-116

The mechanism of the thioether oxidation by MoO$_5$PICO had been previously studied and strong evidence had been obtained on the occurrence of an external, bimolecular reaction not involving an oxidant-substrate intermediate[14]. This is in accord with the scarce effect of the ligand, either PIC or PICO, on the oxidation rates and with the large negative values of the entropies of activation. Following this line, the sizeable effect of the nature of the ligand on the oxidation of cyclohexanol, together with the small entropies of activation observed, may be taken as evidence that, in alcohol oxidations, an associative mechanism is operating.

Concerning the nature of the oxidation step, either etherolytic or homolytic, contrasting information has been obtained.

Scheme 3

OXIDATION OF ALCOHOLS BY MoO_5PICO

- No effect of radical traps or promoters

- No dioxygen interception

- Selective oxidation of cyclobutanol to cyclobutanone

- Low substrate selectivity [1-propanol (1), 2-butanol (2.4), 3,3-dimethyl-2-butanol (2.7)]

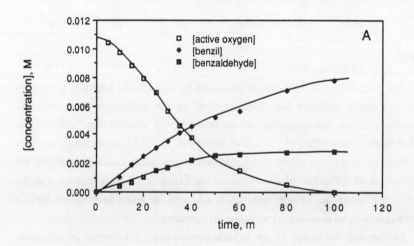

X — ⬡ —OH $\rho = -0.27$

$X = p\text{-OMe, } p\text{-Me, H, } m\text{-Cl, } p\text{-NO}_2$

This is summarized in Scheme 3, where it may be seen that the classical tests for detecting radical intermediates appear to rule out a one-electron oxidation. At the same time, the reaction displays an intriguing feature, *i.e.* a rather low substrate selectivity which does not fit well in an heterolytic mechanism involving a charged transition state usually rather sensitive to electronic effects.

More useful information on the mechanism of alcohol oxidation was obtained, somehow surprisingly, from a study of the oxidation of *meso*-hydrobenzoin by MoO_5PICO in DCE. In such a reaction, the involvement of dioxygen is quite evident resulting in an overproduction of benzil and benzaldehyde compared with the results obtained by carrying out the reaction under argon atmosphere[12]. A typical example of such a feature is shown in Figure 3, where a 5-fold excess of substrate over the oxidant is employed, at 60°C, either under air (A) or under argon (B).

Figure 3

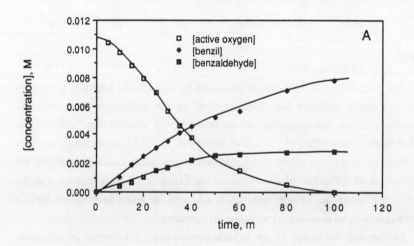

Figure 3 (cnt.)

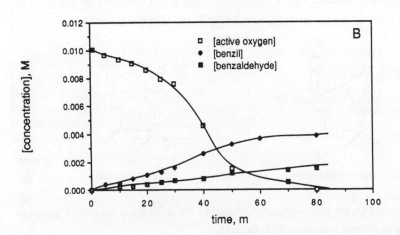

In an effort to rationalize the different behavior of alcohols and *meso*-hydrobenzoin it may be suggested that the life-time of ketyl radicals involved in the one-electron oxidation of the glycol is sufficiently long to allow dioxygen interception before the transfer of the second electron leading to the carbonyl compound takes place whereas such a transfer is much faster in the case of alcohol oxidation.

Having established that MoO$_5$PICO may act as a one electron oxidant, at least in *meso*-hydrobenzoin oxidation, we have investigated in some more detail the glycol oxidation by comparing the behavior of *meso*- and *d,l*-hydrobenzoin. Also for the latter, dioxygen interception is observed. However, the most interesting clue obtained by such a comparison is the observation that the two diasteromers provide an opposite products distribution, as shown in Scheme 4.

Scheme 4

SUBSTRATE	[BENZALDEHYDE] / [BENZIL]
	(O$_{att.}$ = 0)
meso-hydrobenzoin	0.12
d,l-hydrobenzoin	1.7

Based on previous studies reported in the literature, the different behavior of *meso*- and *d,l*-hydrobenzoin should be related to their different ability to act as bidentate ligands, being the chelation by *d,l* isomer easier than that of the *meso-* one mainly for steric reasons. This is immediately clear if one compares the structures of the two peroxocomplexes resulting from the chelation of the two glycols

Scheme 5

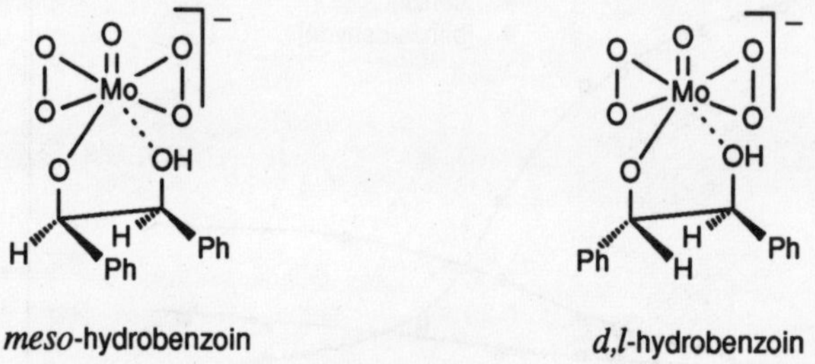

meso-hydrobenzoin   *d,l*-hydrobenzoin

and, in particular, the steric congestion created by the eclipsing of the phenyl groups in the complex formed from *meso*-hydrobenzoin.

A corollary of such an interpretation is that the benzaldehyde should derive from the bidentate association of the substrate whereas benzil should be formed stepwise from the complex where the glycols are coordinated as monodentate ligands, likely through two subsequent oxidations of the alcoholic functions involving the intermediacy of the keto-alcohol benzoin, which has been in fact detected in solution.

A reasonable reaction scheme which takes into account all the observation made above is shown here:

Scheme 6

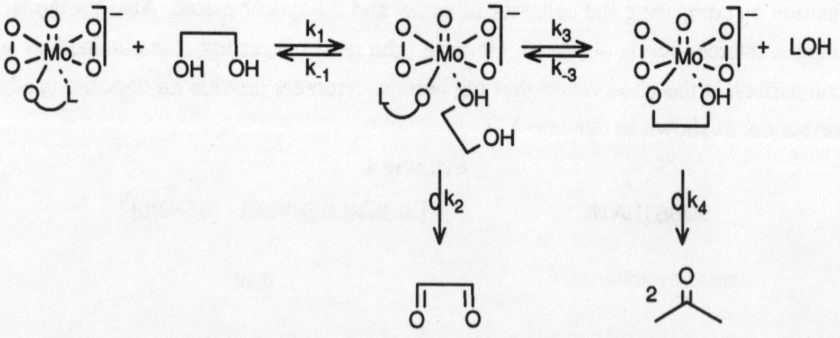

It may be noticed that, in Scheme 6, the pathway leading to the α-diketone bears much resemblance to that which may be envisaged for the oxidation of alcohols.

It has been also possible to prove that indeed both glycols may act as bidentate ligands and that from the resulting complexes benzaldehyde is formed. In fact, according to the equilibrium formation of such complexes which require that the ligand be completely removed from the metal, one should expect that by adding free ligand, the formation of benzaldehyde be greatly depressed. This is indeed observed as revealed by the data of Table 4.

Table 4

SUBSTRATE, 0.025 M	LIGAND, M	[BENZALDEHYDE] / [BENZIL] ($O_{att.} = 0$)
meso-hydrobenzoin	/	0.12
meso-hydrobenzoin	0.03	0.06
d,l-hydrobenzoin	/	1.7
d,l-hydrobenzoin	0.03	0.6

In conclusion, the study of the oxidation of meso- and d,l-hydrobenzoin has shed some light on the mechanism of alcohol oxidation by indicating that an associative process involving two subsequent one-electron steps is a likely possibility. This may be considered a starting point for understanding the intimate details of the mechanism.

5.   REFERENCES

1   Sheldon, R.A. and Kochi, J. K., "Metal Catalyzed Oxidation of Organic Compounds", Academic Press, London, (1981).

2   Di Furia, F. and Modena, G., Rev. Chem. Interm. 6, 51, (1985).

3   Mimoun, H., " The Chemistry of functional groups: Peroxides", S. Patai, Wiley (Ed.), New York, 463, (1962).

4   Bortolini, O., Conte, V., Di Furia, F. and Modena, G.,in W. Ando and Y. Moro Oka (Eds.) "The role of Oxygen in Chemistry and Biochemistry", vol. 33 of "Studies in Organic Chemistry", pp. 301-306, (1988), Elsevier Science Publisher, amsterdam.

5   Haines, A. H.,"Methods for the Oxidation of Organic Compounds: Alcohols, Alcohol Derivatives, Alkyl Halides, Carbonyl Compounds, Hydroxyarenes and Amminoarenes" ch. 2, Academic Press, London, (1988).

6   Vedejs, E., Engler, D.A. and Telschon, J. E., J. Org. Chem. 43, 188 (1978).

344

7   Jacobson, S. E., Tang, R. and Mares, F., J. Chem. Soc. Chem. Commun. 888, (1978).

8   Bortolini, O., Campestrini, S., Di Furia, F and Modena, G., J. Org. Chem. 52, 5467 (1987).

9   Griffith, W. P. and Ley, S. V., Aldrichim. Acta, 23, 13 (1990).

10 Campestrini, S., Di Furia, F., Modena, G. and Bortolini, O., J. Org. Chem. 55, 3658 (1990).

11 Rossiter, B. E.,"Synthetic Aspects and Application of Asymmetric Epoxidation",in "Asymmetric Synthesis", vol. 5, cap. 7, in J.D. Morrison (Ed.), Academic Press, Inc. New York, USA, (1985).

12 Campestrini, S., Di Furia, F., Modena, G. and Novello, F., "Oxidation of alchols and diols by peroxometal complexes". Proceedings of the 4th International Symposium on Dioxygen Activation and Homogeneous Catalytic Oxidation, L.I. Simandi (Ed.), Balatonfured, Hungary, September 10-14, (1990), in press.

13 Conte, V., Di Furia, F. and Modena, G., J. Org. Chem., 53, 1665 (1988).

14 Campestrini, S., Conte, V., Di Furia, F., Modena, G. and Bortolini, O., J. Org. Chem., 53, 5721 (1988).

IMPACT OF HOMOGENEOUS CATALYSIS ON INDUSTRY

W. KEIM

ABSTRACT

Homogeneous catalysis is important academically and industrially. It plays an essential role in the manufacture of a wide range of products ranging from basic chemicals over intermediate chemicals to fine chemicals. In this contribution the impact of homogeneous cataysis on the chemical industry is discussed. After some introductory general remarks the various fields where homogeneous catalysis plays an important role are presented: hydrogenation, oxidation, oligomerization/polymerization, reactions with CO, hydrocyanation, isomerization and metathesis. Special emphasis is given to oligomerization/polymerization, which are especially chosen to demonstrate principles, potential and achievements of homogeneous catalysis.

Catalysis is most important for the chemical industry. There are estimates that more than 70 % of all chemicals produced have seen a catalyst. Of course, most important are heterogeneous catalysts and the share of homogeneous, transition metal based catalyts – following a coordinative mechanisms – amounts to 10-15 % only. But it is remarkable that the majority of homogeneous processes is merely 25 years old and the field is rapidly growing. The question arises: what makes homogeneous catalysis industrially interesting? To elucidate this point, Table 1 exhibits advantages and disadvantages of homogeneous and heterogeneous catalysis.

The advantage to manufacture **new products** is obvious.

Most noteworthy is the **selectivity** with which homogeneous systems can operate. Selectivity is needed to produce pure products in high yields, a characteristic which is very important in the preparation of pharmaceuticals, intermediates for polymers and many other applications. Prices of chemicals vary drastically with its purity grade. Often high purity is also a necessity as in polymer grade olefins or, for instance, as starting materials for metathesis. Generally, the value of an industrial product is determined by: a) cost to manufacture it, b) safety of process and/or product, c) environmental acceptance and compatibility. All three are key features of homogeneous catalysis. To emphasize selectivity in environmental acceptance only the formation of by-products should be mentioned. By-products can lead to market problems in selling and discarding the latter ones. No industry likes processes with two or more products because balance on the market normally is quite difficult, but, furthermore, disposal of by-products will become more difficult and costly.

Table 1: Comparison of homogeneous and heterogeneous catalysis

	homogeneous	heterogeneous
new products	in both possible	
selectivity	often better	
activity	metal atoms are used	only surface atoms are used
reaction conditions	mild (20-200°C)	severe (>250°C)
diffusion	practically unknown	given
reproducibility	given	often difficult (know how)
understanding	in situ spectrscopic methodes (NMR, IR, ESR, etc.) can be applied	difficult, often impossible under reaction conditions
catalyst recycle	full of problems	easy

Selectivity also proves important in saving raw materials, better utilization of reactants and saving of energy (milder reaction conditions).

High chemeoselectivity, regioselectivity and stereoselectivity can be obtained by homogeneous catalysis. So far, regioselectivity has been one of the greatest virtues of homogeneous catalysis. For the future, many applications for stereoselectivity can be forseen. Lately enantioselective catalysis has attracted substantial interest. Although industrial applications are not numerous, the potential is huge. This may be exemplified in Fig. 1, which shows the future market for optically active drugs underlining the importance of chiral selectivity in this field. Other important markets for enantio-selectivity include: agriculturals, polymers, fine chemicals and many more.

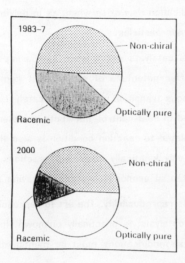

Fig. 1: Market for optically active drugs in 2000

Homogeneous catalyts often impress in their **activity** (turn over numbers ≡ TON). One reason is the easy access of the reactants to practically all metal atoms. In comparison, in heterogeneous catalysis many metal atoms are hidden in the matrix of the support. Utilization of all metal atoms is important, for instance, when applying noble metals as catalysts.

Assessment of the merchant catalyst value of homogeneous catalysts is very difficult. Other than in heterogeneous catalysis homogeneous catalysts are frequently captively used and in situ preparation is very common. Refinery operations, which dominate the catalyst market, rarely see homogeneous, transition metal based catalysts; but lately we see applications emerging (Dimersol technology via propene dimerization). Among the chemical catalysts polymerization is number one. Here definition of homogeneity can be a problem. Homogeneity of a catalyst can be related to particle size, and it can cause difficulties to decide whether a catalyst is homogeneous or hetero-geneous. Polymerization provides well known examples. Often the catalyst solutions are clear to the naked eye, but light scattering experiments suggest the presence of aggregates. An additional complication may arise when, as in polymerization, the cata-lysts is deposited on the polymer particles.

Very often homogeneous catalysts excell when comparing **reaction conditions**. Highly exothermic reactions offer potentials of easier heat removal by working in homogeneous media. Homogeneous transition metal based catalysts in general operate below 200°C. Difficulties related to heat control, hot spots et cetera are less common. An advantageous parameter related to reaction condition is also the lack of **diffusion** limitations, which can lead to only kinetically controlled reactions. In summary, mild reaction conditions offer substantial economic benefits in saving of energy.

A significant advantage is **reproducibility**. The art to reproduce a catalyst, often experienced in heterogeneous catalysis, is practically unknown. In addition, the ease of catalyst tailoring and catalyst modifications must be mentioned.

Homogeneous catalysts are amenable to mechanistic studies under reaction conditions making use of all the physical methods that have been developed for mole-cular species, e.g., NMR, IR, UV, ESR et cetera thus providing a much better **under-standing** of the catalytic steps involved. In addition, homogeneous transition metal cata-lyts in a broad sense are off-springs of the field of organometallic complex chemistry. Here many complexes and reactions are known providing a wealth of information applicable to homogeneous catalysis.

To forward an insight into the wide range of industrial applications of homoge-neous catalysis, Table 2 lists a variety of processes used today.

Among the processes listed in Table 2, oxidations, oligomerizations/polymeriza-tions and reactions with CO have found broadest industrial acceptance.

In the following characteristic examples from Table 2 have been selected to demonstrate the principles, potentials and achievements of homogeneous catalysis in industry.

Table 2: Homogeneous processes practized

Hydrogenation	Reactions with CO
l-Dopa (Monsanto)	Hydroformylation
fine chemicals	Carboxylations
Oxidation	Acetic acid (Monsanto)
Olefins	Acetic anhydrid (Eastman-Kodak)
Alkanes	**Hydrocyanation**
Aromatics	Adiponitrile (Du Pont)
Oligomerizations	**Isomerization**
Dimerization of ethene	Menthol (Takasago)
and propene (IFP)	**Metathesis**
α-Olefins (SHOP-Shell)	Octenamer (Hüls AG)
Cyclooctadiene (Hüls AG, Shell)	Norsorex (CDF-Chemie)
Cyclododecatriene (Hüls AG, Du Pont)	Neohexene (Philips)
Hexadiene (Du Pont)	FEAST (Shell)
Polymerization	SHOP (Shell)
Monoolefins	Telene (Goodrich)
Dienes	

1.   HYDROGENATION

Applications of homogeneous hydrogenation are found in polymer synthesis, hydrogenation of aldehydes to alcohols (in hydroformylation processes), hydrogenation of aromatics and enantioselective hydrogenations. For instance, the hydrogenation of benzene to cyclohexane is an example demonstrating the borderline between homogeneous and heterogeneous catalysis. Originally the hydrogenation of benzene was carried out with a heterogeneous Raney type nickel catalyst. Because of its pyrophoric nature, representing a potential fire hazard, a shift to "apparently" homogeneous systems is going on. Some older plants have been converted already, new plants are being built. The catalysts are obtained by reducing soluble nickel salts with aluminium alkyls thus obtaining clear solutions (Lapporte catalysts[1]).

Among hydrogenations enantioselective hydrogenations grow in importance. Monsanto introduced enantioselective hydrogenation for the synthesis of l-Dopa[2]. The synthesis of Aspartam by Enichem, is an other example[3]. It may be generalized that the enantioselective hydrogenation has been progressed very far and ee valus of > 95 % are common.

2.   OXIDATION

The largest scale application of homogeneous catalysis is found among oxidation of hydrocarbons by molecular oxygen or peroxides[4]. From an industrial point of view a classification in oxidation of olefins, oxidation of alkanes, and oxidation of aromatics can be made. Important examples are given in equation (1) to (6)

$$H_2C=CH_2 \xrightarrow{O_2} CH_3CHO \quad (\text{Wacker}) \quad (1)$$

$$CH_3-CH=CH_2 \xrightarrow{ROOH} \text{propylene oxide} \quad (\text{Halcon}) \quad (2)$$

$$\text{cyclohexane} \xrightarrow{O_2} HOOC-(CH_2)_4-COOH \quad (3)$$

$$\text{butane} \xrightarrow{O_2} CH_3CHO \quad (4)$$

$$\text{xylenes} \xrightarrow{O_2} \begin{array}{l}\text{phthalic anhydride} \\ \text{phthalic acid}\end{array} \quad (5)$$

$$\text{toluene} \xrightarrow{O_2} \text{benzoic acid, phenol} \quad (6)$$

Mechanistically homogeneous metal catalyzed oxidation reactions can be divided into homolytic and heterolytic type of reactions. Homolytic systems are those which involve free radicals as intermediates utilizing the transition metal in one electron oxidation or reduction steps. The metal complex often functions as catalyst to decompose the hydroperoxides. Heterolytic systems are more in line with coordination chemistry. The organic substrate and oxygen/or the oxidising agent are activated by the metal centre. The catalytic cycle can involve a series of two electron steps. Classical examples are the Wacker[5] and Halcon processes (Oxiran)[6].

The Wacker-process is a good example to demonstrate the rapid development of technology. Originally acetaldehyde was made by industry via addition of water to acetylene. This process was displaced by the oxidation of ethene (Wacker). The latter one is loosing rapidly against the Monsanto acetic acid process, because about 50 % of aldehyde is oxidized to acetic acid, which economically is less expensive via methanol carbonylation (one homogeneous process displaces the other one!).

3. OLIGOMERIZATION/POLYMERIZATION

CC-linkage of olefins to dimers, oligomers and polymers belong to industry's most frequently practiced reactions. As Fig. 2 exhibits, linear and branched products are obtainable.

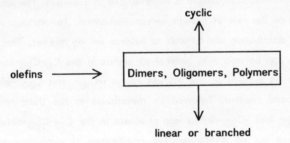

Fig. 2: CC-linkage of olefins

Mechanistically the CC-linkages leading to dimers→ oligmers → polymers possess common reaction features.

3.1 Ethenoligomerization/Polymerization

To demonstrate principles and potentials Shell's SHOP process is chosen, which with one million tons of products produced is one of the biggest applications of homogeneous catalysis.

The SHOP process embraces three catalytic reactions: a) Ethene-oligomerization (homogeneous), b) Isomerization (heterogeneous), c) Metathesis (heterogeneous)[7]. A flow scheme is shown in Fig. 3.

352

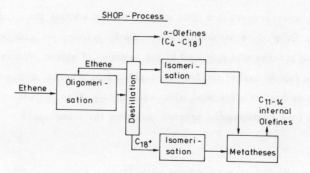

SHOP - Process

Fig. 3: Flow scheme of SHOP

In the first, homogeneous step ethene is oligomerized to α-olefins. The amounts of olefins formed depend on the rate of growth versus elimination. The various olefins produced in a geometric distribution are difficult to balance on the market. Therefore only the α-olefins, which can be sold – in general all olefins in the C_8-C_{20}-range – are distilled off. The olefins outside of the market range ($<C_{10}$- and C_{20}^+-olefins) are isomerized in a second reactor, followed by metathesis in the third reactor. Metathesis converts $<C_{10}$- and $>C_{20}$-olefins into products in the C_{10}-C_{20}-detergent range, which can be taken out via distillation. The combination of isomerization and metathesis paired with distillation and recycle offers an unique technology to tailor the carbon number distribution. This process scheme gives a high dregree of flexibility to provide linear olefins of any carbon number and amount desired.

The key to development was the discovery of a novel homogeneous oligomerization catalyst, which operates at 80-120°C and 50-150 bar ethylene pressure. Olefins of >95 % α-olefin content and >99 % linearity are formed. The selectivity to linear olefins is essential for carrying out metathesis. Branched product olefins react very slowly under metathesis conditions leading to a buildup of non-reactive and branched olefins, which have a low market value. Without the selectivity of the homogenous oligomerization catalyst integration of oligomerization and metathesis would have been impossible, a point, which quite impressively underlines the benefit attached to selectivity.

As pointed out in Table 1, a mechanistic understanding of the reaction steps involved in homogeneous catalytic reactions can be obtained by synthesizing organometallic complexes, which yield active catalysts or which represent intermediate complexes (catalyst precursors). Based on isolated complexes spectroscopic methods can be used to study possible reaction steps under reaction conditions. For the oligomerization the selfexplanatory mechanism shown in Fig. 4 is proposed.

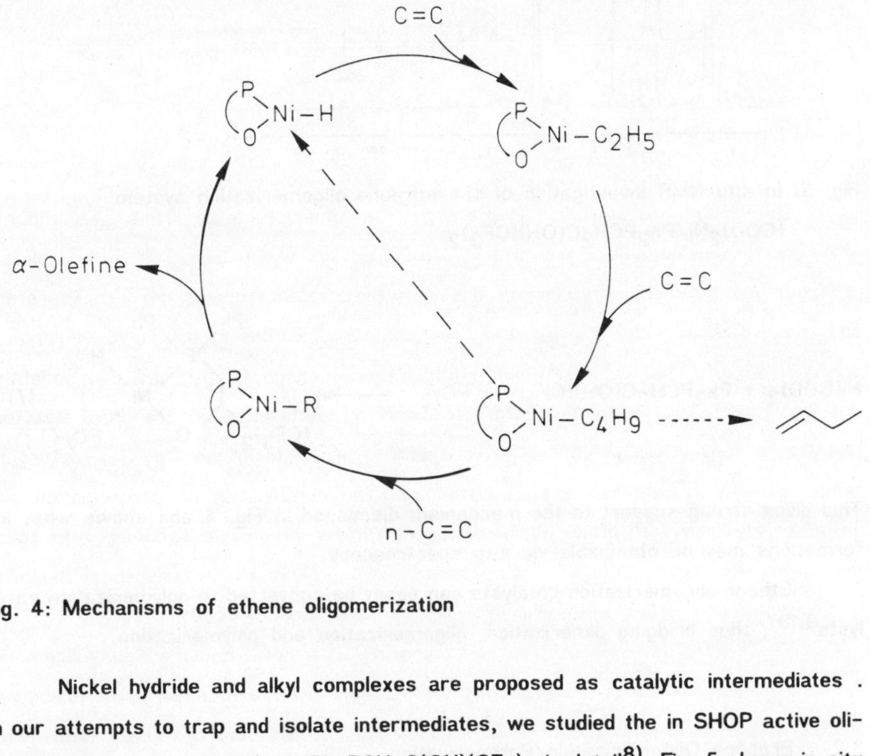

Fig. 4: Mechanisms of ethene oligomerization

Nickel hydride and alkyl complexes are proposed as catalytic intermediates . In our attempts to trap and isolate intermediates, we studied the in SHOP active oligomerization system $(COD)_2Ni/Ph_2PCH_2C(OH)(CF_3)_2$ in detail[8]. Fig. 5 shows in situ experiments.

Spectrum a is obtained at -10°C and shows the nickel hydride signal as a triplet. Upon addition of ethene, the hydride signal disappears and new signals at $\delta = 0.6$ emerge, which can be assigned to nickel alkyl groups (Ni-CH$_2$...). After 10 minutes all ethene is reacted and c shows the final spectrum. Attempts to isolate the nickel hydride were unsuccessful. However, a hydride complex could be isolated and fully characterized (x-ray) according to eq. 7 .

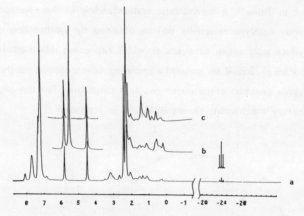

Fig. 5: In situ NMR investigation of the ethylene oligomerization system $(COD)_2Ni/Ph_2PCH_2C(OH)(CF_3)_2$

$$Ni(COD)_2 + Ph_2PCH_2C(OH)(CF_3)_2 + PCy_3 \longrightarrow \quad \text{(7)}$$

This gives strong support to the mechanism discussed in Fig. 4 and shows what informations may be obtainable via situ spectroscopy.

Ethene oligomerization catalysts can easily be converted to polymerization catalysts[9,10], thus bridging dimerization, oligomerization and polymerization.

3.2 Propene Oligomerization/Polymerization

The dimerization of propene applying ligand control was carried out by Wilke and Bogdanovic[9]. Chauvin from Institut Francais du Petrole (IFP) developed nickel catalyts ($Ni^{2+}/AlEtCl_2$) that dimerize propene and/or butenes[11]. These systems are highly active, hence the recycling of catalyst can be dispensed with. The propene dimers are used extensively, especially in the USA, for improving the octane number in gasoline and to provide heptenes and octenes for plasticizers. Since the first plant was established in the USA in 1977, IFP have given about 45 licences.

Of substantial interest is the homogeneous polymerization of propene (α-olefins). The stereoselective polymerization can yield isotactic and syndiotactic polymers.

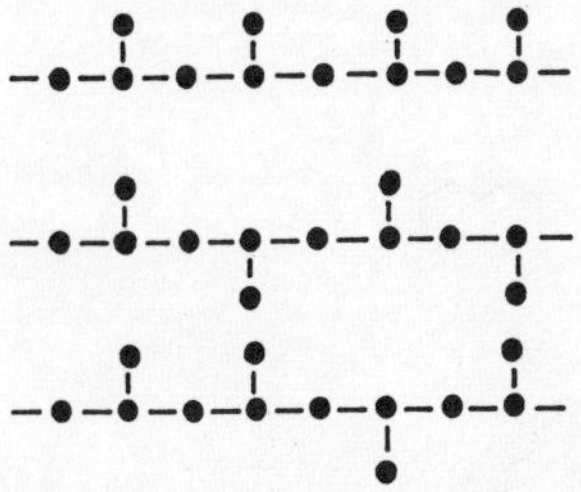

isotactic

syndiotactic

atactic

For a long time it was believed that the stereoselective polymerization of α-olefins was a property of heterogeneous catalysts only. Brintzinger, Kaminsky and Ewen discovered that isotactic and syndiotactic polypropylene can be made homogeneously[12]. Stereorigide complexes are necessary. For instance, complexes with C_2-symmetry yield isotactic and C_s-symmetry syndiotactic polypropylene (Fig. 6).

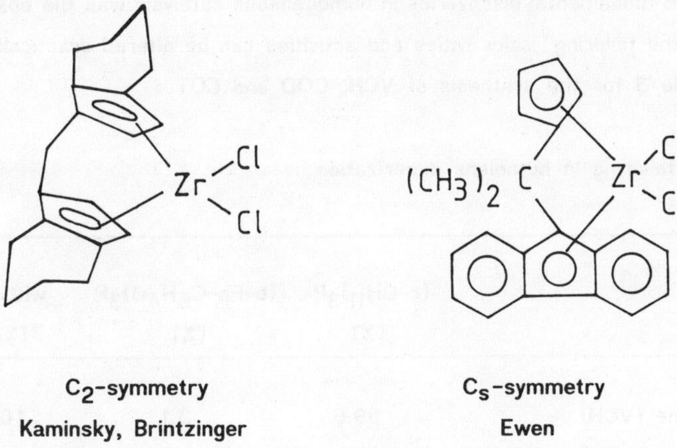

C_2-symmetry
Kaminsky, Brintzinger

C_s-symmetry
Ewen

Fig. 6: Complexes for stereoselective polymerization

3.3   Diene Oligomerization/Polymerization

Wilke discovered that 1,3-dienes can be oligomerized to cyclic products as shown in Fig. 7.

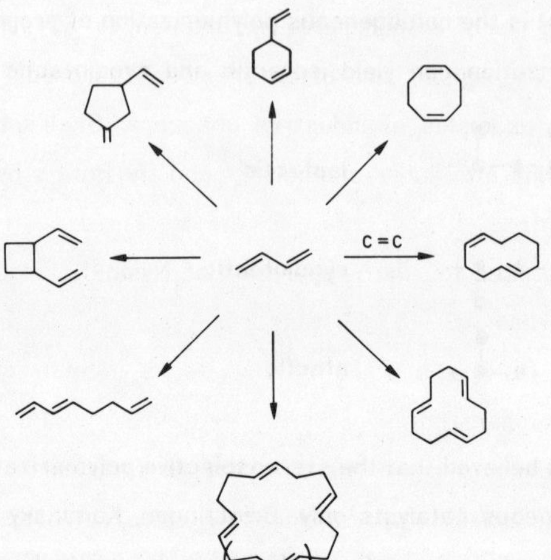

Fig. 7: Cyclic oligomers from butadiene

One of the fundamental discoveries in homogeneous catalysis was the observation that via "ligand tailoring" selectivities and activities can be altered drastically this is shown in Table 3 for the synthesis of VCH, COD and CDT.

Table 3: Ligand tailoring in butadiene dimerization

Product	$(c\text{-}CH_{11})_3P$ [%]	$(o\text{-}Ph\text{-}C_6H_4O)_3P$ [%]	without [%]
4-Vinylcyclohexene (VCH)	39.6	3.1	10
1,5-Cyclooctadiene (COD)	41.2	96.5	25
1,5,9-Cyclododecatriene (CDT)	14.4	0.2	65
Higher oligomers	4.8	0.2	–

This "ligand tailoring" is of considerable importance to all scientists working in homogeneous catalysis. The ligands are often precisely "tailored" to the process envisaged. Two noteworthy examples of industrial uses are: Shell's hydroformylation reaction for converting olefins into linear alcohols[13] and Du Pont's hydrocyanation of butadiene to adipodinitrile[14].

Cyclododecatriene is used for the preparation of Nylon-12. Fig. 8 outlines this synthesis as practiced by Hüls AG (18,000 tons per year) and Du Pont[9]. Valuable textiles are produced from Du Pont's Qiana[R]. Owing to its stability of shape, corrosive resistance, and low-temperature properties, Vestamid[R], manufactured by Hüls AG, has numerous applications in compression cylinders for brakes in automobiles, in fuel pressure lines, in the soles of sports shoes, in cable coverings, in anti-corrosive coatings (coatings for wires, steel pipe construction units) and in the linings of jackets and coats. Hüls AG also manufactures the special rubber Vestenamer[R] from cyclooctadiene (Eq. 8).

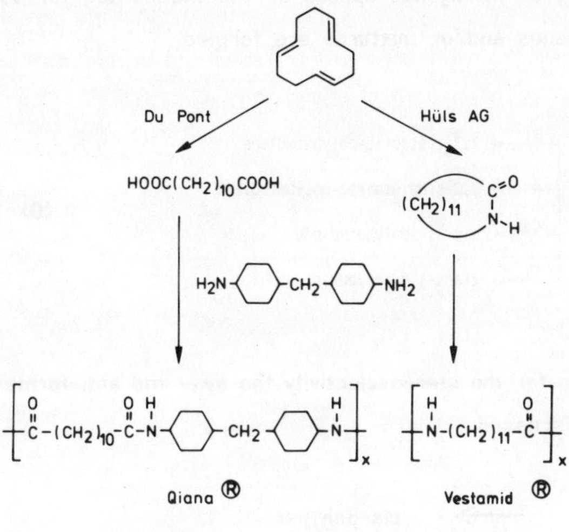

Fig. 8: Synthesis of Qiana[R] and Vestamid[R]

$$2 \diagup\diagdown \xrightarrow{[\text{LNi}]} \bigcirc \xrightarrow{\text{Cat/H}_2} \bigcirc$$

$$x \bigcirc \xrightarrow[\text{Catalyst}]{\text{Metathesis}} \left\{ \diagdown\diagup\diagdown\diagup\diagdown\diagup \right\}_x \qquad (8)$$

Polyoctenamer

Characteristic features of Vestenamer are its partial crystallinity and its relatively low molecular weight. The crystallinity is dependent on the number of *trans* double bonds present. In blends with other rubbers, Vestenamer improves the viscosity and is thus of great help in complicated production procedures, such as those of brake hoses from EPDM (ethylene-propene-diene elastomer), corrugated bellows from poly-chloroprene, tooth crowns from hard plastics, and printing molds from nitrile rubber.

The homogeneous polymerization of 1,3-dienes is also practiced industrially. Depending on the nature of the ligands applied or the metals (eq. 9) used cis-1,4, trans-1,4- or 1,2-polydienes and/or mixtures are formed.

$$\text{butadiene} \begin{cases} \xrightarrow{\text{Ti}} \text{1,2-isotactic-polybutadiene} \\ \xrightarrow{\text{V}} \text{1,2-syndiotactic-polybutadiene} \\ \xrightarrow{\text{Co}} \text{cis-1,4-polybutadiene} \\ \xrightarrow{\text{Ti}} \text{trans-1,4-polybutadiene} \end{cases} \qquad (9)$$

As an explanation for the stereoselectivity the syn- and anti-forms of η^3-allyl systems (eq. 10) are discussed.

$$\overset{\displaystyle \curvearrowright}{\underset{R}{\boxed{M}}} \longrightarrow \text{cis-polymer} \qquad (10)$$

$$R\diagdown\diagup\overset{\curvearrowright}{M} \longrightarrow \text{trans-polymer}$$

4.   REACTIONS WITH CO

Industrial reactions with CO are numerous and they belong to the most frequent and illustrious examples of applications of homogeneous catalysis. There are estimates that close to 10 mio tons/a of products are made via carbonylation. They can be divided into reactions using CO/H_2 or only CO. For an overview reference 15 should be used.

A new chapter of CO-chemistry may be written embracing C_1-chemistry[16]. Uncertainty of oil prices and a dwindling supply of crude oil have given rise to a growing interest in alternative feedstocks such as coal, methane or even biomass. They all can be converted into CO/H_2 (synthesis gas) which than could be used as a feedstock for a variety of direct and indirect reactions[16]. It may be even envisaged that in the future CO_2 may be reduced to CO/H_2 or methanol (green house effect). Homogeneous catalysis will have a great impact on C_1-chemistry. The hydrogenation of CO is exothermic and heterogeneous systems are plagued by problems of heat removal. Homogeneous systems operating in a liquid phase offer advantages. Homogeneous transition metal catalysts are, in a broad sense, offsprings of the field or organometallic complex chemistry. Therefore, homogeneous systems are more amenable to mechanistic studies applying spectroscopy in solution. Applications always live on basic research and basic research and understanding of CO chemistry is far advanced thus implying that new processes may be envisaged here. This is even already reality as may be seen from the acetic acid anhydride process by Eastman-Kodak in which acetic anhydride for films is made from coal (eq. 11).

$$\text{coal} \longrightarrow \text{methanol} \longrightarrow \text{acetic acid} \tag{11}$$

$$\text{acetic anhydride} \xleftarrow{\;CO\;} \text{methylacetate}$$

The key-chemistry involved is based on homogeneous catalysis as may be seen from Fig. 9.

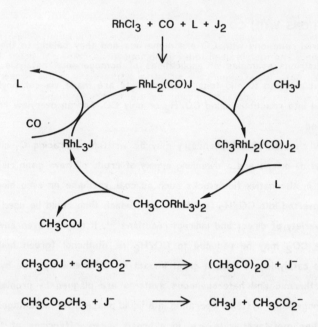

Fig. 9: Mechanism of acetic anhydride synthesis

For **hydrocyanation**[14], **isomerization**[17] and **metathesis**[18] the references given provide detailed informations.

SUMMARY

Great future opportunities for the synthesis of chemicals are foreseen applying homogeneous transition metal based catalysis. Driving forces, for instance, may stem from a change in raw material supply such as synthesis gas and methanol chemistry. The chemical industry always has been influenced by achievements of the scientific world. In a well working system the scientific world will respond to needs of industry. Here rests a great potential for innovation. The field of coordination chemistry in the scientific word has developed to an advanced level and it is the opinion of the author that further breakthroughs in homogeneous catalysis can be anticipated. In analogy a major impulse of the past can be traced back to the Ziegler-Natta catalysis, which in its beginning was more an art, but which has beveloped into a science.

The chances of opportunities may be underlined when considering the periodic table of elements and metals used today in homogeneous catalysis (figure 10). Only 12 metals, so far, have found significant industrial applications. Basic research is challenged to unravel secret catalytic properties e.g. of the lanthanides.

		Sc	T1	V	Cr	Mn	Fe	Co	Ni
Cu	Zn	Y	Zr	Nb	Mo	Tc	Ru	Rh	Pd
Ag	Cd	La	Hf	Ta	W	Re	Os	Ir	Pt
Au	Hg	Ac	Th	Pa	U				

Fig. 10: Metals applied in a significant share in homogeneous catalysis

It also can be anticipated that engineering requirements such as selectivity and mild operation conditions will have an impact on the future of homogeneous catalysis. Finally, environmental constraints regarding the safety and the purity of products (selectivity) may have an influence on the future development (environment driven processes).

LITERATURE

1) Boor, J. in "Ziegler-Natta Catalysts and Polymerizations", Academic Press, N.Y. (1979).

2) Knowles, W.S., J. Chem. Ed. 63, 222 (1986).

3) Fiorini, M. and Giongo, G.M., J. Mol. Cat. 5, 303 (1979).

4) Sheldon, R.A. and Kochi, J.K. in "Metal-Catalyzed Oxidations of Organic Compounds", Academic Press, N.Y. (1981).

5) Smidt, J., Hafner, W., Jira, R., Sieber, R., Sedlmeier, J. and Sabel, A., Angew. Chem. 74, 93 (1962).

6) Weisermel, K. and Arpe, H.-J., in "Industrielle Organische Chemie", VCH Verlagsgesellschaft p. 287 (1988).

7) Peuckert, M. and Keim W., Organometallics 2, 594 (1983); Keim, W., Chem.-Ing.-Tech. 56, 850 (1984); Freitas, E.R. and Gum, C.R., Chem. Eng. Prog. 75, 73 (1979); Behr, A. and Keim, W., Arabian J. Sci. Eng. 10, 377 (1984).

8) Müller, U., Keim, W., Krüger, C. and Betz P., Angew. Chem. Int. Ed. Eng. 28, 1011 (1989).

9) Keim, W., Angew. Chem. Int. Ed. Engl. 29, 235 (1990).

10) Ostoja Starzewski, K.A., Witte, J., Reichert, K.H. and Vasiliou G. in "Olefin Polymerization", ed. Kaminsky W. and Sinn H., Springer-Verlag (1988).

11) Chauvin, Y., Gaillard, J.F., Leonard, J., Bonnifay P. and Andrews, J.W., Hydrocarbon Process. 110 (1982); Leonard, J. and Gaillard J.G., Hydrocarbon Process. 99 (1981).

12) Kaminsky W. and Sinn H., "Olefin Polymerization" Springer-Verlag (1988).

13) Slaugh, L.H. and Mullineaux, R.D., US-Pat. 3.239.569 (1966), Shell Oil Co.

14) Tolman, C.A., J. Chem. Educ. 63, 199 (1986); Tolman, C.A., Chem. Rev. 77 313 (1977).

15) Falbe, J., "New Syntheses with Carbon Monoxide", Springer-Verlag (1980).

16) Keim, W., "Catalysis in C_1-Chemistry", D.Reidel Publishing Company (1983).

17) Mortreux, A. and Petit F. edit. "Industrial Applications of Homogeneous Catalysis", R. Reidel Publishing Comp. (1988).

18) Streck, R., J. Molec. Cat. 46, 305 (1988).

BC